S268 Physical Resources and Environment

Science: a second level course

BLOCK

METALS 2

RESOURCE EXPLOITATION

Prepared for the Course Team by Peter Webb

S268 Physical Resources and Environment

Dedication

Professor Geoff Brown was a member of the Course Team when he was killed on the Galeras Volcano, Colombia, in January 1993. The Course Team dedicates S268 to his memory.

Acknowledgements

The Course Team gratefully acknowledges the contributions of members of the S238 course team (S238 *The Earth's Physical Resources*, 1984).

The Course Team also wishes to thank Sheila Dellow for careful reading of early drafts of the course material.

The Open University, Walton Hall, Milton Keynes MK7 6AA.

First published 1996. Reprinted with corrections 2000. Reprinted 2003.

Edited, designed and typeset by The Open University.

Printed in the United Kingdom by Henry Ling Limited, at the Dorset Press, Dorchester, DT1 1HD.

ISBN 0 7492 5151 4

This text forms part of an Open University second level course. If you would like a copy of *Studying with the Open University*, please write to the Central Enquiry Service, PO Box 200, The Open University, Walton Hall, Milton Keynes, MK7 6YZ. If you have not already enrolled on the course and would like to buy this or other Open University material, please write to Open University Educational Enterprises Ltd, 12 Cofferidge Close, Stony Stratford, Milton Keynes, MK11 1BY, United Kingdom.

Edition 1.3

S268block5part2i1.3

CONTENTS

1 INTRODUCTION TO THE METAL RESOURCES INDUSTRY

We saw in *Metals 1* that a wide variety of metalliferous deposits exist in the Earth's crust as a result of the concentration of elements by natural geological processes. However, these deposits can only be regarded as physical resources if they can be exploited and transformed into useful products. In *Metals 2* we consider the activities of the metal resources industry: how deposits are found; what makes them economic to mine; what form that mining might take; and how ore — essentially rock — is processed and transformed into metal. We also consider the environmental effects of exploiting metal resources, and how the metals industry has changed in line with technological, economic and social developments as well as improved geological understanding.

1.1 Mining activities

Today, the vast majority of primary metals are produced by organized industry, though there remain, especially in poorer parts of the world, individuals who mine with little mechanization, and without the backing or support of organized management.

Small-scale mining requires little more than basic know-how, primitive tools and possibly explosives, and some form of equipment for separating out ore minerals. Thus, little financial investment is necessary, and labour may take the form of 'old-prospectors' or a co-operative workforce — for whom there may be a high health and safety cost in unregulated mining activities. Such operations in the Third World nowadays often have more in common with pre-twentieth-century mining in Europe than with most modern, large-scale mining operations.

Large-scale mining is a very different proposition. The main stages involved in the exploitation of resources were introduced in Block 1, Section 2.4, and we shall be looking at these in more detail. Exploitation of mineral deposits involves a series of activities as outlined in Figure 1 and listed overleaf.

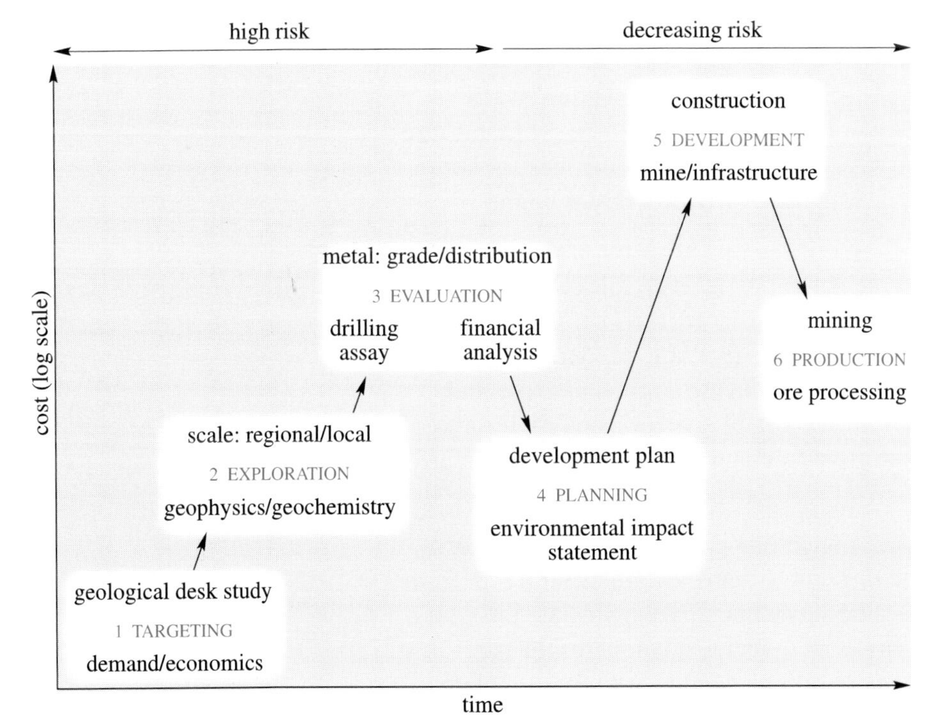

Figure 1 The sequence of activities and the escalation of cost in the exploration and development of a metal mining venture. These activities are explained in the text.

1 *Targeting* — the selection of a suitable region to start exploration, involving desk studies and based on historical knowledge of deposits and/ or geological indicators. It follows a decision to explore, which is based on economic circumstances and the projected demand for a metal.
2 *Exploration* — the systematic search for metalliferous deposits by a variety of methods, starting on a regional scale and becoming progressively more localized.
3 *Evaluation* — the determination of metal grade and its distribution at a specific target, so that decisions can be made on whether or not to exploit the deposit and, if so, how to exploit it.
4 *Planning* — the production of a development plan to support the high level of investment needed to set up the mining infrastructure and ore processing plant. As well as support from investors, approvals are required from governments, and today an environmental impact statement is usually necessary to satisfy the regulatory authorities that the site will neither have an unacceptable impact nor cause unacceptable pollution.
5 *Mine development* — the development and construction of the operational infrastructure necessary to gain access to the ore as well as to process and ship it. This usually involves installing power supplies, building accommodation for the work force, and constructing ore-processing plant and road or rail links for shipment of ore and concentrates. Accessing the ore may involve excavating overburden to create an open pit, or sinking shafts and tunnelling underground.
6 *Mine production* — the removal and processing of ore; sometimes the on-site extraction of metals.

It is important to appreciate that each of the first three stages requires financing at high risk. There is no income during these stages and no guarantee of a successful outcome. Through stages 4 and 5 the risks lessen, but costs are even higher, especially in stage 5 and there is still no income. Indeed, there can be no income until the ore is sold and that might not be until well after mining starts. Changes in world economic or political circumstances could put a stop to development at any stage of the project.

At each stage up to full production, *financial evaluation* and *risk analysis* are necessary to justify the increasing investment required. Decisions to continue must take into account the cost of likely geological problems, the economic and political vagaries of world markets and the price that the product is likely to command in the future. Many projects under development have to be written off when their viability cannot be demonstrated. To be profitable, the mine must not only be productive enough for the income to cover operating costs and repay the capital outlay, it must also provide a return on the investment.

The stages outlined in Figure 1, from the initial decision to explore, to entry into production, take varying lengths of time. Indeed, the *lead time* for a mining project (the time from discovery of a prospect to production) is generally between 3 and 20 years, depending on the size, complexity and location of the operation. Profits from successful operations might have to support the cost of developing new projects that might be terminated before the production stage.

If the development costs of a project escalate or if it takes a long time for production to start, it will be more difficult to achieve a financial return from mining comparable with that of a 'safe' investment. To appreciate this point, look at Figure 2a, a hypothetical financial model that compares the net cumulative return (profit) from a major mining venture with the compounded return on capital 'safely' invested. A breakdown of annual income and expenditure is given in Figure 2b. In the first few years the venture makes a loss because injection of capital is necessary and interest is payable on loans. In this example, the mine starts to make an operating profit in year 11, and only then can loans be repaid.

- Examine Figure 2a and decide when the venture will break even — that is, when cumulative costs are balanced by cumulative income.

- Break even occurs about 14 years after the project started (or 5 years after mine production started).

- How long after the major capital investment in years 8 and 9 does the mine bring in a return exceeding that of capital 'safely' invested?

- The curves in Figure 2a intersect about 18 years after the project started, and thereafter the mine out-performs the 'safe' investment. This occurs about 10 years after the main injection of capital seen in Figure 2b.

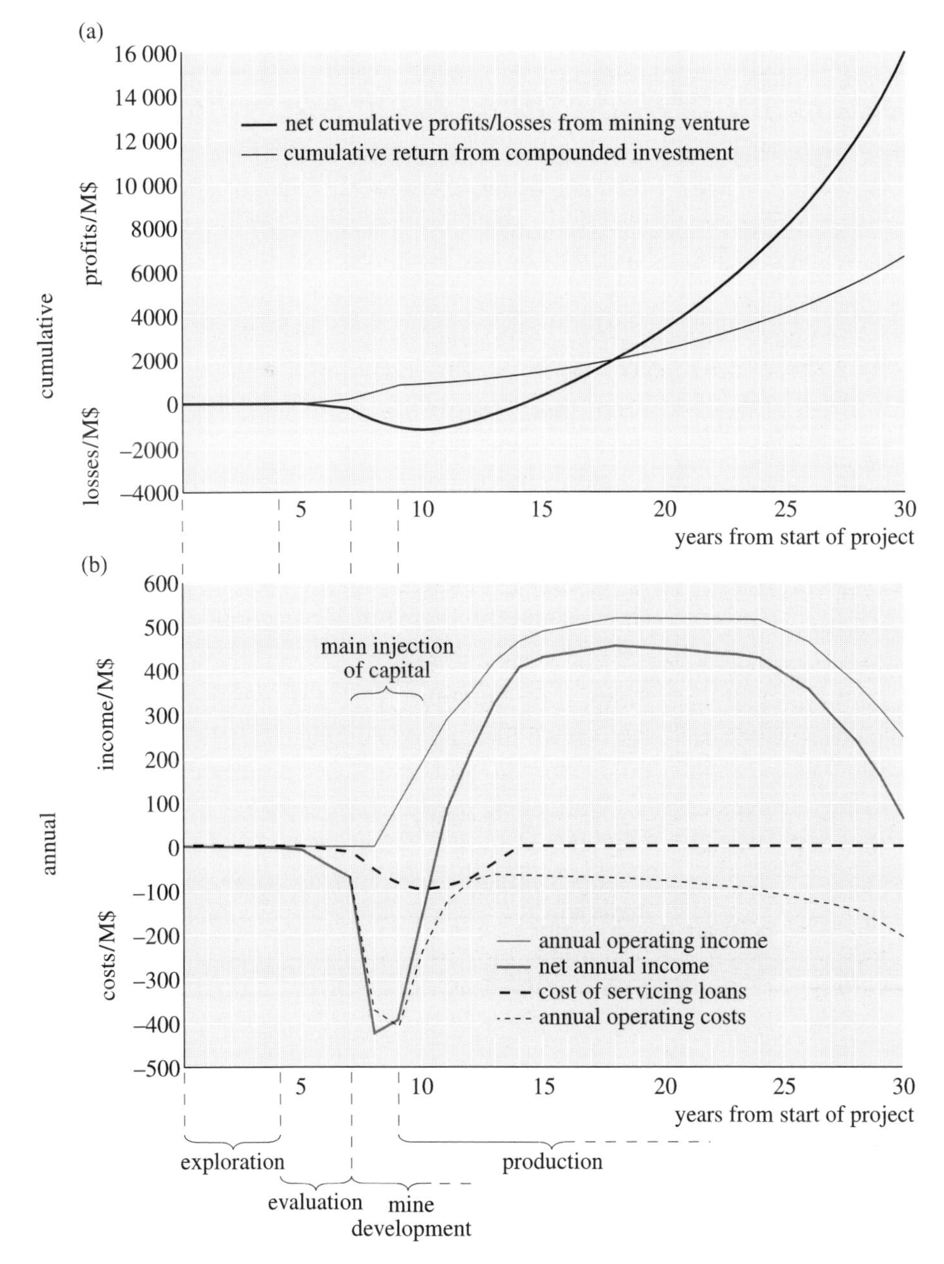

Figure 2 Profit–loss curves for a hypothetical major mining venture with a productive life of about 20 years: (a) net cumulative profits and losses derived from net annual mining income and expenditure compared with the return from equivalent capital safely invested (based on compound interest of 10%; calculations include 10% compound interest on operating profits, once achieved); (b) annual income and expenditure for the mining venture — net annual income and losses are derived from the annual operating income less development and operating costs and the cost of servicing loans at 10% per annum.

Although Figure 2b shows annual income far exceeding annual costs after year 11, suggesting a high level of profit, it is an appreciable time before the cumulative returns from mining out-perform those of a 'safe' investment, because of the high capital outlay without return in the first few years of development. Therefore, it is important to start production quickly and gain a high return once production is under way to compensate for the lack of return on capital invested and costs incurred during development. Clearly, large-scale mining is a long-term investment.

Question 1

You have $1 million cash. You may either (a) invest at 7% compound interest or (b) buy out a mine at the point of production with an expected profit of $200 000 per year.

Use your knowledge of doubling time (approximately, 70 divided by the percentage change) to work out which would be the better investment over a 10-year period and explain why.

To illustrate the evolution of a mining venture before it comes into full production, let's examine the development of the Olympic Dam Mine in South Australia.

A modern mine development: Olympic Dam, South Australia

The Olympic Dam deposit in South Australia was discovered by Western Mining Corporation (WMC) in July 1975. There followed extensive drilling over several years to prove the extent of the deposit. This led to the developments shown along the timeline in Figure 3. By the early 1980s, the deposit was heralded as one of the world's largest resources of copper and uranium extending over an area of 20 km^2, and was believed to be a total *resource* of 2000 million tonnes (Mt) containing a *reserve* of 450 million tonnes with metal contents as shown in Table 1.

What is the essential difference between resources and reserves?

Reserves contain grades of metal that can be extracted profitably under prevailing conditions; total resources include lower grades of conditional resources that have the potential to be exploited given realistic changes in methods of extraction, metal prices or legal conditions (Block 1, Section 2.2).

The deposit lies within a 1600 Ma old, highly brecciated and extensively altered granite body, overlain by about 300 m of barren, flat-lying sediments. The breccias are haematite-rich and contain copper sulphides and pitchblende, low grades of gold, silver and some rare earth elements. In these circumstances, mining the ore had to be an underground operation.

From discovery to the official opening, when the mine came into production, was about 13 years, and required the investment of A$750 million (about £350 million). The lead time and the size of the investment is typical of large underground mines and is in striking contrast to the short lead times (indeed, short overall lifetimes) of the open pits featured in Video Band 14: *Gold Rush in the 1990s*.

Further investment was necessary to optimize mining operations and improve output. By 1994, however, production had still not reached projected levels (Table 2). Figure 3 reveals some of the resources used at Olympic Dam and the scale of the infrastructure needed to provide water power, fuel and construction materials.

Table 1 Announced resources at Olympic Dam

	Size Mt	Copper %	Uranium (as U_3O_8) kg t^{-1}	Gold g t^{-1}	Silver g t^{-1}
total resource (1982)	2000	1.6	0.6	0.6	3.5
probable reserve (1983)	450	2.5	0.8	0.6	6.0
probable reserve (1993)	572	2.1	0.6	0.7	5.0
conditional resource (1993)	1560	1.1	0.4	0.4	2.5

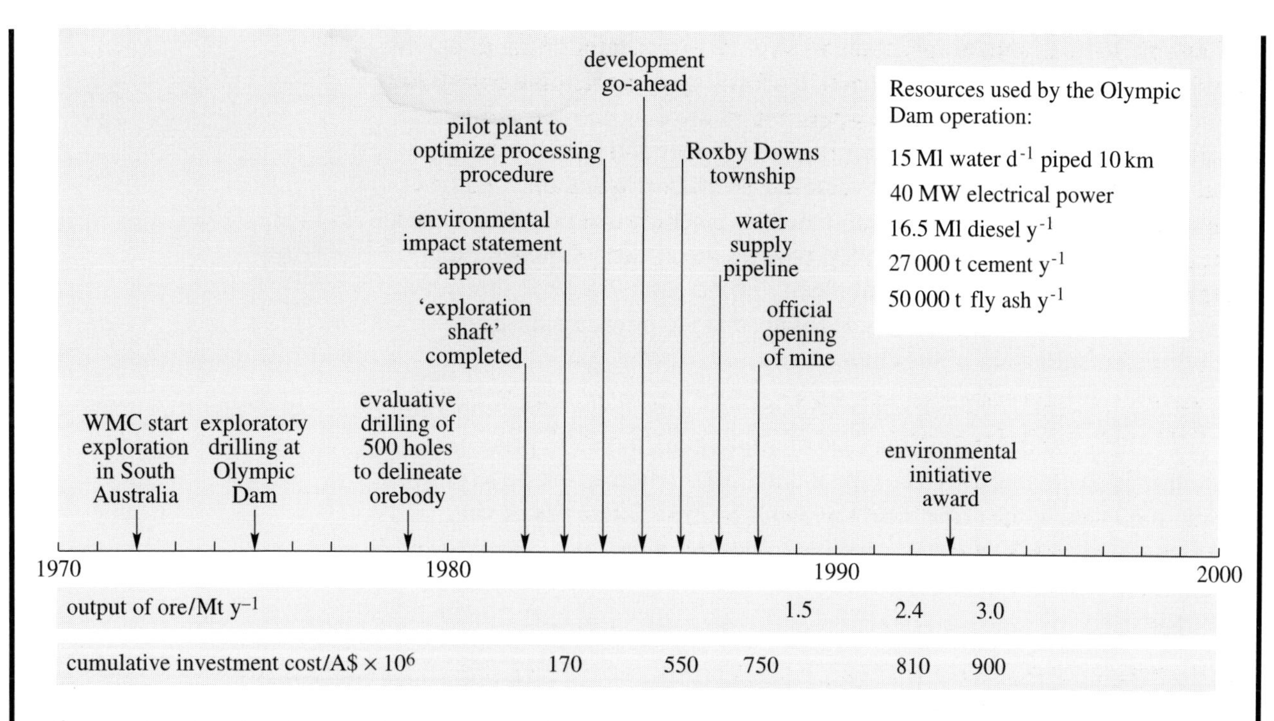

Figure 3 Timeline showing development activity, cumulative investment cost, and the amount of ore produced from the Olympic Dam deposit, South Australia.

The data in Tables 1 and 2 and the events shown in Figure 3 demonstrate several important points:

- the increasing investment necessary for exploration, evaluation and development of a mine before full-scale production is possible;
- the lead time between the initial discovery of a deposit and entry into production;
- the refinement of information about expected output and reserves as geological constraints and technical solutions become better defined.

Table 2 Production of metals at Olympic Dam

Annual output	Ore Mt	Copper 1000 t	Uranium (as U_3O_8) 1000 t	Gold t	Silver t
projected (1988)	6.5	150	3.0	3.4	23.0
actual (1994)	3.0	70	1.4	0.62	15.5

Although Olympic Dam is regarded as a major deposit on the world scene and might not yet be at its peak of production, Question 2 will help you put into perspective the contribution of Olympic Dam to world production. Bear in mind that copper mined from Chuquicamata, the world's largest producer, amounted to 8.3% of world copper production in 1992 (*Metals 1*, Section 2.4).

Question 2

(a) At the 1994 rate of output (3 Mt y^{-1} of ore) at Olympic Dam, how long would the probable reserve of 572 Mt of ore (quoted in 1993) last? What kind of changes in global markets would reduce the lifetime of the reserve? Similarly, what changes would lengthen it?

(b) In terms of 1993 *world* output (9 Mt Cu, 2290 t Au and 14 900 t Ag), for which of these metals is Olympic Dam most important at the 1994 rates of output quoted in Table 2?

We saw in *Metals 1*, Section 1.2 that often only a small proportion of an ore is useful, so the cost of shipping metal, even if impure, is much less than the cost of shipping an equivalent amount of ore or ore concentrates. Therefore, metals obtained from low grade ores, such as copper and gold, are now commonly extracted at or near the mine site. Richer ores and ore concentrates are usually transported in bulk to smelters that are often located where energy costs are low. However, costs of metal extraction (smelting) are generally high owing to the complexity of the plant, the large amount of energy required to run it, and the safeguards that are now demanded to minimize contamination of the environment.

Ore processing and metal extraction costs can be appreciated by comparing the prices of ore and metal. In the case of aluminium, the 1992 price of bauxite ore (containing 25% Al) was about $\$18\,t^{-1}$ whereas the price of aluminium metal at the same time was about $\$1250\,t^{-1}$. Ore prices vary according to the grade of the ore and the impurities it contains, whereas metal prices depend on the purity achieved — because additional refining increases costs.

1.2 Trends in primary metals production

Recent (1992) production levels of the more important metals were considered in *Metals 1*, Section 1.1. Based on the same data, Figure 4a shows the relative importance of metals in terms of the quantity produced from ore. Iron dominates because of the importance of steel. The relative importance of manganese when compared with the lesser major metals, such as zinc and lead, is explained by the fact that most manganese is alloyed with iron and makes up a small proportion of many steels. The relative *notional values* (price × production) of metals produced in 1992 are shown in Figure 4b. This is a better way of assessing the relative importance of different sections of the metals extraction and refining industries. On this basis, chromium and nickel (both high-cost metals that are important in steel production) are seen to feature quite strongly, yet their presence does not register in Figure 4a.

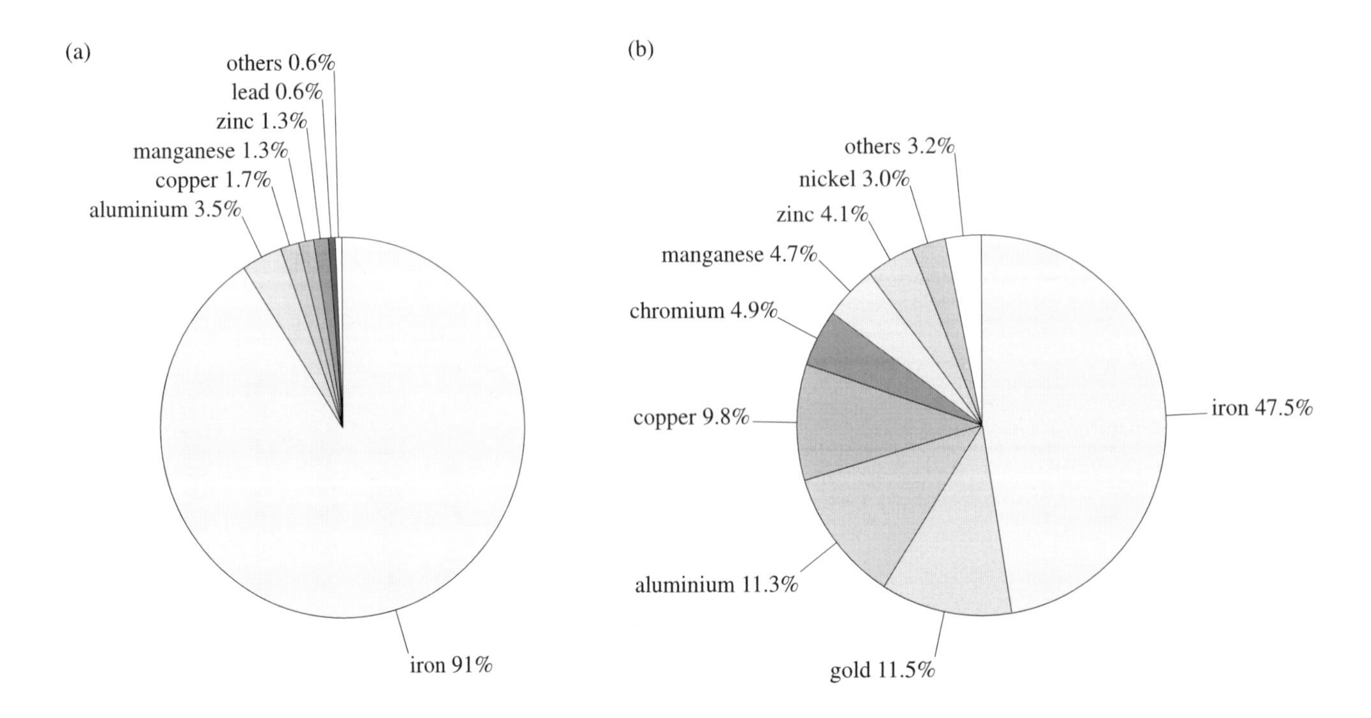

Figure 4 Metals production in 1992: (a) as a percentage of the total weight of metals produced; (b) as a percentage of the total notional value of metals produced.

Estimating the true value of metals that are used in alloys is difficult because the component price is not the same as the pure metal price. Because a large proportion of a metal's value is added in smelting and refining, the values estimated in Figure 4b do not represent income to the mining industry alone, but to the whole of the metals mining and refining industry. Historically, most smelters were owned by mining companies; today this is less often the case.

Question 3

Which metal not mentioned above appears in Figure 4b but does not feature in Figure 4a? Explain this discrepancy.

Figure 5 shows how levels of world metals production have changed during the present century. Production levels for each metal fluctuate according to the demand for and availability of metals, but a number of important features are apparent.

Copper, zinc and lead were produced in roughly equal amounts in the early 1900s. In recent years, copper has been more important, in terms of production, than zinc, and both are more than twice as important as lead production, which has been declining since the late 1970s. Very little aluminium was produced in 1920, but now aluminium production is roughly equal to the combined production of copper, zinc and lead.

- Given the exponential growth of aluminium production in the period 1955–72, from about 3 million tonnes to about 12 million tonnes, as shown in Figure 5 (and Block 1, Section 2.1), what is the difference between the production you might have expected to see by 1989 and the production that actually occurred? What implication does this have for the lifetime of aluminium reserves?

- If growth had continued at the 1955–72 rate (doubling about every 8.5 years), production in 1989 would have reached 48 million tonnes. In fact, production in 1989 was less than 20 million tonnes because growth did not continue to rise at the same rate (Figure 5). Therefore, any estimate of the lifetime of aluminium reserves made in 1972 would be inappropriate for the 1990s.

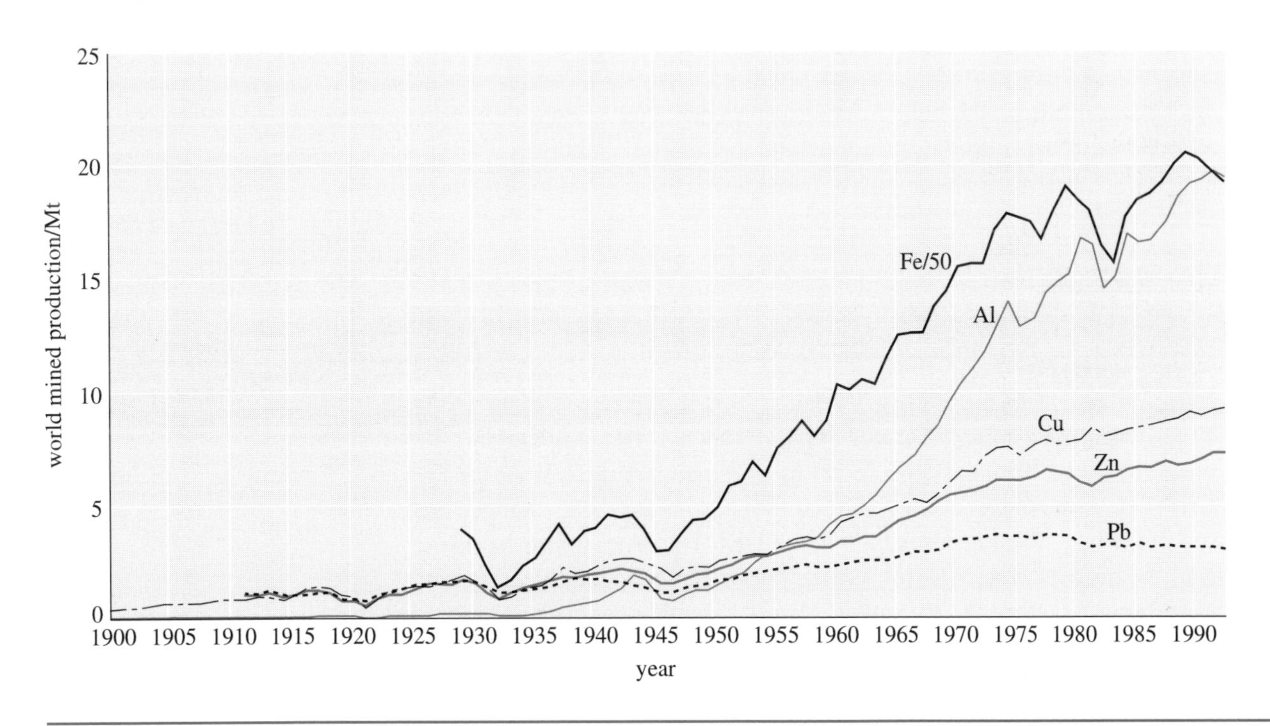

Figure 5 World annual mined production of the major metals 1900–90. Note that iron production is shown as *one-fiftieth* of its value in order to fit on this graph.

The production patterns for copper and zinc also show growth in the 1960s, but much less than for aluminium. A roughly linear increase in copper and zinc production has been a feature of the 1980s. Figure 5 also shows that growth in world iron production was roughly linear from 1945 to about 1972. Since then, there have been fluctuations but little overall growth. This probably reflects the tendency to substitute lighter materials (aluminium and, more especially, plastics) for iron in order to save energy in both transportation and use.

Let's now consider some of the reasons underlying the changes in the proportions of major metals produced today, compared with production in the early part of this century.

Why has aluminium become so important in use? And why is it now produced in large quantities?

Aluminium is easily the lightest of the common metals and is very versatile in manufacturing and use (*Metals 1*, Section 1.1). Its lightness is especially important because less energy is required to transport it than many cheaper but denser metals, iron in particular. So, use of aluminium keeps transport costs down and conserves fuel. However, the extraction of aluminium from its ores is an energy-demanding process (Block 1, Section 4.3), and the increasing production since World War II only became possible when electricity became available more cheaply and in sufficient quantity. Today, large-scale production and use of cheap energy help to keep prices down.

Why have primary production and the use of lead declined?

Largely because of the reduction in demand for lead as its toxic properties have been more widely appreciated. In the 1980s, regulations were introduced to reduce its use in areas where toxicity is important. Increased use of unleaded petrol, and of titanium dioxide to whiten paint, are just two forms of substitution that have occurred. In addition, the amount of lead being recycled has been rising (*Metals 1*, Section 1.4.2).

To summarize, trends in primary metal production this century generally reflect the increased use of metals that are either light or versatile or non-toxic, such as aluminium and copper. Metal prices also play a part, and the prices of aluminium and copper have remained competitive despite a high demand, because of large-scale production and relatively cheap energy supplies.

1.3 Global trends in the exploitation of ore deposits

The UK was once the leading producer of metals such as tin, copper, lead and iron. In the mid 1990s, only one metal mine remains in the UK — the South Crofty tin mine in Cornwall. Some of the reasons for these changes are discussed in the box 'Mining for metals in the UK'. Unsurprisingly, world patterns of metals production do not remain static; they respond to economic, political and social factors. As we saw in *Metals 1*, geological circumstances determine where mineral deposits occur (and thus where new deposits can be found) as well as the form and grade of a deposit, but many other factors determine whether or not a deposit is economic to mine.

Table 3 compares world patterns of metals production in 1930 and 1990. Answering Question 4 will help you to appreciate the major changes that have occurred.

Table 3 The main producers of iron, copper, zinc, lead, tin and gold in 1930 and 1990, in order of decreasing share of world production

Year	Iron	Copper	Zinc	Lead	Tin	Gold
1930	USA	USA	USA	USA	Malaya	South Africa
	France	Chile	Germany	Mexico	Bolivia	USA
	UK	Congo	Mexico	Australia	East Indies	Canada
	Sweden	Canada	Australia	Canada	Thailand	Russia
	Russia	Japan	Poland	Spain	Nigeria	Mexico
	Luxemburg	Mexico	Canada	India	China	Rhodesia
1990	USSR	Chile	Canada	USA	China	South Africa
	China	USA	Australia	China	Brazil	USSR
	Brazil	USSR	China	USSR	Indonesia	USA
	Australia	Canada	USSR	Canada	Malaysia	Australia
	USA	Zambia	Peru	Peru	Bolivia	Canada
	India	Zaire	USA	Mexico	Thailand	China

Question 4

Use Table 3 to answer the following:

(a) What country dominated world metals production in 1930 and how had its position changed by 1990?

(b) How did the major producers of iron change from 1930 to 1990? What reasons can you suggest for these changes?

(c) For copper, zinc, lead and tin, which countries have elevated their position in terms of world production since 1930?

According to Table 3, the countries that have become increasingly important as producers of metals are China, the former USSR, Australia, and Canada, whereas the previously strong position of the USA has declined and many of the former producer countries of Western Europe have faded out of the picture. Today's producers are generally large countries in which deposits are often mined far from centres of industry. The reasons for these changes include political, social, technological and environmental factors, as well as geological ones. For instance, some large ore deposits have been found only by exploration in remote areas. With bulk transportation, many ores now have a much lower *place value* than they used to have and there is a growing trend towards use of low-grade ores with a high place value that demands the extraction of metals on site. China's success is based on cheap labour, few or no environmental safeguards, and no overriding need for its metals industry to make a profit. Under these circumstances metals can be produced cheaply — consequently, demand is high.

Mining for metals in the UK

Metal mining has been carried out in Britain for at least 3500 years. Indeed, there was trade in tin between Cornwall and the Mediterranean by the fourth century BC. In prehistoric times, tin was obtained mainly from alluvial deposits, copper and lead were mined from veins by digging crude pits, and iron was mined from outcrops of nodular and bedded ores. Most early mining was in trenches, open pits and shallow shafts, but gradually, as easily accessible ores were worked out, tunnelling was necessary and by the late seventeenth century, there were extensive underground mines in many parts of Britain.

Base metal ores have been mined in many upland areas of England and Wales, and parts of Scotland. The main mining areas are shown in Figure 6. Copper, tin, lead and zinc ores were mined from the hydrothermal veins associated with the large granitic intrusions of south-west England (*Metals 1*, Section 4.3.2). Lead, copper and zinc ores came from veins in the Ordovician and Cambrian sedimentary rocks of north and central Wales, the Lake District, the Isle of Man and the Southern Uplands of Scotland. Lead, zinc and some copper were worked in the Carboniferous limestone of the Mendips, north Wales and the Pennines. In some areas, silver was recovered from the lead ores, and gold was mined in central Wales.

By the seventeenth century, northern England had become important for its lead mining and Cornwall for its tin mining. The technological advances and demands for metals during the Industrial Revolution led to the emergence of an important copper mining and smelting industry, together with iron production from the coalfields. In the mid-eighteenth century, copper became more important than tin in Cornwall and dominated world supplies, but before the end of the century, the Parys Mountain Mine in Anglesey (Video Band 2: *Copper Resources and Reserves*) was producing cheaper copper ore and Cornwall's prosperity declined. But then, as the deposits of Anglesey became more difficult and costly to mine, copper prices increased and copper mining in Cornwall thrived again during the early and mid-nineteenth century. With its major competitors in central Europe weakened by wars and difficulties in working their mines, the British mining industry dominated world markets in the eighteenth and early nineteenth centuries.

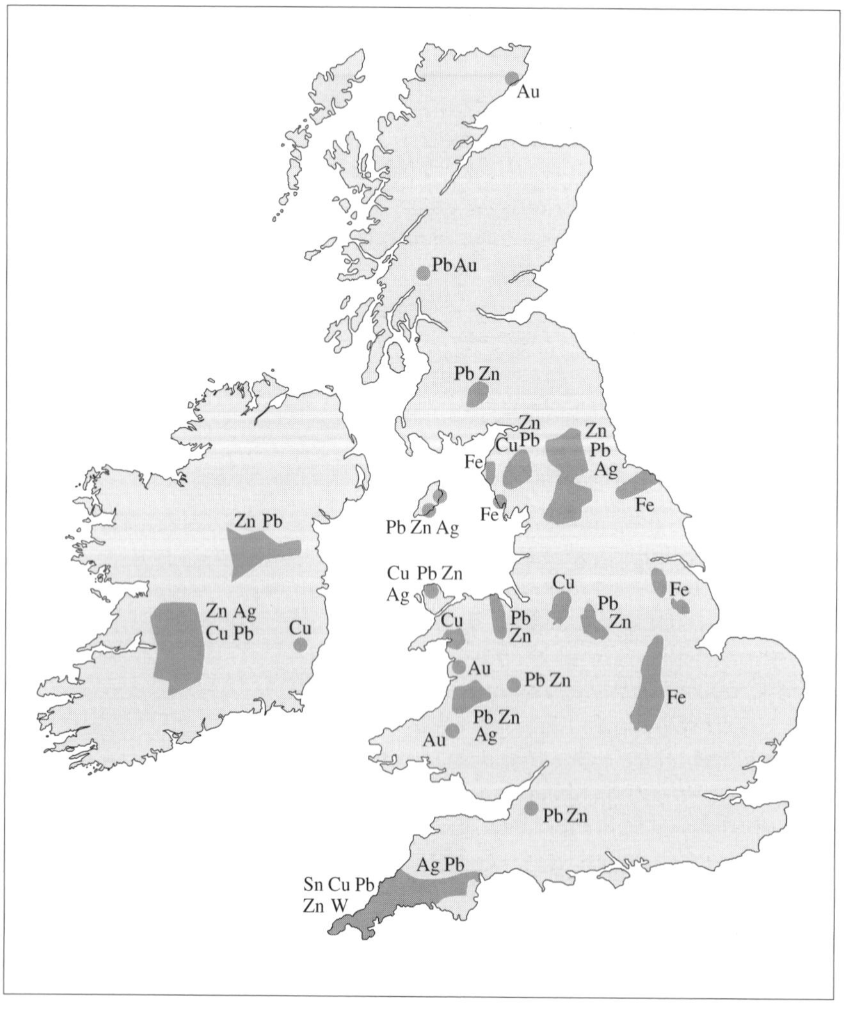

The importance of mining in mid-nineteenth-century Britain is illustrated by statistics for 1862, when British mines employed over 80 000 people and produced metal worth an estimated £13.5 million (at a time when the yearly wage for most people was no more than £50). A survey of mines in south-west England, north Wales and the north Pennines at the time showed that many were small operations (Table 4). In all, over half employed fewer than 50 miners underground. At the same time, fewer than 6000 miners were employed in the silver, lead, and iron mines of the Erzgebirge of Germany which had been the premier mining region of Europe in the Middle Ages.

Figure 6 Metal mining areas of the British Isles.

Table 4 Numbers of mines by size of workforce in major British base metal mining areas in 1862.

No of men employed underground	Devon and Cornwall mines	Central and north Pennine mines	Central and north Wales mines
600+	–	–	–
500–599	1	–	–
400–499	2	–	–
300–399	3	1	2
200–299	13	3	3
100–199	45	4	3
50–99	49	12	6
1–49	78	71	8
Totals	191	91	22

In which area, according to the numbers of men working underground (in Table 4), did the mines tend to be larger — in south-west England or the north Pennines.

Nearly 80% of the north Pennines mines had less than 50 workers underground whereas a third of those in the South West had more than 100 workers underground. So, mines were generally larger in the South West.

Metal mining was an important factor in the development of industry generally in mining areas, especially Cornwall. As well as people employed in the actual extraction and processing of ore, there were jobs in associated industries; especially engineering, transportation and finance. Indeed, from the 1820s, mining equipment and mining engineers were exported all over the world.

Towards the end of the nineteenth century, world production of ores gradually moved to large low-grade ore bodies as mechanization had an impact on ore processing, transportation, and mining. These deposits were often cheaper to work than British mines, because of bulk handling and low wages, but lack of fuel often made local smelting expensive. In the second half of the nineteenth century, therefore, British mining started to decline (as shown by the data for home-produced lead in Figure 7) but imports of foreign ores to Britain continued because the smelting industry was well established. By 1880, Spain supplied 71% of Britain's imports of lead and, because Spain regularly undercut the price of British lead by between 5 shillings (25p) and £2 per ton, the British mining industry rapidly succumbed to the cheaper imports.

By the eve of World War I, much of Britain's base metal mining industry was dead. Some mines were saved by switching production to fluorspar (for flux in iron making) or barytes (for drilling mud); these were the gangue minerals which had hitherto been discarded. Others switched to producing zinc ores, but usually lasted only a few more years because of the low zinc price. The last major lead mine, at

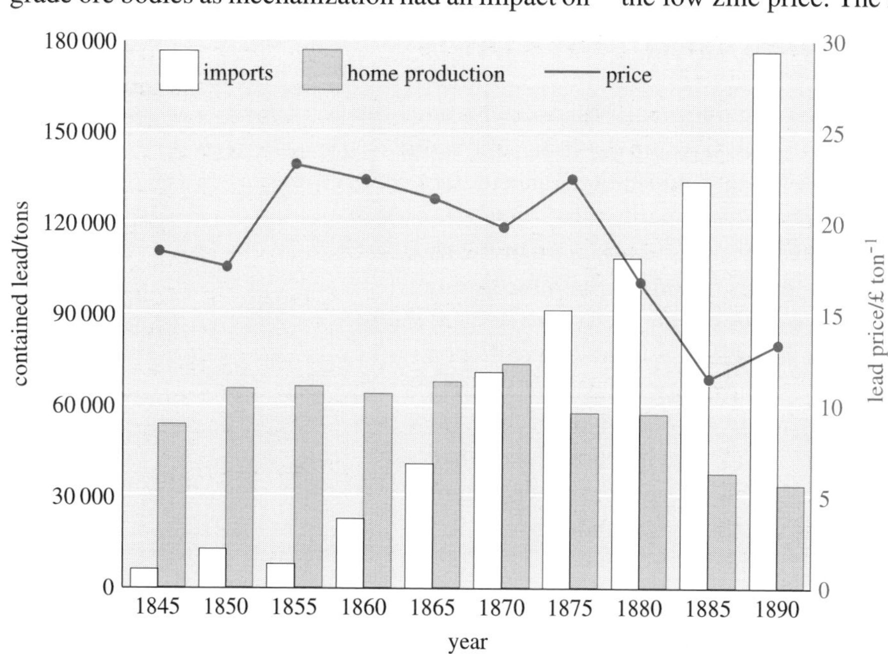

Figure 7 Graph showing levels of home-produced lead, imported lead, and lead prices in Britain, 1845–90.

Greenside in the Lake District, closed in 1962. Since then, lead ore has been raised only as a by-product of fluorspar or barytes mining.

Iron ores have been obtained from a variety of sources in Britain, as mentioned in Video Band 1: *The Great Iron and Steel Rollercoaster* and shown in Figure 6. These sources include nodules in Weald clays; 'Black Band' ores in most Carboniferous coalfields; bedded ironstones in the Jurassic rocks of Cleveland, Lincolnshire and Northamptonshire (*Metals 1*, Section 3.3.1); and haematite replacement deposits in Carboniferous limestone along the Cumbrian coast (featured in Video Band 3: *Resource Geology*).

In the eighteenth century, most of the ironstone was worked from the coalfields but Cleveland iron ores accounted for 30–40% of the total between 1860 and 1910. The Jurassic ores of Lincolnshire and Northamptonshire became important in the present century when they were worked in highly mechanized opencast mines (Video Band 1). Iron ore output reached a peak of nearly 20 million tonnes during World War II. This was mainly due to expansion in Northamptonshire, which continued to dominate until iron ore mining declined in the 1970s; by the early 1990s, it had all but ceased. Ironstone mining in Cleveland ended in 1964 but had been in decline since 1920. The decline of British steel-making in the 1980s and generally low commodity prices has also caused the closure of most fluorspar mines.

In the mid-1980s, the collapse of the tin cartel and the resulting fall in prices meant that high-cost Cornish mines closed, leaving only South Crofty Mine, in Camborne. Gold mining in mid-Wales shifts in and out of production as the price of gold fluctuates, but it operates only on a small scale. There was new prospecting for copper and zinc in the 1980s at the Parys Mountain Mine in Anglesey, where a deep shaft was sunk; there was also prospecting for gold at the Tyndrum mines in Scotland.

Mineral production statistics for 1991 showed that metal mining had almost ceased in the UK: only 2300 tonnes of tin, 1000 tonnes of lead, 1100 tonnes of zinc, 300 tonnes of copper, and 59 000 tonnes of iron ore were mined.

Question 5

Use the information in the box 'Mining for metals in the UK' and Figure 7 to answer the following questions.

(a) In 1880, home-produced lead amounted to 56 900 tons and total imports of lead were 109 000 tons (Figure 7). Did Spain or Britain supply more lead to the British market?

(b) When did imported lead start to exceed levels of home-produced lead?

(c) How do you think changes in the price of lead affected British lead mining, particularly after 1875? Identify the cause and effect.

1.4 Strategic supplies and stockpiles

As we saw in *Metals 1,* metal resources are not evenly distributed around the world. For example, the USA is rich in molybdenum deposits, and South Africa in platinum group metals (PGM). Many consumer countries lack important deposits, and in times of unrestricted supply these countries tend to obtain supplies from the most convenient source, which is often the cheapest rather than the most reliable. When supplies become vulnerable through conflicts or international embargoes, supplies from alternative sources might have to be sought. At such times, it is important to be able to call upon **strategic resources** — sources of minerals that are crucial to a country's economy and military strength, which might be located either in its own territory or in nearby friendly countries. It may be no coincidence that reluctance (for 'environmental reasons') to develop resources in many Western countries also serves a political strategy for the long-term preservation of strategic resources.

Strategic resources include not only reserves based at home or in friendly countries, but also *marginal* (sub-economic) deposits. For example, the USA lacks sufficient economic deposits of chromium, nickel and PGM. At times of international conflict it could call on strategic supplies from Mexico and Canada, but in addition, the Stillwater Complex in Montana is an important strategic resource (*Metals 1*, Section 2.2.1). It contains sub-economic deposits of chromite and has been mined since 1986 for PGM, although output in the early 1990s represented only about 5% of US consumption. However, the USA has another strategic reserve, the National Defence Stockpile: enough refined metal to support industry and manufacturing at a level sufficient to sustain a conventional global war for 3 years. In the 1990s, the end of the Cold War has raised questions concerning the need for this stockpile.

- What is the likely consequence to world markets of reducing a major stockpile such as this?

- In the short term, if supplies were rapidly released, they would flood world markets causing a reduction in prices and thus reduce the profitability of mining operations. Mines might be forced to close.

The same thing can happen when countries where mining is under state control — for example, China or the countries of the former Soviet Union — have a policy to supply cheap metal and ore concentrates in return for vital foreign exchange. Prices are held down and this might lead to the closure of marginally economic mining operations in regions where mining is *not* subsidized and must be profitable to survive.

The metals markets also create their own stockpiles, partly as a buffer to fluctuations in supply and demand, and partly as an investment. For example, the London Metal Exchange (LME) has stocks of copper as shown in Figure 8. Such stockpiles are often built up at times when demand and prices are low. An effect of stockpiling is to create a demand that prevents prices from dropping too far and so helps to stabilize the market. If stocks become depleted and demand holds up, prices may rise until mine production is increased and supplies catch up. The interaction between metal stocks, prices, demand and supply is both complex and dynamic; the moving targets of supply and demand were discussed in Block 1, Section 2.

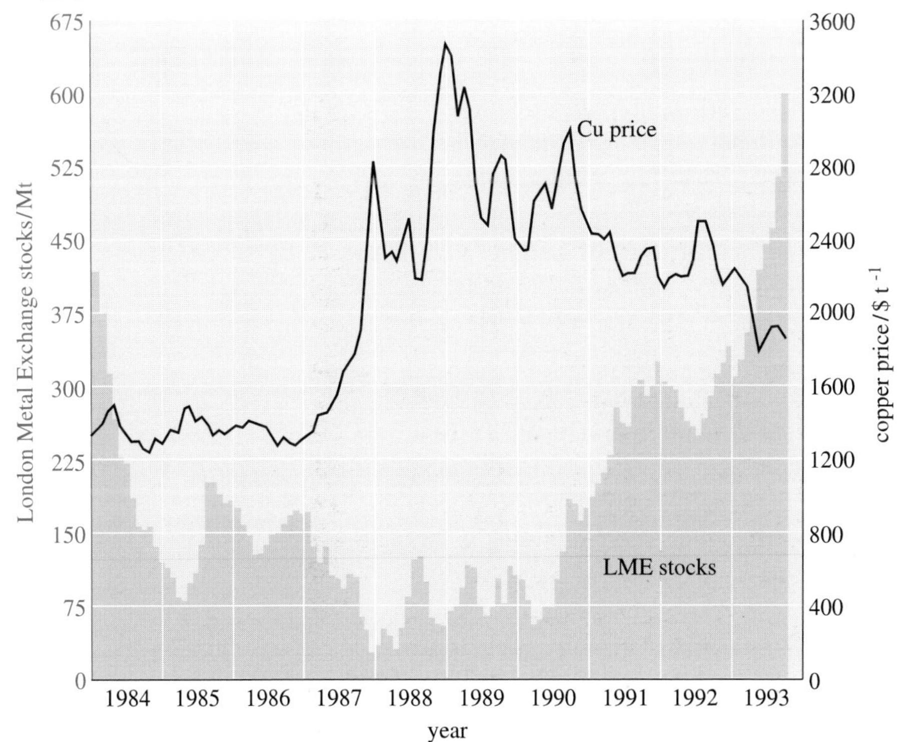

Figure 8 Copper price and London Metal Exchange stocks at monthly intervals, 1984–93.

In Figure 8, the rapid rise in copper price towards the end of 1987 (which suggests demand was high) is mirrored by the decline in LME stocks. Usually when shortages occur and prices are high, production increases to counter the demand. How long did it take for stocks to recover to 1986 levels?

About 2.5 years. During that period there were fluctuations in prices and stocks, but only from the middle of 1990 does it appear that a steady recovery of stocks occurred.

The metals for which strategic reserves are especially important are those that have extensive military use, those obtainable from only a few countries, and those that are generally scarce. Manganese, for example, is an important constituent of steel, and manganese dioxide is in high demand for dry cell batteries. Although several countries produce manganese ore, the *supply* in 1993 was dominated by China (23%) and the Ukraine (25.5%); moreover, the former Soviet Union and South Africa together account for 84% of world *reserves*. North America, a major consumer, currently has no reserves but there is a large sub-economic resource in Mexico. Such resources might be compared with the ironstones of the UK, which remain a strategic resource, although they are uneconomic to mine today.

Question 6

A considerable period of time elapses from the initial discovery of an ore deposit to production of ore. What reasons can you give for this?

1.5 Summary of Section 1

1 Metal resources are exploited on various scales that range from small-scale operations involving individuals to multinational companies. Large-scale mining operations require major investment, careful planning and financial assessment at each stage of development. There is often a long lead time from discovery to production. Mining ventures operate at a loss until production is well under way.

2 Iron production dominates world metals markets in terms of both tonnage and value. Many of the minor metals, especially manganese and chromium which are mainly used in steel, are as important as some major metals, such as zinc and lead.

3 Trends in metal use in the twentieth century are towards weight reduction (to save energy during transportation and use), versatility, and avoidance of toxicity in use and manufacture. The aluminium and copper industries have thrived, largely at the expense of iron and lead.

4 During the twentieth century, mining has tended to move from centres of industry to more remote locations, often in Third World countries, as a result of technological advances, and political, social and environmental pressures. The importance of mining in the USA and Western European countries has declined over the period 1930–90, whereas mining in large countries such as China, the former USSR, Australia and some South American countries has flourished.

5 Britain once had a thriving metals mining industry that was at the heart of the Industrial Revolution and led the world in base metal production. Towards the end of the nineteenth century, base metal mining declined

as deposits became increasingly difficult to work and cheaper ores became available from abroad. Iron ore continued to be successfully mined in the first half of the twentieth century but it too declined when cheaper ores became available from foreign sources.

6 Although sub-economic resources do not contribute to current reserves, they can have great strategic importance. They represent an insurance against the threat of restricted supplies. A stockpile is an alternative form of strategic resource, but its creation and disposal can have a major effect on prices and, therefore, the prosperity of the metal resources industry.

2 EXPLORATION FOR ORE DEPOSITS

2.1 Background

Both the exploration for and the evaluation of ore deposits depend on geological knowledge, but both are costly mining activities and are therefore controlled by economic considerations. In the end, mining companies must make a profit, and the amounts of money they make available for exploration vary depending on the probability of finding a deposit, company circumstances, and the anticipated profitability of the type of ore deposit likely to be found. Exploration budgets range from subsistence levels for individuals panning for gold in the rivers of South America to the many millions of dollars invested annually by large multinational companies in extensive exploration programmes.

Why do mining companies need to explore?

Companies must continue to be profitable or else they cease to exist, and most mines have a working life of only 15–30 years, many much less. Therefore, it is essential to discover new ore deposits for tomorrow's mines.

● In Block 1 (Section 2.5) an examination of reserves lifetimes showed that levels of reserves for most metals are sufficient for many years into the future at current rates of production. So, why do you think exploration is still necessary today?

○ You might consider several reasons, including the three below.

(i) The lead time between the discovery of a deposit and the start of mining can be as much as 10 years and is sometimes several decades. Therefore, it is important to explore for reserves many years in advance of the time when they are likely to be needed.

(ii) Few ore deposits are located where they are required (i.e. at the point of demand) so there is often a need in the major consumer countries to identify alternative, more accessible resources, in case of difficulty in maintaining existing supplies through international conflict, political or economic circumstances.

(iii) There is also the possibility that the economics of exploiting a newly discovered deposit might be more favourable than continuing to exploit an existing one.

Other, less obvious, reasons for exploration include the protection of a company's long-term interests by keeping likely mine prospects away from a rival company, and the fact that in many countries, money spent on exploration can be written off against tax on today's profits.

It can take a long time to realize a return on the initial investment in exploration (Section 1.1), and in that time all sorts of changes in technology and in the demand for the ore can occur to make the venture no longer profitable; nonetheless new exploration programmes must be launched for continuity of supply.

● What changes in circumstances do you think would encourage companies to expand their exploration programmes for a particular metal?

- Events that might encourage exploration could include any of the following.

  (i) Existing supplies of a metal suddenly become restricted, typically because of a change in the economic or political climate. For example, the Sudbury workers' strike in the 1960s threatened world supplies of nickel, and the Rhodesian sanctions of the 1960s and 1970s resulted in a shortage of chromium. Both are essential metals in steel production and, at the time, few other major sources were known. The prices of both these metals rose and, consequently, exploration efforts were increased.

  (ii) Changes in industrial technology create new uses for metals that were previously in little demand. For example, there was a high demand for uranium in the 1950s and 1960s when the prospects for nuclear power were first appreciated (Block 4 *Energy 2*, Section 2).

  (iii) Improvements in mining technology mean that previously uneconomic deposits can become worth targeting for further exploration. For example, the development of large-scale heap leaching has allowed gold to be extracted economically from very low-grade deposits (Video Band 14).

Other occasions might arise according to a company's circumstances. For example, if a mine turns out to be less profitable than had been anticipated, but the necessary mining equipment had already been purchased and installed, there would be a considerable incentive to find new deposits nearby. There could also be direct economic incentives, such as changes to the tax laws in a particular country, or even changes in the amount of money a government is prepared to invest in exploration. In Japan, for example, government agencies financed 75% of Japanese domestic exploration in 1979, whereas in Australia at that time, government investment in exploration was only about 5%.

Conversely, exploration programmes are cut back, discontinued or simply not begun, when the economic climate is poor. The recession of the late 1970s and the early 1980s brought about the closure of many metal mines worldwide, and, as there were ample reserves, there was little incentive to invest in major new exploration. However, even in times of economic recession, mining companies keep teams of geologists at work. They need to ensure that when the economic climate improves, they can quickly take advantage of the greater demand and higher metal prices.

What do they look for?

The first issue to be addressed in any decision to set up an exploration programme is clearly what to look for. Historically, many companies concentrated on particular metals or ores. This had the strategic advantage of building up considerable specialized company expertise in the exploration and marketing of those metals. However, if markets change and new opportunities for other metals open up, it is much more difficult for companies specializing in one or two metals to respond quickly. Thus, the trend is for companies to diversify. Anglo American, for example, was already a major metalliferous mining company before it developed a very successful coal division. Similarly, some of the major oil companies now have large interests in the minerals sector. An exploration strategy needs to fit in with company policy on the range of minerals and other deposits it mines. It's particularly advantageous when an exploration target turns out to have profitable amounts of more than one metal. In practice, the exploration geologist is likely to be told which metal or type of mineral deposit to look for, and will be required to advise on likely locations for specific types of deposit.

Where do they look?

The second part of the decision-making process is to determine whether exploration should locate deposits in a new area, or find additional ores in an existing mining area and ensure that all available ore is worked before a mine is abandoned.

An exploration programme designed to find new deposits is likely to be a large-scale operation that requires a high level of understanding of the geological conditions under which those deposits form, and how they can be recognized. However, just how much scientific understanding is necessary has long been debated within the mining industry. Arguably, the highest priority is for the exploration geologist to be well acquainted with available exploration techniques and their applicability to the type of deposit targeted — and that applicability depends on the form of the deposit and on its physical and chemical properties. Traditionally, there has been the view that if one example of a particular deposit was known to exist, there must be more: 'it doesn't matter how they were formed, just go and find another'. However, it is increasingly accepted that understanding the origins of ore bodies is important because certain types of deposit are more likely to occur in particular geological settings, or to have formed during particular periods of geological time (*Metals 1*, Section 5). Such information allows exploration programmes to be better focused and thus save money.

It's important to appreciate that *geological factors* dictate where to search for deposits of particular metal ores, but *economic and political factors* determine whether or not the size and the grade of a particular metalliferous deposit is worth exploitation.

- How would the minimum size of deposit that could be mined profitably in an existing mining area compare with that of a deposit in an undeveloped area?

- Where an infrastructure, including expensive transport networks and processing plants, already exists, smaller, less profitable deposits can be worked economically.

Levels of royalties and taxes, as well as environmental constraints, differ in different countries, and some countries may be more susceptible to sudden changes in policy towards mining than others. Each of these factors affect profits, and so a particular grade and tonnage that is attractive in one region will not be worth the risk in another.

The decision to set up an exploration programme must take account of all these factors, but also requires an assessment of the likely risks in order to justify further investment. The most obvious risk, and the one that is directly related to the geology, is that even in a favourable geological setting, a profitable deposit might not be found. In principle, the amount worth investing in exploration can be estimated on the basis of the likelihood of finding a deposit, how big that deposit might be, and the value per tonne of the extractable ore. The outcome of exploration in an established mining area is easier to judge than that in a remote and less well known region. The chances of making a profitable discovery in an unexplored area and the value of metals that might be present per square kilometre can only be estimated from the distribution of ore deposits and production records in geologically similar areas of active mining.

It is not unusual for companies to undertake major exploration programmes in which the chances of finding a profitable deposit are quite low, perhaps 1 in 200 or 1 in 500. With long lead times, even if exploration is successful and a mine is opened, it might be 10 years or more before an operating profit is made (Figure 2), so these are clearly medium to long-term, high-risk investments.

2.2 Exploration programme

Until the late nineteenth century, most ore deposits were discovered by a combination of luck and the experience or 'instinct' of prospectors who had little or no formal training in geology. Indeed, a close look at the records of many modern mines reveals that they were found as a result of the persistence of individuals making direct observations of rocks and soils on the ground. However, most of the more easily discoverable deposits have long since been found, and many such deposits have been worked to the extent that they are no longer economic to mine.

Historical methods of prospecting

Figure 9 Sixteenth-century prospecting: the divining twig and trenching.

In 1556, the first detailed documentation of mining and geology, *De re metallica*, by Georgius Agricola was published, based on mining in the Erzgebirge region of Germany and Czechoslovakia. It provides evidence that even then prospectors had a good understanding of indicators that might lead them to metal ore deposits. For example, there was early recognition that vegetation could be affected by the presence of mineralization.

> ...there are trees whose foliage in spring-time has a bluish or leaden tint, the upper branches more especially being tinged with black or with any other unnatural colour, the trunks cleft in two, and the branches black or discoloured. ... Therefore, in a place where there is a multitude of trees, if a long row of them at an unusual time lose their verdure and become black or discoloured, and frequently fall by the violence of the wind, beneath this spot there is a vein. Likewise along the course where a vein extends, there grows a certain herb or fungus which is absent from the adjacent space, or sometimes even from the neighbourhood of the veins. By these signs of Nature a vein can be discovered.
>
> *Georgius Agricola*

We shall return to similar forms of prospecting at the present day in Section 2.6.4. Agricola also reported the use of the divining twig for prospecting for metallic ore mineral veins (Figure 9). Although divining is based on no known scientific principles, water divining is still commonly used today to find underground water and was used well into the nineteenth century for mineral prospecting.

The early prospectors employed many forms of direct observation that are still in use today. They would search the ground surface for signs of mineralization, such as vein outcrops; colourful gossans or weathering crusts (*Metals 1*, Section 3.2.2); pieces of ore uncovered by the action of streams, moles or the plough; ore mineral grains in sands; discoloration of trees and grass; mineral waters and the position of springs. These indications were then tested by digging exploratory pits; today, boreholes would be used.

Prospecting was directed both at finding new deposits and at finding additional ores in existing workings. Where veins were not visible, prospectors would use methods such as hushing, boring, and driving crosscuts.

Hushing was used especially in northern England, but only where the terrain was suitable. A reservoir was built at the top of a slope and, when full, it was breached and the water allowed to rush down in a torrent, tearing up the soil as it went. This laid bare the underlying rock and, where the flow was powerful enough, also removed ore and rock. Hushing was also used to work veins, by flushing out the debris of open-cast workings. However, many landowners disliked hushing because it did extensive damage to their property.

Borings were used to find coal seams by the early seventeenth century, but they could easily miss mineral veins because veins tend to form vertical sheets more often than horizontal ones. Early borings were comparatively shallow, made with simple chisel bits, or borers that consisted of little more than a hollow pipe with a sharp cutting edge at one end and a cross-piece handle at the other.

Crosscuts are horizontal tunnels driven across a line of veins from underground workings or from the surface. They were more likely to encounter new veins than borings. Crosscuts serve equally well for the underground movement of men and materials or for mine drainage, so they became an important form of exploratory activity by the end of the eighteenth century.

Only in the nineteenth century were major exploratory projects undertaken to discover and prove new veins in advance and to allow steady and regular mine development. In the north Pennines, for example, about 200 km of exploratory adits and crosscuts were driven in one lead mining area during the period 1818–76, when almost 400 000 tons of lead ore were produced.

Until the introduction of diamond drilling in the late nineteenth century, miners lacked the means to prove mineral deposits without first sinking shafts or driving adits. Their inability to assess accurately the precise location, true extent and real value of mineral veins was a major difficulty. Even when veins were proved, the industry had a reputation as a precarious and speculative investment because of large and unpredictable fluctuations in mining costs and profits.

With the growing demand for metals and depletion of the more obvious ore deposits, new deposits have generally become more difficult to find by direct means. To compensate, however, there is now a great deal more information available about how and where ore deposits occur. The modern exploration geologist has access to geological maps, to rapidly increasing amounts of ground imaging data from aircraft and satellites, and to sophisticated geophysical and geochemical techniques for detecting ore bodies. Often, favourable areas for exploration can be selected without leaving the office.

Once the metal and, therefore, the type of mineral deposit to be targeted have been established on the basis of company expertise, market constraints, and so on, there are several stages to follow in a typical exploration programme (Figure 10).

1. *Desk studies* identify broad areas where deposits are likely to occur. They are based initially on an understanding of the geological settings in which different ore bodies form, and information compiled from geological maps, satellite images, and any previous exploration studies.
2. *Reconnaissance surveys* on a regional scale (thousands of square kilometres) are designed to identify the most promising areas for more detailed survey. They might include airborne geophysics, regional field mapping, and geochemical stream sampling. All these activities involve personnel and equipment, so this is when the exploration costs start to rise, but costs are still relatively low per square kilometre.
3. *Localized surveys* on promising areas (tens of square kilometres) are aimed at detecting potential ore bodies. They involve largely ground-based studies; detailed field mapping, ground-based geophysics, and geochemical analysis of soil samples to identify specific targets worthy of further investigation. Most of these methods are labour and equipment intensive and costs per square kilometre rise steeply.
4. *Evaluation* of favourable targets by drilling, trenching, and geophysical logging, in order to prove an ore body and define its size. These are costly operations and practical only over specific targets. Drilling costs are particularly high.

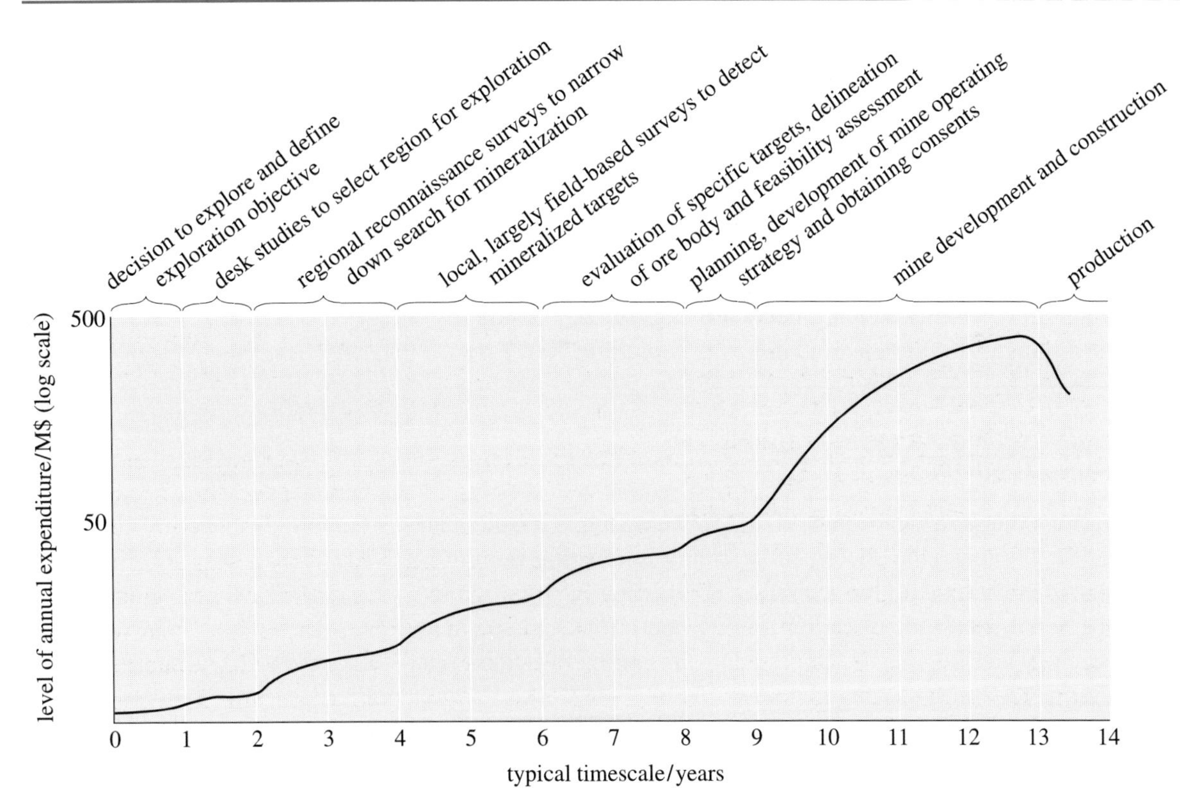

Figure 10 Stages and relative levels of expenditure in a mineral exploration and mine development programme on a scale similar to Olympic Dam (Section 1.1). Note that the costs scale is logarithmic.

At every stage of mineral exploration and mine development, costs become greater (Figure 10), and risk analysis is necessary to assess whether the information available justifies progressing to the next stage or whether the risks are too great and the programme should be stopped.

Before we look at these stages and some of the methods used in more detail, this would be a good time to view again Video Band 14: *Gold Rush in the 1990s*. The exploration and mining aspects are relevant as background for Sections 2 and 3 of this Block. Notes are provided in the video box to highlight features of the video, and you can test your understanding of the main points of the video by answering Questions 7 and 8. It will help if you read the questions through before viewing.

Video Band 14 Gold Rush in the 1990s

Speakers

John Wright	The Open University
Bruce Braginton	Lone Tree Mine
Billy Loughlin	Independent consultant

Gold was mined extensively in Nevada in the mid-nineteenth century, but declined as the rich veins were worked out. In the 1980s it became apparent that rich vein deposits lay beneath the alluvium that floors the valleys in the 'Basin and Range' province and that extensive low grade deposits occurred in both hydrothermally altered rocks and silicified rocks (jasperoid) often associated with fault breccias. The large scale mining and extraction methods of today are quite different from those used in the nineteenth century, and are particularly suitable for extracting extremely fine-grained gold from low grade ore. Notice that conventional prospecting still has its value, but both exploration for and evaluation of deposits benefit greatly from modern technology. Shallow open pit mining of the kind featured is notable for its short lead time to production and the relatively short lifetime of mines.

Question 7

(a) What was the main method of exploration for gold in Nevada in the nineteenth century?

(b) What modern-day exploration methods are described in Video Band 14?

Question 8

Which twentieth-century mining developments are largely responsible for making open pit mining of low-grade gold deposits economic?

2.3 Desk studies

After an exploration objective has been defined, the next step is to select an area for exploration, often an area geologically similar to existing mining areas. This means identifying a region, collating all existing information in the form of maps, reports, records of earlier mining operations and so on, and using geological understanding of the factors controlling mineralization (as described in *Metals 1*) to interpret these data.

Question 9

In which of the crustal settings 1–3 would you begin to search for each of the types of deposit a–c?

Crustal settings

1 Ancient continental interiors, i.e. cratons

2 Ancient oceanic crust in collision zones

3 Shale–limestone–evaporite sequences of sedimentary basins

Types of deposit

(a) Limestone-hosted lead and zinc deposits

(b) Magmatic segregation deposits of chromite

(c) Banded ironstone formations

You saw in *Metals 1* that certain metals occur in higher concentrations in particular rocks, and that the occurrence of certain rock types can indicate the presence of specific ore deposits. Thus, once a suitable region in which to explore for a particular type of deposit has been selected, it is important to locate appropriate rock types, because these direct the geologist to specific areas.

Question 10

Ore deposits of nickel, tin, uranium and titanium occur in crustal rocks. Use your knowledge from *Metals 1* to answer the following.

(a) Which of these deposits tend to be associated with granitic rocks and which are more likely to be associated with gabbroic rocks?

(b) For which of these metals would you prospect for ore minerals in gravel and sand deposits of modern stream channels?

Knowledge about mineralizing processes is useful, but there's still a lot we don't know. So, we cannot predict *exactly* where ore deposits will be. That's why we need to use systematic exploration methods. For example, we know that porphyry copper deposits occur as stockwork vein systems associated with granodioritic rocks where hydrothermal fluids have extensively altered the minerals of the host rock (*Metals 1*, Section 2.4). We cannot always say why some granodiorites contain porphyry copper deposits, whereas others in similar geological settings do not. We do know that volcanic arc settings (sites of modern or extinct subduction zones) are the best places to look for large-scale copper mineralization. Similarly, there is a very well known association of lead and zinc sulphide ores with limestones, especially faulted limestones associated with shales (*Metals 1*, Section 4.3). We know that the ores are of hydrothermal origin, but we cannot always tell why some limestones are mineralized whereas others are not.

One form of desk study has become increasingly important since the 1970s — gathering information obtained from a distance by aircraft and satellites. This is known as **remote sensing**.

Remote sensing

Making maps of different kinds, whether topographic or geological, once relied solely on surveying on the ground with theodolites, compasses and measuring chains. This is still important, but since the 1930s much mapping has used photographs looking vertically downward from aircraft and, more recently, electronically captured images from satellites. The use of high precision satellite navigation systems has supplanted much of the precise positioning through conventional surveying by an even more precise form of geographical location. The Global Positioning System, developed for the USA military but accessible in a slightly degraded form for civilian use, makes it possible to define locations anywhere on Earth to within 10 m horizontally and 5 m vertically. Accurate location is important in field surveys, and in airborne surveys where large amounts of data are acquired rapidly and height positioning is important. Then, using computer techniques, maps of any kind can be produced very quickly and at relatively low cost.

An aerial or satellite photographic image contains much more information than most maps, since it records everything from topography to vegetation, soil cover, rock outcrops, roads and buildings. The information encompasses a far greater area than anyone working on the ground could see — even during a protracted period of work — and it may cover areas that, for one reason or another, are physically inaccessible. The box 'Aerial photograph interpretation' illustrates how rapid geological interpretation is possible.

Geologists have used aerial photography since the 1930s. Since the 1960s, many of its limitations have been overcome by using parts of the electromagnetic spectrum that are invisible to the human eye. This is a more sophisticated form of remote sensing that uses information about natural features carried by infrared and ultraviolet radiation as well as visible light. Although surface materials reflect radiation, they also absorb it (heating up), and, on cooling, they emit different wavelengths of radiation according to their composition. Thus, information about different kinds of surface material can be obtained by recording their electromagnetic spectrum and measuring the strength of different wavelengths. By using computers to analyse and combine these measurements (as demonstrated in Video Band 14), visible false-colour images can be produced to reveal areas with distinctive geological characteristics.* As a result, many minerals in soils and rocks, as well as different kinds of vegetation, can now be distinguished. This form of remote sensing is shown in Plate 70 and can be used for both geological mapping and the detection of particular geological features that might relate to metalliferous mineral deposits.

* False-colour images are produced when intensities of different spectral characteristics are represented as red, green and blue images, and these images are combined. Locations where all three characteristics are strong show up as bright spots (white).

Aerial photograph interpretation

Figure 11a is a black and white aerial photograph of an area in northern Canada. At first sight, the surface appears extremely complex; this is not surprising as it is a mixture of water, lakes, vegetated areas and rock outcrops. There are several geological features that control the form of the rock outcrop patterns. Beginning to interpret such an image relies on recognizing different combinations of tone, image texture and patterns, and relating them to geological features through ground control.

- What do you think the scattered, irregularly shaped, dark patches in the photograph represent?

- They have distinct outlines and are sometimes elongate, following the textural 'grain'. They are small lakes.

Figure 11b is a geological interpretation that may help you follow this description of Figure 11a. The palest areas are outcrops of granitic rock and large quartz veins, and the mid greys represent either sedimentary rocks or vegetation. About halfway up the image is an arcuate east–west boundary between an area to the north with many pale granitic outcrops separated by grey patches of vegetation, and an area to the south that is dominated by grey sediment outcrops with very similar patches of vegetation and a number of irregular, often elongate patches of pale quartz veins. In the lower left quadrant there is an elliptical body of pale granite, partially surrounded by a lake, and lying within the sediments. If you look carefully at the sediments, you might be able to see patterns that form a set of parallel 'swirls'; these are ridges and valleys shaped by folding of the bedded sedimentary rocks. The sedimentary 'grain' in this area is *cut across* by the elliptical granite and the quartz veins, which are, therefore, younger than the folding. Finally, there are some strong linear features, particularly on the left side, that extend through the pale granite mass and the sediments. Since they appear to control the form of the lakes, they must represent some sort of easily eroded ground.

- These linear features are not explained in the key to Figure 11b. What type.j of geological feature do you think they might represent?

- They could be faults, or fracture zones, picked out by erosion — but there is no evidence of displacement in the main east–west boundary. Following two of them from NNW to SSE they can be seen to cross the elliptical granite, where they show as parallel-sided grey bands. In fact, they are basaltic igneous dykes that intrude both the sediments and the granite — but we would only know that by *direct observation* of the rocks on the ground or by a more sophisticated form of remote sensing.

(a)

(b)

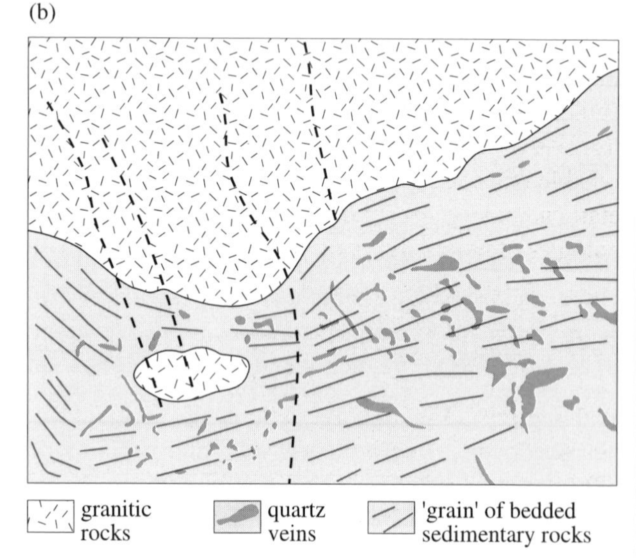

Figure 11 Part of northern Canada (the area is about 5.5 km across; north is to the top): (a) aerial photograph; (b) geological interpretation of the photograph.

You may not have seen all these features easily, but you will have seen some of them. Figure 11b is a geological interpretation of Figure 11a made in 30 minutes or so by an experienced photo interpreter without any field work. To make the same map by traditional means would have taken at least a week, for much of the area is almost impenetrable pine forest and swamp. However, it is still essential to establish 'ground truth', that is, to *prove* the nature of particular types of feature on the image, but once this is established, the principle can be applied across a whole area.

Many low-grade ores, such as porphyry-type deposits, can be seen by remote sensing because of the effects on soils where groundwaters have been made acid by the weathering of sulphide minerals (*Metals 1*, Section 3.2.2). Sometimes the soils are bleached because soluble iron(II) has been removed. At other times a highly coloured capping or gossan of insoluble iron(III) minerals may form, resulting from oxidation of iron-rich sulphides. Both effects result in a visible **anomaly** (an area of the image that stands out as being different) that can be detected by remote sensing. An example is the 'gold' anomaly featured in Video Band 14.

The *resolving power* of the system is an important property that limits the size of the details that can be made out by remote sensing. Resolution depends on a number of factors, including the flying height of the imaging system, its optics and the recording medium. It is analogous to the grain size of a film which limits the enlargement of photographs.

The potential of remote sensing is primarily economic. On average, a geologist in the field using traditional mapping methods would take upwards of 100 days to produce a simple map of an area of 100 square kilometres at a scale of 1:100 000. This could cost in the region of $200 000. Using satellite imagery, the same area could be mapped to very much the same level of detail in around 10 days at one-tenth of the cost. Moreover, by using information that simply cannot be seen in the field, either because it is invisible or on too grand a scale to be grasped from the ground, much more detail can emerge. In addition, the satellite 'sees' all the area, while the geologist cannot visit every location.

2.4 Regional reconnaissance surveys

Sooner or later, predictions made from desk studies must be tested. The geologist must investigate a target, either by going into the field or by commissioning other forms of remote sensing over regions of interest. This is when exploration costs begin to rise substantially (Figure 10). Let's first consider what techniques are suited to regional-scale exploration.

2.4.1 Geophysical techniques

- You were introduced to some geophysical exploration techniques when considering how to search for petroleum in Block 4 *Energy 1*. What were they?

- There were three techniques:
  - seismic
  - gravity
  - magnetic.

Seismic surveys

Seismic surveys are invaluable to the petroleum industry for determining geological structures, particularly in stratified sediments, and for identifying structures in which oil and gas might be trapped. However, they are expensive and only appropriate in ore mineral exploration where deposits are confined to sedimentary layers, where geological structure is important, or where alternative methods of exploration would be even more costly. Seismic surveys have rather restricted applications in the search for ore bodies, so we can leave them to one side.

Gravity surveys

Gravity surveys measure variations in the Earth's gravitational field and, therefore, indicate differences in the *density* of rocks at or close to the Earth's surface. The results are usually displayed in the form of a gravity contour map showing *deviations* from the gravitational pull that would be *expected* at the Earth's surface, thus revealing any rocks of abnormal density in the upper part of the crust. A positive gravity value indicates relatively high-density rocks beneath the surface, whereas a negative gravity value indicates relatively low-density rocks.

Magnetic surveys

Magnetic surveys measure the Earth's magnetic field, which is locally distorted by magnetism in rocks caused by the magnetization of magnetically susceptible minerals. Only three reasonably common minerals, normally present in rocks as accessory minerals, are sufficiently magnetized by the Earth's magnetic field to produce a measurable magnetic response. In order of decreasing magnetic strength or *susceptibility*, they are magnetite (Fe_3O_4), ilmenite ($FeTiO_3$), and pyrrhotite (FeS). Consequently, magnetic variations reflect the presence of particularly iron-rich rocks, such as basalts, that typically contain significant amounts of these magnetic minerals.

Question 11

Given what you know already about the properties measured by gravity and magnetic surveys, briefly summarize the likely results of such surveys in an area that contains gabbroic intrusions with associated sulphide mineralization.

It was noted in Block 4 *Energy 1*, Section 4.3.1, that geophysical exploration methods lend themselves to reconnaissance surveys that cover large areas because they are rapid and relatively inexpensive per square kilometre. Both gravity and magnetic surveys are particularly useful for determining the location of basaltic intrusions, some of which may be associated with sulphide ore. When it is necessary to locate anomalies more accurately, localized geophysical surveys — the subject of Section 2.5 — may be necessary.

2.4.2 Geochemical methods

We can take rock samples from the field and measure the abundance of just about every element of the Periodic Table, but most geochemical analysis techniques require laboratories with specialized equipment and skilled operators — which means they are expensive.

- Would it be desirable to analyse all the rocks that are exposed in an area of regional exploration?

- Ideally, yes, but mineralization may be very localized and rocks containing it may not be exposed, especially if the area is largely covered by soil and vegetation. So, the analysis of bedrock samples is unlikely to be helpful without continuous exposure and a high sampling density; and then it would be extremely expensive.

It would be far better to analyse fewer samples, with each representing and recording the mineralization of a large area. How could such a form of sampling be possible? This can be answered by considering processes active at the Earth's surface.

- What happens naturally to rocks exposed at the Earth's surface?

- They are subject to weathering, which breaks up rocks; some (resistant) minerals may be released, others may be chemically decomposed, and soluble materials distributed in surface and ground waters (*Metals 1*, Section 3.1).

The products of weathering are soils, sediments and soluble material in solution. When an ore body is weathered, unusually high levels of metals end up in weathering products that are then distributed by surface processes. This dispersion provides samples that not only reflect bedrock chemistry of a large area, but also contain a compositional *signature* of any ore bodies — just what is needed for geochemical exploration surveys.

- In what circumstances should we analyse (i) stream water or (ii) stream sediment samples?

- (i) Stream water analyses are suitable for detecting metals that are soluble in water and are taken into solution when ore minerals are weathered. Water moves faster and further than sediment, so water samples represent a wider area.

  (ii) Stream sediment analyses are suitable for detecting ore minerals that are stable under weathering (or form stable weathering products). Sediments move less readily than waters, and, therefore, are better for targeting sources. They also provide information about the minerals in the deposit.

The final point to consider here concerns the form of ore deposits and their ease of detection.

- *Confined* and *dispersed deposits* were discussed in *Metals 1*, Section 1.3. Which do you think would be easier to find by geochemical exploration techniques and why?

- The metals in dispersed deposits are widely disseminated over large areas, so anomalous levels of diagnostic elements would be difficult to miss. In contrast, concentrations of metals in a confined deposit are very restricted, and a corresponding geochemical anomaly might also be localized and so more easily missed. Although the *levels* of metal concentrations are likely to be higher locally for confined deposits, the *area* of elevated metal concentrations is likely to be larger for dispersed deposits. Therefore, dispersed deposits are more likely to be detected in geochemical surveys because the density of measurement is commonly around 0.5 to 2 samples per square kilometre.

Activity 1 gives you an opportunity to think through an exploration problem, and demonstrates how reconnaissance surveys serve to direct subsequent localized surveys.

Activity 1 Interpretation and planning during the reconnaissance stage

You have a topographic map of a selected area (Figure 12a), and a limited amount of money in your exploration account. There is not much rock exposed. The vegetation is a thin cover of grass in an area of low rainfall where streams flow only in the wet season.

Figure 12b summarizes the results of a gravity survey of this area. The most obvious feature is that many of the gravity contours tend to run from north-west to south-east, and we know from what little geological field work already done that this trend is broadly parallel to the outcrop pattern of the major rock units. To find out what else can be inferred from the contour pattern on Figure 12b, and how far that helps in planning an exploration programme, answer the following questions.

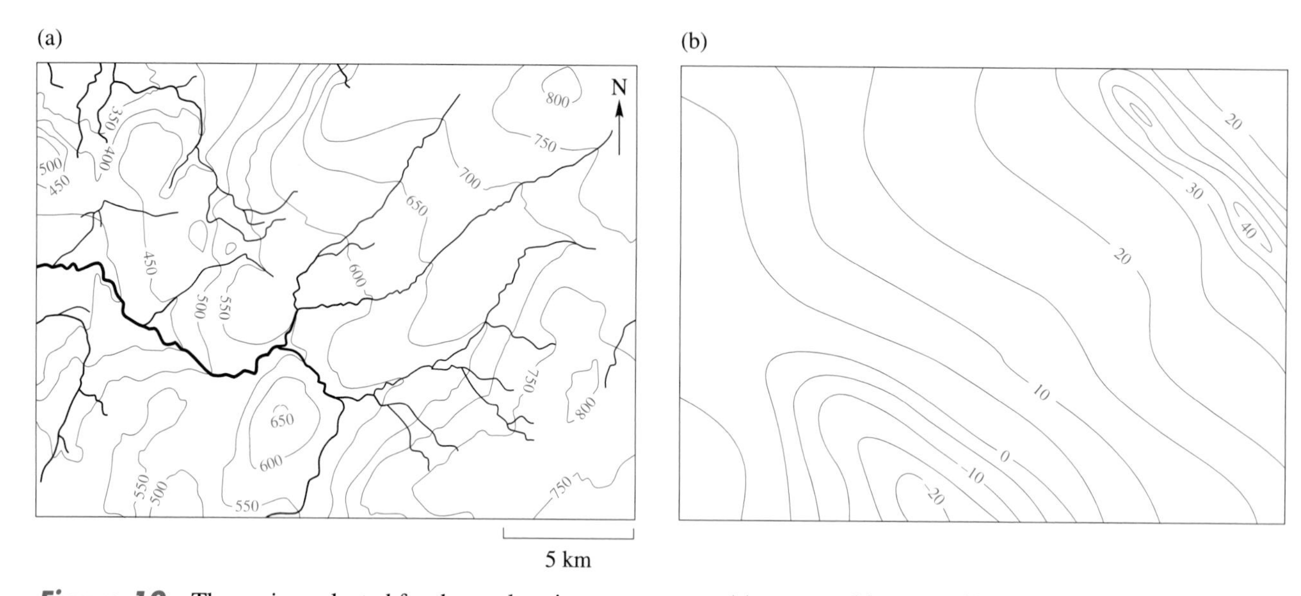

Figure 12 The region selected for the exploration programme: (a) topographic map with drainage channels, contours in m; (b) results of a gravity survey of the region, contours in mgal.

(a) A lot of gravity contours are clustered together in the north-east corner, and near the southern margin of the gravity map. Do they depict areas of particularly high or low gravity?

(b) Which of these areas is likely to be associated with high-density rocks and which with low-density rocks — that is, which cluster of contours is likely to be associated with basalts or gabbros, and which could be associated with a granitic intrusion?

(c) As there are no rock exposures in the areas of the gravity highs and lows, consider each of the following exploration options and suggest whether or not they would be appropriate for determining the presence of mineralization and explain why. The options are (i) more detailed geophysics — gravity or magnetics, (ii) geochemical sampling, (iii) field mapping, (iv) drilling.

(d) If your target was sulphide mineralization associated with basaltic intrusions, and you decided that the next step should be to undertake a geochemical survey of the drainage channels, would you analyse water samples or sediment samples? Why? Roughly which area on the map in Figure 12a would you select for your survey of drainage geochemistry?

(e) If the results of this drainage survey indicated anomalous concentrations of metals, what would you then do to locate the source of the anomaly?

2.5 Localized geophysical surveys

Geophysical techniques that can be undertaken on a regional scale from satellite or aircraft are particularly effective as reconnaissance techniques. The same techniques can also be undertaken on a local scale to identify specific targets. In addition, there are other geophysical methods that are suitable only for localized studies as they require simultaneous measurement of surface rocks at different places. In this Section, we consider a range of geophysical methods; but first, there are three points that should be borne in mind about geophysical surveys.

1. Airborne geophysical techniques are used early in an exploration programme because they cover large areas rapidly and relatively cheaply. The same is true for gravity reconnaissance studies, which require perhaps only one measurement on the ground per square kilometre. In contrast, small-scale ground-based techniques (especially electrical methods) are slower and far more costly per unit area.
2. Geophysical techniques — especially at the reconnaissance stage — are best at detecting differences in the physical properties of large volumes of rock. They are more often used to detect the presence of particular rock types associated with ore deposits than ore minerals themselves, which are not often detectable when dispersed.
3. Most geophysical techniques can be used on different scales, but, in general, the greater the distance between the point of measurement and the rocks, the poorer the resolution (definition) of the acquired data. This is analogous to vision — it is possible to resolve more detail in close objects than in distant ones. Ground-based geophysical surveys generally take longer to complete than airborne ones, but they provide much more detailed information. We shall look at a selection of techniques that can be used to *pin-point* rocks with distinctive properties — including potential ore deposits. *Proving* the presence of a deposit, however, requires direct sampling and mineralogical or geochemical analysis.

2.5.1 Gravity surveys

Gravitational forces are measured using a gravimeter. This device contains a small object on a spring and measures how much the object is attracted by the Earth's gravity. Corrections are necessary to account for the elevation at which the measurements are made, and for the shape of the ground surface. Any remaining variations in the Earth's gravitational field can be presented as a contour map (such as Figure 12b) and are the result of variations in the density of underlying rocks.* The size of a local variation in the gravity field depends on three factors:

- the difference in density between an anomalous body of rock and the surrounding rocks;
- the distance between the body and the point of measurement;
- the size of the body.

The deeper a body of unusually high or low density rock, the less obvious is the response at the surface; thus, a large, deep body may produce a gravity response of similar magnitude to a smaller, shallower one. This effect is illustrated in Figure 13.

* Strictly speaking, any *deviation* in the gravity field from that expected at any point on the Earth's surface is called a gravity anomaly; the contour map Figure 12b is, therefore, a gravity anomaly map. However, it is quite common practice to refer to areas of particularly high or low gravity values as 'gravity anomalies' when they are distinct from the regional gravity field.

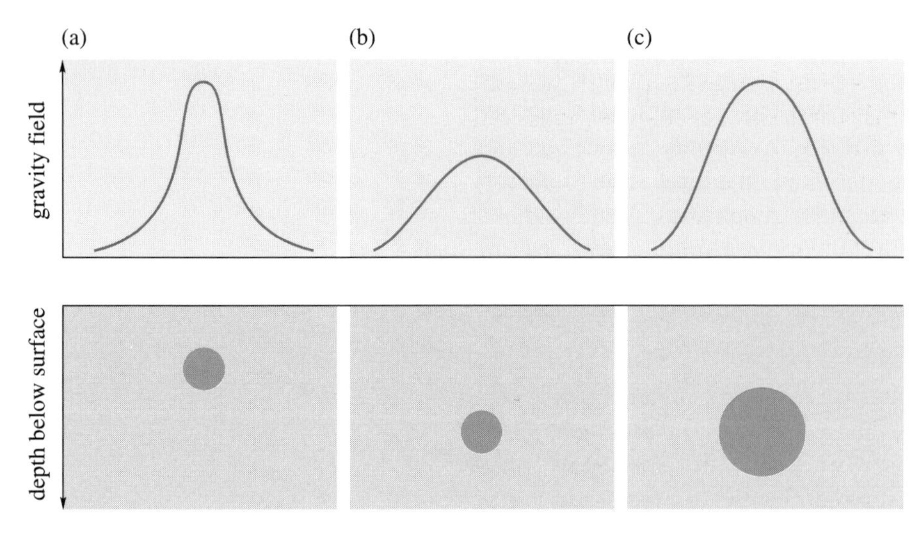

Figure 13 Deviations in the gravity field over an anomalous sphere of rock: (a) and (b) show how the field varies with depth for similar size bodies, (b) and (c) show how the field varies for bodies of different sizes at the same depth. Note that the deviation for a large body at depth (c) may be of similar magnitude to that caused by a smaller body at a shallower depth (a) but is broader.

- The deviations in the gravity field shown in Figure 13 all have positive values. Does this mean that the rock bodies have relatively high or relatively low densities? Would they be likely to have high or low iron contents?

- Positive gravity values are produced by rocks with relatively high densities (Section 2.4.1). The density of a rock is often correlated with its iron content, so those bodies featured in Figure 13 are all likely to have relatively high iron contents. Rocks with low densities produce negative gravity values, and would form trough-like mirror images of the peaks in the gravity fields illustrated in Figure 13.

- Many ore minerals have high densities. Do you think ore bodies themselves are likely to produce detectable deviations in the gravity field?

- The size of the deviation in the gravity field depends on the size of a region of contrasting density. It is unlikely that many ore bodies would contain a large enough proportion of dense ore minerals to be detected; most ores contain a high proportion of gangue with average density.

What use then, are gravity surveys in mineral exploration? Only if the volume and the density contrast of a body of rock containing both gangue and ore minerals is large enough can it produce a detectable deviation in the gravity field. A narrow vein deposit or a porphyry deposit would be unlikely to show up. On the other hand, ore bodies such as massive sulphide deposits (*Metals 1*, Section 4.2) and sulphide-bearing magmatic segregation deposits (*Metals 1*, Section 2.1.2) are typically associated with large volumes of dense rocks (basalts, gabbros) that are likely to produce significant positive gravity values. However, a gravity survey would detect basaltic rock masses among less dense rocks, whether or not sulphides were present. Thus, gravity surveys cannot directly prove the presence of an ore body, but they can often provide important information on the variation in density of rocks underground. This information can then be used to *direct* more localized exploration programmes.

Question 12

Using your knowledge of ore deposits from *Metals 1*, say whether or not a gravity survey would be useful in the search for the following types of ore deposit and why:

(a) pegmatite deposits;

(b) layered magmatic sulphide deposits;

(c) porphyry copper deposits.

2.5.2 Electrical surveys

There are a number of methods of electrical surveying. These either make use of naturally occurring electrical fields within the Earth, or they require electrical current to be applied to the ground.

Conduction of electricity in rocks depends on their resistivity (box 'Electrical resistivity') and, as shown in Figure 14, resistivity values for common rocks and minerals vary over several orders of magnitude. Most rock-forming minerals have high electrical resistivity and are good insulators, so it is hardly surprising that most rocks have high resistivity. However, there is another factor to consider. Most rocks have interconnected pores and cracks that usually contain water, and water normally contains dissolved salts (and, therefore, charged ions) that allow electrical currents to flow by the movement of the charged ions in solution. The resistivity of rocks is, therefore, significantly *reduced* by the presence of pore water. Porosity is a major influence on the resistivity of rocks: resistivity of water-saturated rocks decreases as porosity increases. In fact, the conductivity of most rocks is essentially that of water occupying the interstices of an insulating material.

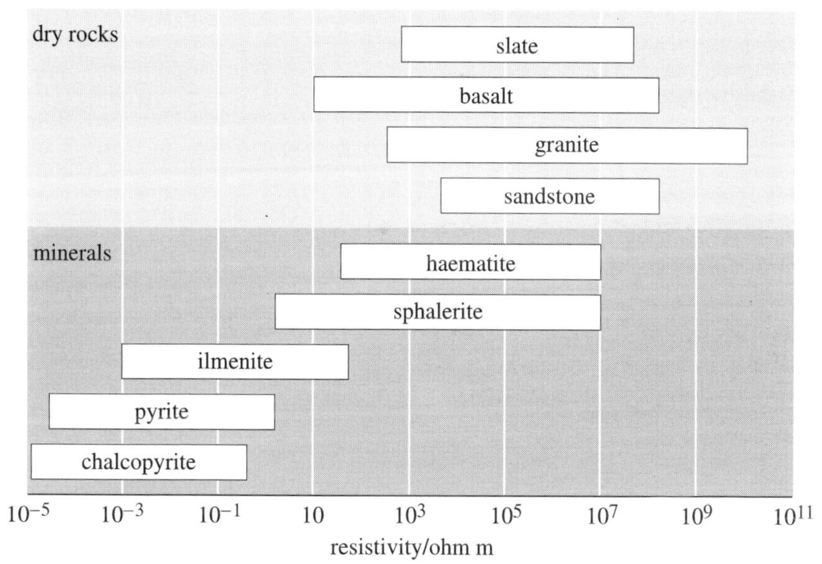

Figure 14 Resistivity values for some common rocks and ore minerals.

There are three electrical techniques that can be used in exploration for ore deposits.

1 **Resistivity surveys** detect variations in the electrical conductivity of rocks underground, and may reveal bodies of rock with unusual conductivity. They are also widely used in engineering and hydrogeological investigations because resistivity is reduced by the presence of underground water (Block 3, Section 3.8).

2 **Spontaneous polarization surveys** measure electrical currents that sometimes flow naturally in the ground.

3 **Induced polarization surveys** depend on an applied electric current and measure the ability of some rocks to charge up more readily than others.

Electrical resistivity

Electrical current is the flow of charged particles, for example, electrons and ions, and occurs much more readily in some materials than others, depending on their **electrical resistance** — the ability of a material to resist electrical conduction. For an electrical current to flow in any material, there must be a difference in electrical potential. Water flows through a pipe only when the pressure is higher at one end than the other; similarly a difference in electrical charge provides the **potential difference** that enables an electric current to flow from one point to another in a conducting medium.

There is a simple relationship known as Ohm's law that relates these electrical parameters. The current, i, (measured in amps) that flows in a material is the ratio of the electrical potential difference, V, (measured in volts) to the resistance, R, of the material (measured in ohms).

i.e. $i(\text{amps}) = V(\text{volts})/R(\text{ohms})$

Thus, the greater the voltage across a piece of material, the larger the current that flows through it. Conversely, if we keep the voltage the same and measure the current that flows in a number of different materials, we find that the current varies depending on the electrical resistance of each material. The *resistivity* of a material is its ability to resist a current passing between the opposite faces of a one-metre cube, and is measured in ohm metres.

Certain rather rare minerals such as native metals and graphite have free electrons in their atomic structure. Are they likely to be good or bad conductors of electricity — and will they have high or low resistivity?

As the movement of electrons is easy in these minerals they will be good conductors of electricity and have low resistivity.

Resistivity surveys

Resistivity surveys were introduced in Block 3, Section 3.8.3. These surveys distinguish between 'wet' rocks and 'dry' rocks because 'wet' rocks are generally the better conductors. In a similar way, some mineral deposits are better conductors than the surrounding rock because they contain sulphide ore minerals, which are generally better conductors (except for sphalerite) than most rock-forming minerals (Figure 14). Resistivity surveys cannot identify ore deposits but, used alongside other methods, they help build up a picture of the sub-surface geology that may help to define a deposit.

What two methods used in resistivity surveys were described in Block 3?

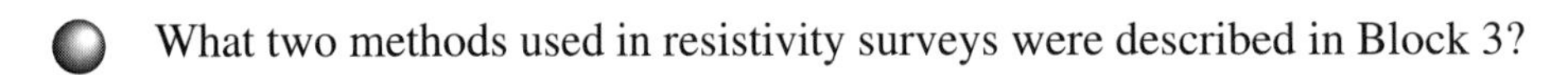

Horizontal profiling where electrodes are moved in formation along the surface to measure the horizontal variation of sub-surface resistivity. This formation is shown in Figure 15, where the distance of separation (a) remains unchanged; the depth of penetration remains fixed.

Vertical sounding to measure the variations in resistivity with depth. This involves keeping the array of electrodes centred on the same place but changing the distance (d) between them.

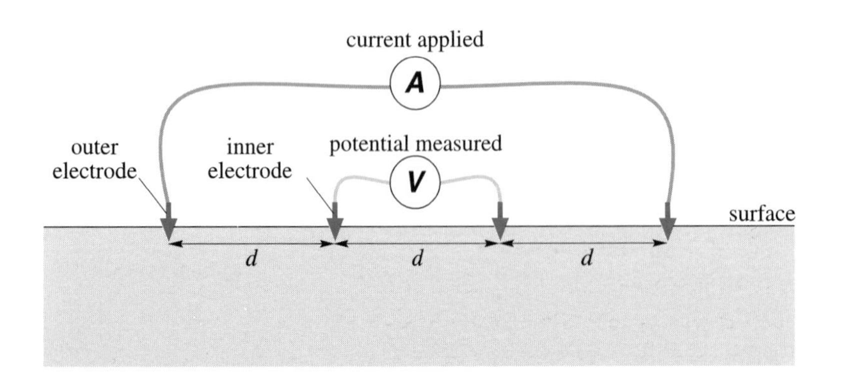

Figure 15 A commonly used linear arrangement of electrodes for resistivity surveys: a fixed current (A) is applied to the ground via the two outer electrodes, and the resultant voltage (V) is measured using the two inner electrodes. In horizontal profiling, all the electrodes are moved along the surface keeping the distances (d) between them constant. In vertical sounding, the distance (d) between electrodes is changed, the array remaining centred at the same point.

Spontaneous polarization

Under certain conditions, electrical currents flow naturally in rocks, an effect known as spontaneous polarization (SP). This happens particularly in sulphide ore bodies that extend across the water table as shown in Figure 16a. The electrical potential is thought to be caused by oxidation of the ore body in the weathered zone (producing free electrons) and reduction beneath the water table (producing positive ions). An alternative explanation is that the ore body acts as a conductor of currents caused by oxidation–reduction reactions that occur at the water table. In any event, the result is a build-up of negative charge above a conductive ore body such that the electrical potential can be detected at the surface by electrodes connected to a voltmeter (Figure 16a). Simply by stepping these electrodes along the surface, variations in potential can be detected and lines of equal potential mapped out (Figure 16b). This rapid technique is largely limited to conductive, sulphide ore bodies that extend across the water table.

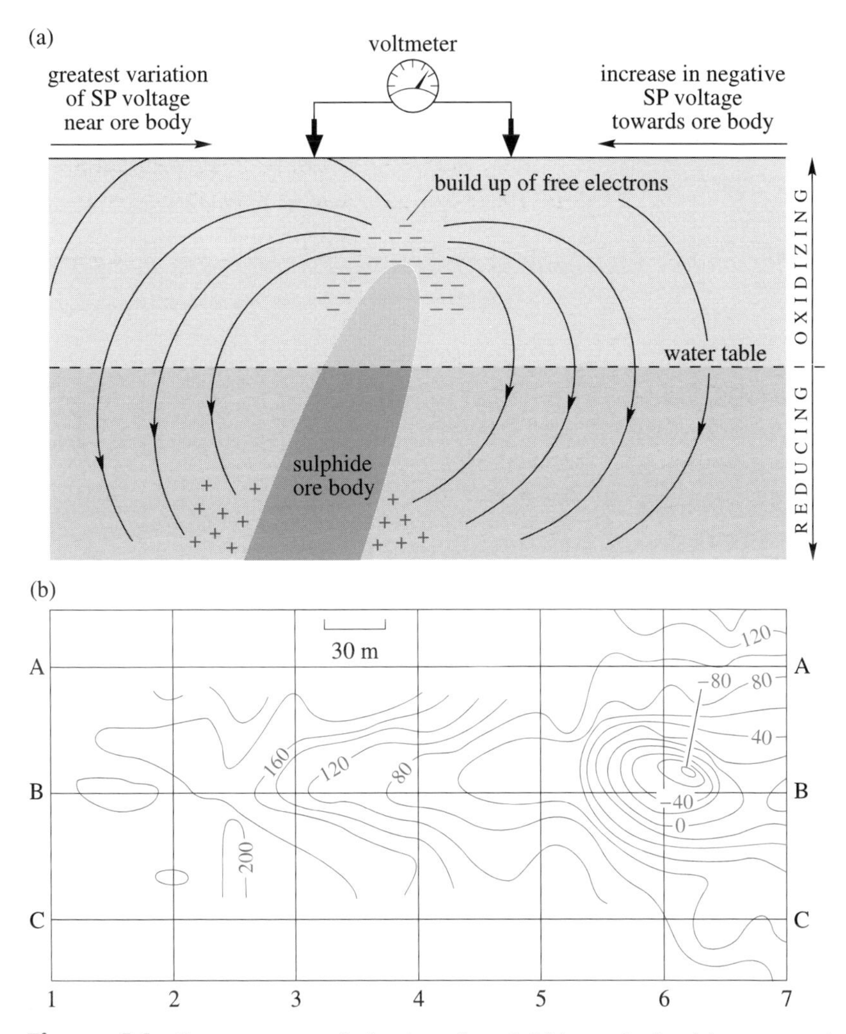

Figure 16 Spontaneous polarization of a sulphide ore body: (a) cross-section showing the build-up of negative charge above the ore body and the flow of electrical current around the ore body; (b) map showing lines of equal potential resulting from spontaneous polarization, contours in mV.

Question 13

Examine Figure 16b. Bearing in mind that there can be a build-up of negative charge around sulphide ore bodies due to spontaneous polarization, give the grid reference at which you might expect to find such an ore body.

Induced polarization

Not all sulphide ore bodies give rise to spontaneous polarization. This may be due to a number of factors including:

- the presence of poorly conducting sulphides, such as sphalerite;
- a lack of electrical continuity within the ore body;
- the ore body doesn't extend across the water table.

Thus, SP has its limitations. However, conductive minerals can have charges induced in them when subjected to a powerful electric field. This is the basis for an electrical method called induced polarization (IP). Passing an electric current at high voltage through the ground induces a polarity in minerals, rather like charging a battery. After the current is switched off, a small current flows in the reverse direction and the potential decays gradually rather than immediately (Figure 17). The time taken for the potential to decay is a measure of the *chargeability* of the rocks, and hence the amount of conductive sulphide minerals in the ground. Chargeability depends only on the presence of conductive grains, they don't have to be in electrical continuity, so IP is an important method for detecting most kinds of sulphide deposit.

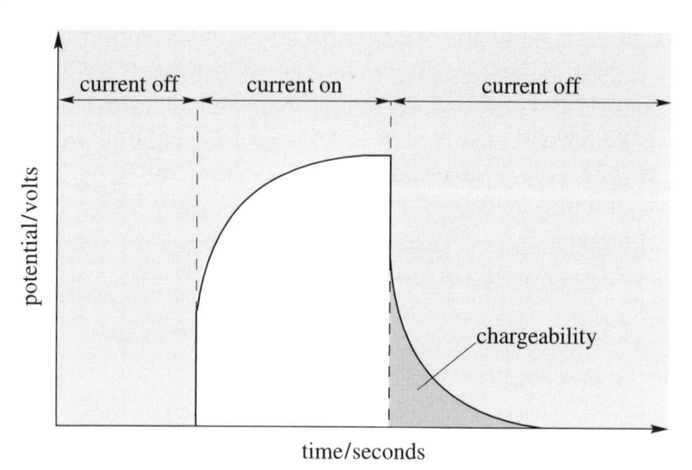

Figure 17 Electrical potential plotted against time to show the effect of induced polarization when a high voltage is applied to the ground. The shaded area under the curve is a measure of the chargeability of the rock.

This would be a good time to view the second part of Video Band 16: *Pine Point: origin and exploration*. It follows on from the part that you viewed in *Metals 1*. After watching the video, test your understanding by answering Question 14.

Video Band 16 Pine Point: origin and exploration

Speakers

Steve Drury and John Wright	The Open University
Doug Shearman	Imperial College, London
Jeanie Owens	Pine Point Mines

The account of exploration at Pine Point shows how IP can be used to define ore deposits in an area that is covered by many metres of glacial boulder clay. The full details of the procedure need not concern us. In essence, a strong current is passed into the rock for a short time, and the electrical potential is measured with an array of electrodes. While the current is on, the voltage increases to reach a constant level, and when the current is switched off, the voltage drops and then decays gradually, as illustrated in Figure 17. The time taken for the voltage to decay is a measure of the chargeability of the rock. In the video, chargeability is explained in terms of the extent of oxidation of mineral surfaces — but this video was made in 1983, and today the explanation would be expressed differently. Chargeability is now considered to be the size of the charge physically induced by the applied current at the surfaces of conductive minerals rather than the extent of any oxidation reaction. Disregarding the explanation given in the video, however, does not detract from the demonstration of a valuable exploration method.

Question 14

Why was it so important at Pine Point to use geophysical methods of exploration as opposed to geochemical methods or direct geological observation?

Figure 18 is an example of the results obtained by geophysical prospecting at Pine Point. An IP survey identified an area with high levels of chargeability, where resistivity was low (Figure 18a). Gravity, which can detect high density minerals if they form large bodies, was employed as a backup and gave a weak positive response (about 1 mgal in Figure 18b). From the geophysical information, boreholes were drilled and defined an ore body containing a reserve of 3 175 000 tonnes averaging 2.9% lead and 9.1% zinc (Figure 18c).

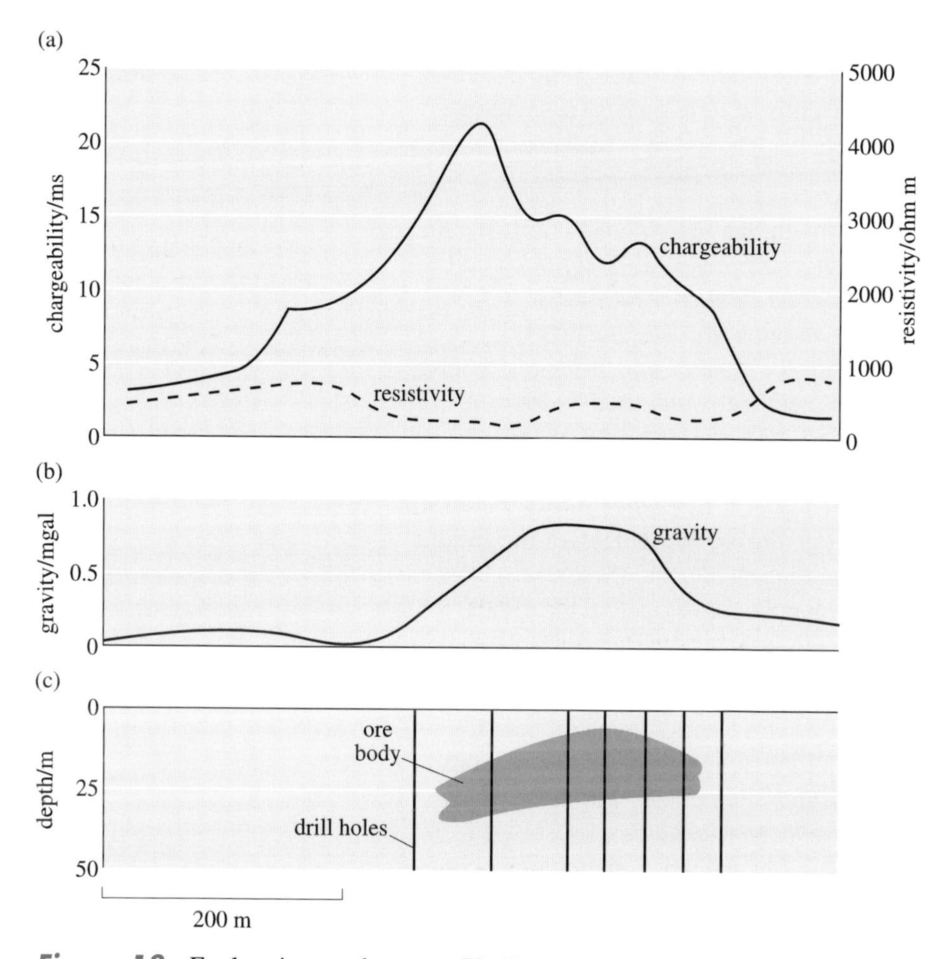

Figure 18 Exploration results over a Pb–Zn ore body at Pine Point: (a) induced polarization and resistivity profiles; (b) gravity profile; (c) drill holes and ore body.

Setting up an array of electrodes for an IP survey requires a large field crew, so the method is more expensive than many other ground-based geophysical techniques. Nonetheless, induced polarization is one of the most widely used exploration techniques in the search for sulphide ores. For instance, it was the main technique used in the definition of the major lead–zinc ore body at Navan, Ireland (Section 2.6) where the ore bodies were found in calcareous sedimentary rocks that provided a marked polarization contrast against the sulphide ore bodies. Unlike resistivity, which depends on conductive grains being connected, IP works well whether a sulphide ore body is massive (continuous) or disseminated (dispersed), as is the case with porphyry deposits.

2.5.3 Electromagnetic surveys

An electrical current flowing in a conductor produces a magnetic field. Conversely, when a conducting body is exposed to electromagnetic radiation (a varying magnetic field), alternating currents are induced within that body. This, in principle, is how a radio aerial converts radio waves into alternating electrical currents that are modified and amplified in a radio receiver and then converted to sound by a loudspeaker. The opposite happens in radio transmission, when alternating currents flowing in a conductor cause electromagnetic radiation (radio waves) to be emitted. Since most sulphide and some oxide ore minerals are good electrical conductors compared with common rocks, it is possible to exploit these induction phenomena and to detect ore bodies containing them through **electromagnetic (EM) surveys**.

All conducting ore bodies can have alternating currents induced in them by electromagnetic radiation, providing the radiation can penetrate to the depth at which they are buried. When such a body emits electromagnetic radiation with long enough wavelength (i.e. sufficiently low frequency) to penetrate rock, the *secondary radiation* emitted can be detected by a further aerial or antenna.

The traditional EM survey involves traversing the search area with two coils, a primary (transmitting) coil and a search (receiving) coil. The search coil is tuned to detect the secondary electromagnetic field created by any conducting geological structure, such as an ore body. The method is particularly sensitive to native metals. Indeed, it's the same principle that is exploited on a much smaller scale in the metal detectors used by treasure hunters and by the military to detect mines. EM prospecting is a form of remote sensing that can be carried out from the air in fixed-wing aircraft or in helicopters. Some submarine detection systems carried by military aircraft operate on a similar principle. Increasingly, the receiving devices for ground EM surveys have become smaller and more portable, and the sources have become more distant and powerful. One system, developed in the 1960s, utilizes the very low frequency (VLF) radio systems devised for communication with submerged nuclear submarines.

Particularly deep-penetrating VLF (10–20 kHz) electromagnetic radiation is produced by lightning strikes and certain EM prospecting devices rely on these as their primary signal source. This radiation passes with little loss of signal right through the Earth. VLF surveys can now be carried out using a single search aerial, hand-held, or mounted on an aircraft, thereby reducing costs and allowing rapid, routine, field measurement.

- Why would airborne magnetic or EM surveys be of little use in exploration of porphyry ore deposits?

- Porphyry deposits are low-grade and disseminated. Irrespective of the magnetic or electrical properties of the ore minerals they contain, any effects would be diluted by common nonconducting minerals.

2.6 Localized geochemical methods

The rocks, soils, water or vegetation in the vicinity of ore deposits commonly become enriched in ore metals or associated elements as a result of a variety of surface processes (Section 2.4.2). Geochemical exploration is the systematic search for unusual or anomalous concentrations of elements in these surface materials, with the aim of locating nearby ore deposits.

In exploration terms, a **geochemical anomaly** is a concentration significantly above the normal range of values for an area, which are known as **background concentrations**. The magnitude of an anomaly and the background value for any element varies from region to region and according to whether rock, soil, water or vegetation is being analysed. The boundary between background values and anomalous values is known as the **threshold**. We are dealing here mainly with metals that are present at trace abundances in common rocks, which means that they must be detected and measured at parts per million (ppm) levels.

Figure 19 shows copper concentrations in soil along a traverse where there is a clear-cut subdivision between background and anomalous values. The threshold between anomalous and background values might not always be so obvious and selecting the threshold correctly is a critical step in any interpretation.

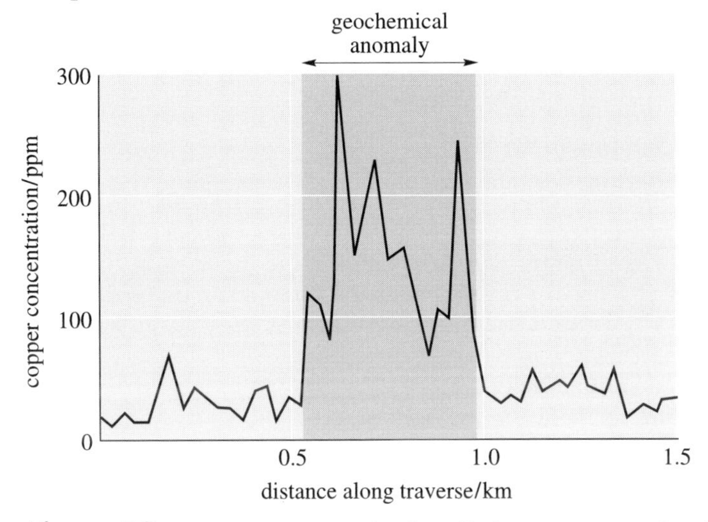

Figure 19 Copper concentration in soil along a traverse showing a zone of anomalous concentrations.

- Looking at Figure 19, what range of values do you think define the background?

- The background values are those that occur most frequently, mainly in the range 10–70 ppm.

By taking a threshold that just exceeds the background, in this instance about 80 ppm, all values that exceed the threshold are defined as anomalous.

Figure 20 presents the results of analysis for copper on 100 soil samples taken at evenly spaced intervals across a 9 × 9 km grid. The purpose of this exercise and the subject of Question 15 is to identify areas of anomalously high copper concentration that might be worth following up in the next stage of an exploration programme.

Question 15

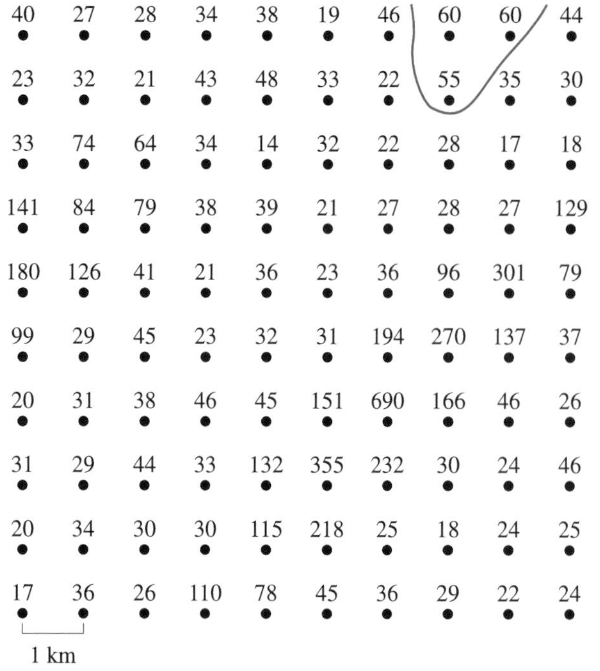

40 27 28 34 38 19 46 60 60 44
23 32 21 43 48 33 22 55 35 30
33 74 64 34 14 32 22 28 17 18
141 84 79 38 39 21 27 28 27 129
180 126 41 21 36 23 36 96 301 79
99 29 45 23 32 31 194 270 137 37
20 31 38 46 45 151 690 166 46 26
31 29 44 33 132 355 232 30 24 46
20 34 30 30 115 218 25 18 24 25
17 36 26 110 78 45 36 29 22 24

1 km

Figure 20 Copper concentrations (ppm) in soil in a gridded reconnaissance survey.

(a) On Figure 20, outline the areas where soil concentrations of copper exceed the following thresholds: (i) 50 ppm (one area is shown for you), and (ii) 250 ppm.

(b) Your plans for further exploration might differ according to the level of threshold chosen. What effect would these thresholds have on the size of the area selected for follow-up studies?

(c) What are the implications, in terms of cost and likely targeting of mineralization, of choosing the higher threshold?

Where possible, concentrations of metals that are of economic importance are measured directly, as in the case of copper in Figure 20. However, some elements, such as gold, are extremely difficult to analyse at low concentrations, particularly at background levels, and are not easy even at anomalous concentrations, which may be at low to sub-ppm levels. Moreover, such analyses can be extremely expensive. Thus, it is common practice to analyse for elements that usually accompany such an element but are more abundant and easier to analyse. These elements are called **pathfinder elements**, and they are used as *proxies* for the target metals. For example, arsenic (As), bismuth (Bi), and antimony (Sb) are frequently used as pathfinder elements for gold. (Arsenic, antimony and mercury were the pathfinders referred to as 'toxic elements' in Video Band 14).

Stream sediment surveys have been carried out systematically by the British Geological Survey in many parts of the British Isles. Concentration ranges of elements are divided up and colour-coded to produce maps showing the distribution of metals in stream sediments. Plate 71 is such a map showing the distribution of copper in northern Britain. Notice that the annotated scale along the bottom gives pairs of numbers, for example, 75/45. The second number shows the concentration of copper in ppm at the upper boundary of that division; the first shows the proportion of the data-set (the percentile) below that division. Thus, only 1% of the data-set occupies the top dark red band with copper concentrations above 183 ppm. Activity 2 will clarify the value of this type of survey.

Activity 2 Stream sediment reconnaissance survey: copper in northern Britain

Use Plate 71 and the geological map of Great Britain in *The Geological Map* booklet to answer the following:

(a) How do the areas coloured blue on Plate 71 compare with the geological map? What geological divisions do they represent?

(b) What geological divisions on the geological map correspond with the areas coloured red on Plate 71?

(c) What are the approximate background levels for copper in (i) the red and (ii) the blue areas of Plate 71?

(d) Different levels of copper could constitute an anomaly in each area. Suggest approximate thresholds in each of the red and blue areas.

(e) Where would you look for possible sites of mineralization, and why?

(f) Is there anything about the correlation between the geological map and Plate 71 to suggest that the stream sediment information could be used as an aid to geological mapping? In what circumstances might it be most useful?

Even supposing that an interesting geochemical anomaly is found, how likely is it to lie directly above an ore deposit? Assessing this probability is crucially important because to explore further might mean using ground-based geophysical methods or drilling — and both are usually much more expensive than geochemical methods. To understand the relationship between a surface geochemical anomaly and its source in an ore deposit, it is important to understand in a little more detail how these anomalies develop in soils, sediments, and water.

2.6.1 Geochemical dispersion

By now it should be clear that an ore deposit is rather like a needle in a haystack — very small but very anomalous. Most deposits for which geochemical exploration is appropriate are tiny compared to the size of the areas in which they are sought, often only a few hundreds of metres across and very rarely extending for a kilometre or more. The larger parts of most deposits are probably buried, although if their depth is much greater than about 1 km they may not be economic to exploit anyway. Various geological processes, however, help to reveal deposits by dispersing the high concentrations of the elements of a deposit into much larger volumes of rock or surface material. This process is called **geochemical dispersion**, and it produces a dispersed anomaly that is larger and therefore much easier to find than any localized and extreme anomaly associated with the ore body itself (Section 2.4.2).

Two main types of dispersion are recognized: primary and secondary. *Primary dispersion* occurs through the geological processes that are responsible for the development of an ore deposit itself. *Secondary dispersion* occurs as a result of weathering processes and groundwater movement long after an ore deposit has formed. Secondary dispersion includes the transportation of ore mineral grains or metal ions in surface drainage water, soil, wind-blown sand, and glacial deposits. Linked to this is the fact that plants growing in areas rich in certain elements may absorb those elements to anomalously high levels. The levels may be high enough to stunt growth or allow only adapted, or metal tolerant, species to thrive (Section 2.6.4).

Porphyry-type ore deposits produce some of the best examples of primary geochemical dispersion, because the fluids involved in the mineralization process (*Metals 1*, Section 2.4) penetrate surrounding rocks for hundreds of metres and give rise to high concentrations of many metals. Figure 21 shows how such dispersed anomalies usually extend well beyond the actual deposit, thereby enlarging the target for exploration. Zones with anomalous concentrations of metals are often arranged concentrically to form a 'bull's-eye' around the main ore body. Although geochemical exploration using rock samples could reveal primary dispersion, it would be a very expensive procedure for regional surveys. In fact, the wide zone of primary dispersion around a porphyry deposit is usually subjected to secondary dispersion processes that further enlarge the overall area in which anomalous metal values are distributed.

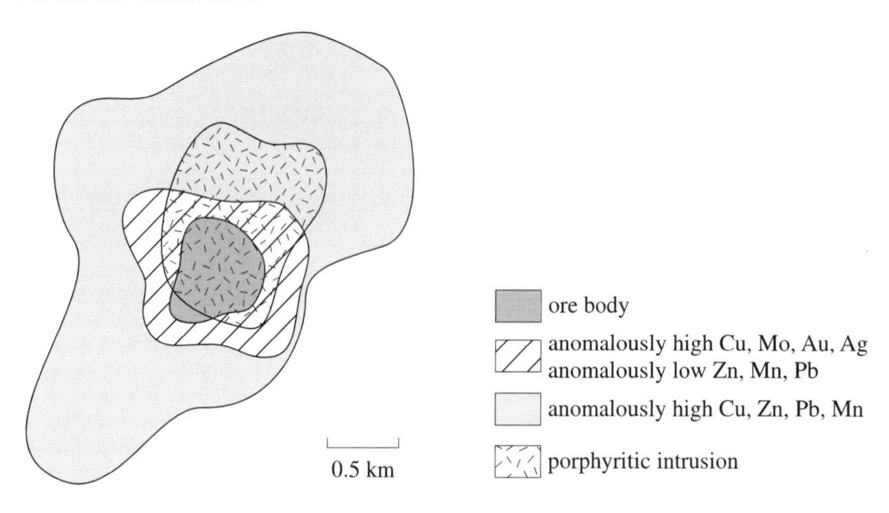

Figure 21 Plan of the 'bull's-eye' effect of mainly primary dispersed metal anomalies centred on a porphyry ore body.

Primary dispersion is related to the process of mineralization itself, so you might wish to refer back to *Metals 1* when tackling Question 16.

Question 16

For each of the ore deposits listed below, briefly describe the main process that controls the distribution of ore minerals and therefore the primary dispersion. Which deposit is likely to have the broadest primary dispersion?

(a) A magmatic segregation deposit of nickel sulphides.

(b) A porphyry copper deposit.

(c) A lead–zinc sulphide deposit in limestone.

(d) A placer deposit of tin.

Figure 22 shows some examples of secondary dispersion. There are two important points to bear in mind: first, secondary dispersion can involve solutions or solid particles — this is significant because soluble elements released from unstable minerals travel much further than those forming stable mineral grains; second, the most efficient agent of transportation is water.

A stream flowing over a metalliferous deposit (Figure 22a) can pick up ore mineral grains and take metal ions into solution and transport them downstream. Anomalous metal concentrations progressively reduce downstream through dilution with barren sediment and uncontaminated water entering from tributaries. On entering a lake, the composition of the water may change sufficiently for dissolved metals to be precipitated from solution, but in many cases stream water anomalies still persist downstream of lakes.

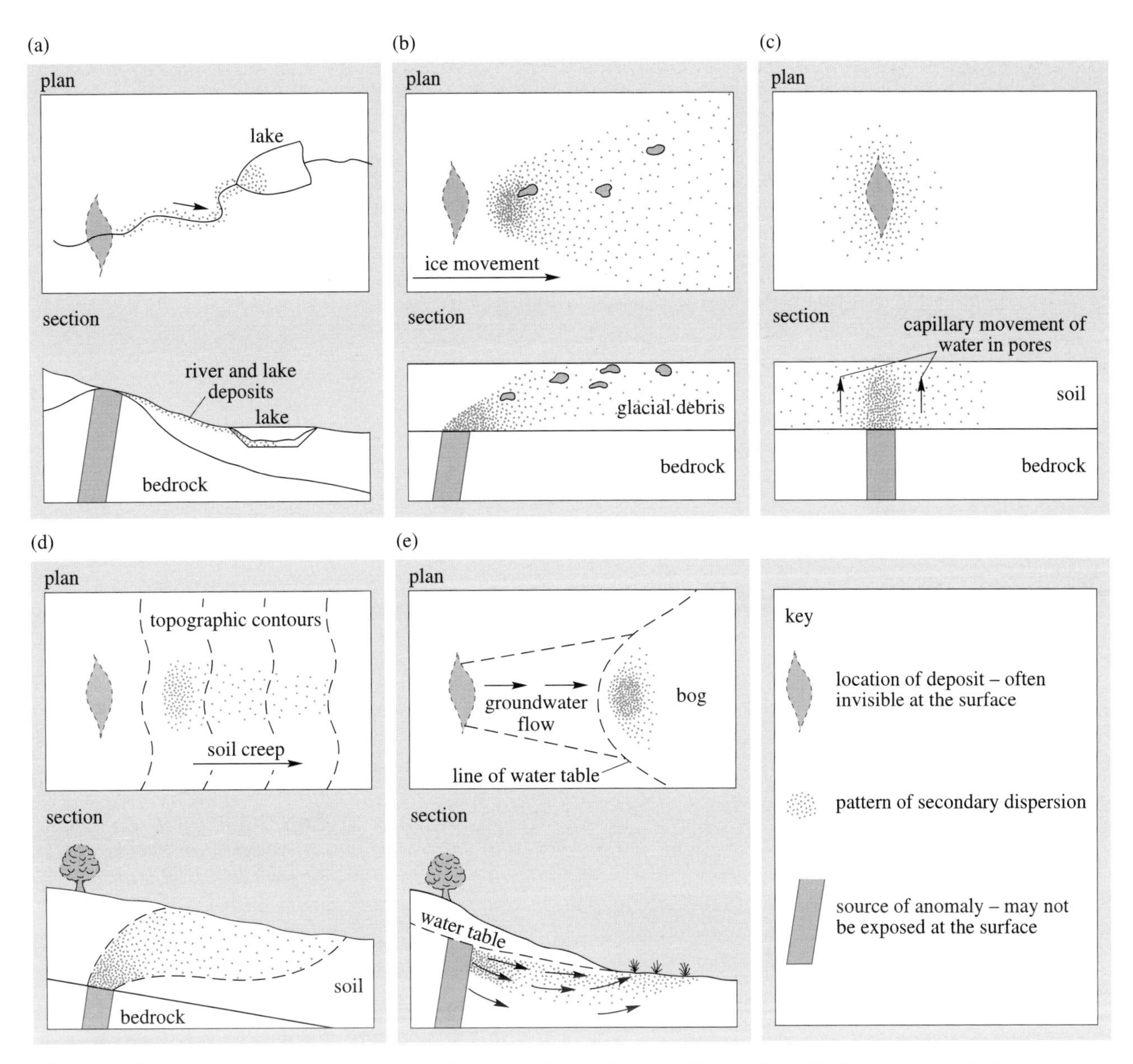

Figure 22 Secondary dispersion patterns due to (a) river and lake sedimentation; (b) glacial transport; (c) movement of water in soil; (d) soil creep; (e) groundwater flow.

The dispersion pattern in Figure 22b is typical of the smearing effect of ice movement preserved in glacial deposits, where there may be 'trails' of mineral grains and large blocks that lead back to the deposit, sometimes extending for tens or even hundreds of kilometres.

In Figure 22c, moisture containing soluble metals moves upward by capillary action to form a 'halo' of anomalous soil chemistry that is available for absorption by vegetation.

In Figure 22d, weathering of the deposit has contributed anomalous levels of metals to the overlying soil. Because of the slope, the soil creeps slowly downhill so displacing the surface anomaly.

In Figure 22e, groundwater within permeable rocks flows downslope through a buried deposit and carries away dissolved metals. If it then comes to the surface as a spring or in a swamp, the surrounding vegetation and soil are likely to concentrate the metals from solution and will have anomalous chemistry. With this form of dispersion, geochemical anomalies can be recognized by analysing water from wells downslope of the deposit, as well as from the spring or swamp itself.

2.6.2 Drainage surveys

Dispersion patterns affect both stream water and stream sediments, and in a geochemical survey either or both may be sampled. They provide an effective means of sampling soils and bedrock extending over a large area. Drainage channels are also particularly attractive for geochemical sampling because locating sampling sites is easy on both maps and aerial photographs, a minimum of equipment is needed to collect samples, and, as a glance at almost any topographic map such as Figure 23 will show, most areas are crossed by numerous drainage channels.

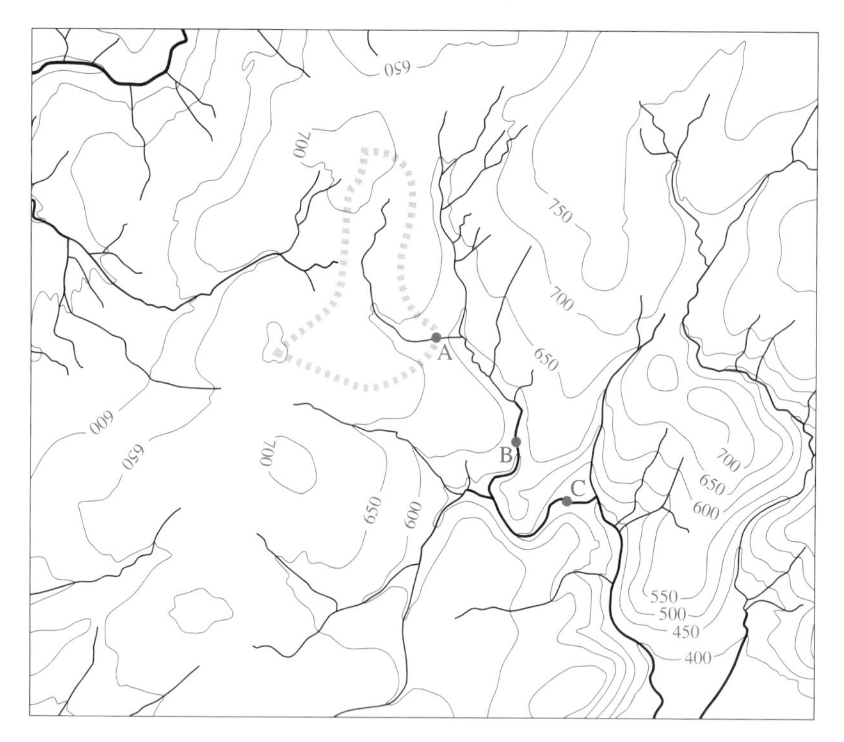

Figure 23 Drainage-pattern map showing the catchment area for point A; catchment areas for points B and C are to be added when you do Question 17.

In drainage surveys it is important to appreciate that the geochemical analysis of a water or sediment sample at a particular point reflects the composition of soils, sediments and groundwater of the area draining through that point. This contributory area is known as the **catchment area** of the stream.

Question 17

Examine Figure 23 then outline the catchment areas associated with samples taken from the stream at points B and C. The catchment area for point A is done for you. You will find it is easiest to mark the divides between adjacent catchment areas to give the boundaries you need.

It is clear from Question 17 that the size of the catchment area represented by a drainage sample increases downstream because of the increasing number of tributaries that enter the channel. Sampling a stream near its source with few tributaries reduces the probability of finding a geochemical anomaly, but increases the chance of defining the precise source of a known anomaly.

 Why do you think the magnitude of geochemical anomalies tends to decrease downstream as more tributaries join the stream being sampled?

 The more tributaries carrying background levels of metals in sediments and water that join, the more dilute any stream geochemical anomaly becomes.

We need not concern ourselves here with analytical methods, except to say that it is sometimes possible to perform rapid measurements using standardized field methods for specific metals. A semi-quantitative method for drainage water surveys is shown in Video Band 16: *Pine Point: origin and exploration*. The method uses indicator paper, which changes colour when high levels of particular soluble metals are present, However, anomalous metal contents in water depend on both the solubility of the metals released on weathering of the ore deposit and the pH of the water. Also, changes in water chemistry might cause dissolved ions to be precipitated onto the stream bed; this could prevent an anomaly from spreading further downstream. Thus, drainage water surveys are not as reliable as drainage sediment surveys — water may transport soluble elements over much greater distances, and its metal contents are harder to interpret.

The degree to which processes involved in geochemical dispersion are able to transport various elements over different distances is clearly important when deciding which elements to look for, and how to interpret data from both water and sediment samples. The aims of a geochemical survey are to detect a geochemical anomaly and (assuming the anomaly is related to secondary dispersion) to determine the source of the secondary dispersion. An important feature of any anomaly is its **persistence** (that is, how far from its source the anomaly can be detected).

- The persistence of a geochemical anomaly depends on several factors. What factors do you think might be important in determining the persistence of geochemical anomalies in (i) sediment and (ii) water?

- (i) The persistence of a geochemical sediment anomaly (which involves mineral grains) depends on the density of the key minerals (how easily they are deposited), on their hardness (how easily they are broken up), and on their chemical stability (how easily they decompose).

  (ii) The persistence of a geochemical water anomaly depends on how the solubility of relevant metals changes in the prevailing water conditions.

Question 18

Comment on whether the persistence of a stream *sediment* anomaly is likely to be high or low in the case of these examples:

(a) a low-density, easily-broken mineral;

(b) a high-density, hard mineral;

(c) a low-density, chemically unstable mineral.

In principle, by looking for minerals or elements exhibiting different levels of persistence, we can obtain both reconnaissance and more localized information. An element with high persistence that is dispersed over a wide area helps *detect the presence* of a deposit in a particular catchment area, at least until the anomaly fades out. An element with low persistence records an anomaly from a relatively small area, so, once found, it helps to *pin-point the source* of the anomaly. In practice, if sampling of the main drainage from a catchment area looks promising, samples are taken progressively upstream at the inflow of each tributary. An anomaly at an inflow directs the search area to that tributary until the point is reached where anomalous levels give way to the background values upstream. This *cut-off point* marks the source of the anomaly. Question 19 (overleaf) illustrates this point.

Question 19

Examine Figure 24 and trace the anomalous levels of copper upstream to identify cut-off points. Show where you might expect to find a copper ore body. What form does it have?

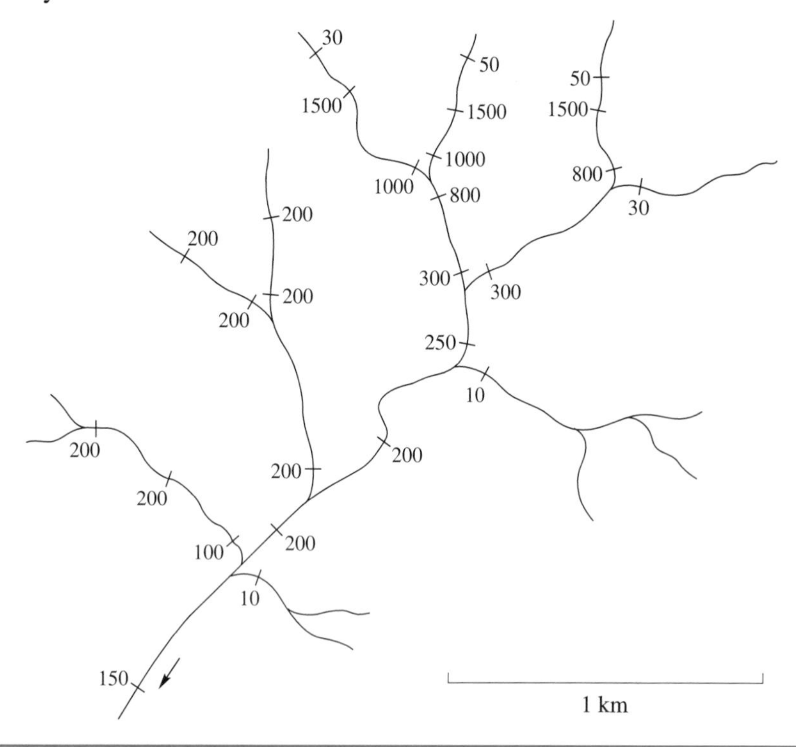

Figure 24 A drainage system showing copper concentrations (in ppm) in the stream sediments.

2.6.3 Soil surveys

A basic assumption in soil geochemical surveys is that the soil is derived more or less directly from underlying bedrock.

In terms of distance from the ore deposit, how will a geochemical anomaly in soil compare with one in stream sediments?

In streams, free-flowing water can transport an anomaly for great distances. In soil the anomaly should be more restricted in extent, and located closer to the ore body.

In practice, however, soils are complex. Forms of dispersion include downslope movement of solid material (Figure 22d), and the addition of soluble material transported and precipitated from groundwaters (Figures 22c and 22e). Also, the soil may be derived from a layer of transported sediment such as glacial till that blankets underlying rock (e.g. at Pine Point), as shown in Figure 22b. Moreover, all soils have a layered structure, and the extent and form of layering depends on a large range of climatic and organic factors. Some layers can be 'leached' of soluble elements (*Metals 1*, Section 3.2.1) and might appear barren even if situated close to an ore body. Other layers, such as those associated with laterites, may concentrate some elements well above their levels in underlying rocks, so giving misleading anomalies.

The first stage in a soil survey is to decide which parts of an area have soils that are derived locally and to select a soil layer that is most representative of bedrock geochemistry. Samples are then taken at an appropriate depth to reach this layer or 'horizon'. Because of the complexity of soils, soil surveys are more appropriate as detailed follow-up to reconnaissance surveys. They are usually organized on regular, closely-spaced grid patterns and often accompany ground-based geophysical surveys.

The discovery of the Navan ore body in Ireland

The Navan ore body lies in County Meath in the Irish Republic (Figure 25), within an area of mineralization that was not discovered until 1961. Prior to that date it was thought that Ireland possessed few mineral deposits, although there was a well-known historical mining site at Silvermines. Two highway engineers were struck by similarities between the terrain of the famous mining camps in the Superior Province of Canada and the poorly exposed bog-covered Central Plain of Ireland. Advice from the Director of the Geological Survey of Ireland took them to the area around Tynagh where copper-stained, red sandstone boulders occur locally in the glacial till. Soil analyses revealed extraordinary concentrations of lead and zinc with significant copper and silver values, and a few years later the first mine was opened at Tynagh.

This started a mineral rush in the area and many Canadian companies engaged in systematic exploration by modern geophysical and geochemical methods in central Ireland. By 1969, a number of deposits had been found, when attention was drawn to the Navan area, 120 km north-north-east of Tynagh because of a report indicating high metal contents in streams and waters drunk by cattle. Geologists sent to the area found mineralized limestone in postholes dug for power lines. A regional shallow soil geochemical survey was begun, with samples collected on a regular grid spacing of 152 m, and typically from a depth of 0.15 m. North of the main river in the area, the River Blackwater (Figure 25), a distinct geochemical anomaly was located, measuring 900 × 400 m. The background values were 90 ppm for zinc and 45 ppm for lead; peak anomaly values were up to 5000 ppm for zinc and 2000 ppm for lead. These results were the basis for a more detailed soil survey using a 30 m square grid of soil samples with sampling depths of 0.6–0.9 m. This confirmed and extended the anomalous area. The highest anomalous metal values occurred in a fairly small area where 1.5–3.0 m of overburden lay on top of highly mineralized calcareous sedimentary rocks of Lower Carboniferous age.

South of the River Blackwater only one anomalous value was detected, which might suggest that the ore body did not occur to the south of the river. However, as it turned out, that is where the mine was opened. The lack of high metal values in the soil south of the river was because of a marked thickening of the overburden, up to 25 m, in the preglacial course of the river, and the fact that in this area the ore lies below relatively thick limestones. The zinc anomaly persisted almost 1400 m from the ore body, reflecting secondary dispersion following the dominant drainage direction. Induced polarization surveys (Section 2.5.3) were carried out over the area of the anomaly and outlined the target for drilling. By 1972, 355 diamond drill holes had been completed, defining reserves of nearly 70 million tonnes of ore at a grade of 10% zinc and 2.6% lead. The Tara Mine came into production in June 1977, working the ore body to the south of the River Blackwater, and was, for a time, the largest zinc–lead mine in Europe.

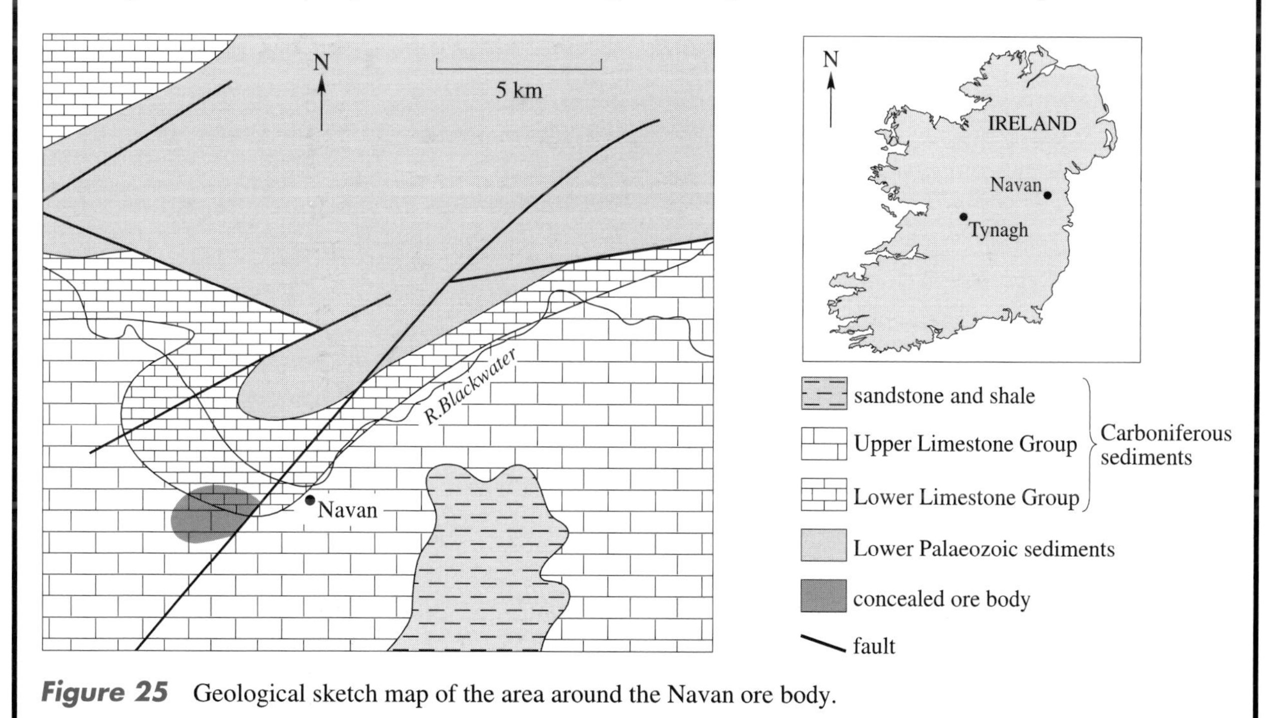

Figure 25 Geological sketch map of the area around the Navan ore body.

2.6.4 Vegetation surveys

Where water is accessible to roots, plants become involved in the uptake of metals and therefore in geochemical dispersion. Figure 26 shows that not only are many primary (ore body) and soil anomalies reflected in the chemistry of leaves and stems, but fallen leaf litter also becomes incorporated in soil and adds to local anomalies. These geologically induced chemical anomalies in plant material are called *biogeochemical anomalies* and are the basis of **biogeochemical surveys**. These surveys involve the collection of leaves and twigs for geochemical analysis to detect elevated levels of metals and hence underlying mineralization. They are more time-consuming and expensive than many surveys involving direct measurement in the field and are only conducted when other methods are precluded. They are particularly useful where roots penetrate transported soils and tap deeply buried water in bedrock. As in every form of geochemical exploration, it is important that analyses are carried out on comparable samples and conclusions are drawn from statistically acceptable data. Therefore, vegetation samples must be taken from the *same species* of plant at the *same stage* of growth. If this is not the case, then apparent 'anomalies' may simply reflect differences in the metal uptake by different species, or in the same species at different stages of growth.

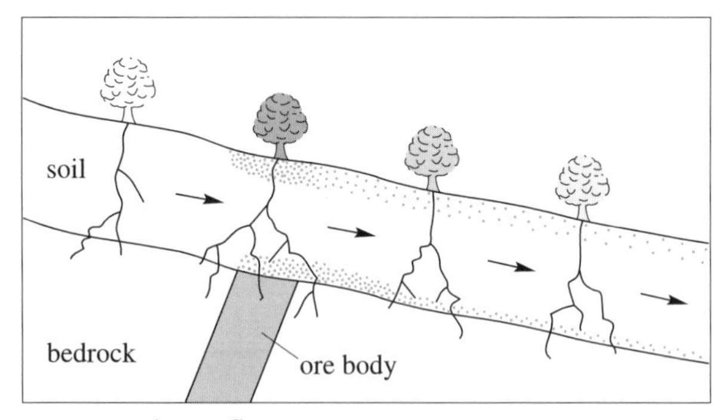

Figure 26 Biological dispersion of an element (coloured dots) in leaves and soils (through leaf fall) from a mineral deposit covered by thick soil. The shading of the trees represents take-up of metals.

Geobotanical surveys involve the recognition of specific plant species that tend to grow on soils unusually rich in metals. Such plants are distinctive because they tolerate very high metal concentrations, and even thrive on them, forming highly specialized plant communities. Examples include the yellow calamine violet that is associated with zinc deposits in central Europe and the spring sandwort (leadwort) associated with lead deposits in northern England. However, most plants have a limited range of tolerance to the chemistry of the soil and the water that nourish them. There are minimum requirements for elements such as nitrogen and potassium, and also many trace elements that are vital in cell metabolism; if *essential* elements are not present above these minimum concentrations, plants will not thrive. On the other hand, an element may be *toxic* to plants if it is present at concentrations above a certain level (*Metals 1*, Section 1.4). Both excesses and deficiencies can cause plants to develop discoloured foliage, shed leaves early, or show stunted growth — characteristics of **stressed vegetation** (recognized at the time of Agricola, Section 2.2). Many metal-rich soils or groundwaters support no growth at all, forming barren areas in otherwise well-covered ground.

2.6.5 Rock geochemistry

To analyse a rock geochemically usually involves powdering a sample to homogenize it. Because this is time-consuming and costly, and because rock analyses may represent only the composition of the rock unit from which they are taken, they are rarely used in exploration except where there is insufficient soil or sediment cover for secondary dispersion processes to have been effective. Rock analyses become especially important when exploration has finally identified a promising target where the probabilities for success and the associated financial risks demand detailed evaluation.

2.7 Evaluation

Once an exploration program has revealed geochemical and/or geophysical anomalies that point to the presence of a mineral deposit, the next stage is to evaluate whether the grade and size of the deposit justify the major investment necessary to mine it.

- How might the 3-D form and grade of a deposit be determined?

- By geochemical analysis of a 3-D array of samples obtained by drilling.

Drilling, retrieval of chippings or core samples, and assay for their metal contents provide the simplest method of determining the grade of a mineral deposit. Drilling on a grid pattern and sampling at regular depth intervals is necessary to establish the form of the deposit and generate a 3-D computer model for use in evaluating the distribution of grades and planning mine development. Figure 8 in *Metals 1* shows simplified diagrams of this kind contoured for grade. Because of the high cost of drilling, preliminary boreholes may be drilled to plan the best orientation and spacing of the detailed sampling grid. Here, geological knowledge is important.

- How might drilling strategy differ for (i) a dispersed porphyry-type deposit compared with (ii) a confined massive sulphide deposit only 50 m thick and oriented vertically?

- (i) For a dispersed deposit, where the grade varies gradually over a considerable area, widely spaced holes would be adequate (Figure 27a). These should be drilled vertically to intersect any flat-lying zone of secondary enrichment (related to the water table) rather like the Inspiration Deposit (*Metals 1*, Section 3.2.2).

  (ii) A close-spaced pattern of drilling would be required to define a confined deposit. Vertical drill-holes might well miss a vertically oriented or steeply inclined deposit only 50 m thick. Inclined drilling to intersect the body at different depths would be preferable (Figure 27b).

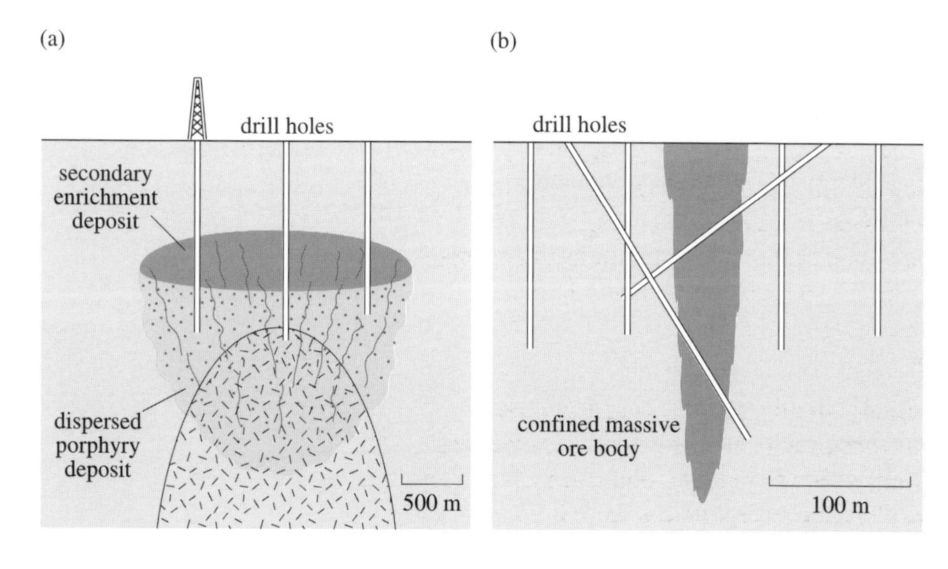

Figure 27 Drilling strategies for (a) a dispersed deposit and (b) a vertically oriented confined deposit.

The last few minutes of Video Band 16, following the coverage of IP surveys used to locate the Pine Point lead–zinc deposits, looks at the acquisition of borehole assay data and its use by mine engineers in drawing up a mining plan. These activities are all part of evaluation. Without evidence that a certain amount of ore at a given grade exists and can be mined economically, a mining venture would not be given the go-ahead. Computerization of data-processing is now more sophisticated than that in the Pine Point video, but the requirements are the same — to identify if and how a deposit can be mined for profit. Different forms of mining, depending on the form and location of the deposit, have different cost implications, as we shall discover in Section 3.1.

Preliminary investigation of the technical and engineering problems associated with mining and ore processing are an important part of evaluating mining costs. Feasibility studies are carried out to determine, for example, how much crushing would be needed to liberate ore mineral grains and what the energy requirement would be (Section 3.2.1). Such studies would involve measuring the grain size of the ore minerals and determining the strength of the rock.

During evaluation, the costs of setting up the infrastructure to support the mining operation must also be taken into account. Several questions then arise. How accessible is the area? Will a new road, railway or port have to be built? Is there an electricity supply or will a power station have to be built? Is there a local water supply or will water have to be piped in? Will the mine have to be self-sufficient, or can food and spares for equipment be bought locally? Can operations continue throughout the year or does the climate prohibit work during some seasons? What laws govern pollution control during operation and the eventual restoration of the mine area? Are there sites where waste can be dumped cheaply, safely and legally? Who are the owners of the adjoining land and will they hinder development? Is there an indigenous skilled workforce or will a mine township have to be built for immigrant labour? What wages are necessary to attract suitable personnel to the mine? The list can go on and on, even to the extent of investigating the best lubricant for surface vehicles under the prevailing climatic conditions.

The economics of mining are an essential part of evaluation and depend not only on local circumstances but also on metal (and thus, ore) price and world markets. The case study 'Molybdenum at Quartz Hill, Alaska' describes the exploration and evaluation of a molybdenum deposit that had progressed to an advanced stage when it had to be shelved due to unfavourable market prices, thus illustrating the high risk of investment in mining.

Question 20

(a) What is it about a potential ore body that must be evaluated in order to define the potential reserve?

(b) What fundamental economic evaluation must be made to justify investment in mine development?

Molybdenum at Quartz Hill, Alaska

Molybdenum is a metal that is present at only a few parts per million in most rocks. Demand for it is high because it is widely used to improve the durability and high-temperature performance of high-strength steels. It typically forms highly charged Mo^{6+} ions which, because of their large charge, do not readily substitute into the crystal structures of common silicate minerals. Molybdenum is, therefore, concentrated into magma remaining during processes of fractional crystallization, but is soluble in the aqueous fluid that separates when wet dioritic magma rises and crystallizes. These processes may lead to the formation of porphyry molybdenum deposits (*Metals 1*, Section 2.4), which are the most important source of molybdenum.

Throughout the 1960s, the USA consumption of molybdenum increased and the future for the molybdenum market appeared good (Figure 28a). Therefore, an exploration programme was started in southern Alaska in 1971, an area chosen because the geology was similar to that across the border in British Columbia where molybdenum and copper porphyry mineralization were already known. After three years of reconnaissance geophysical surveys and geochemical sampling, an area of highly promising mineralization with anomalous levels of molybdenum, copper, gold and silver was found at Quartz Hill. There followed a further 7 years of drilling and some underground working to evaluate the deposit in more detail, until, in 1981, it was estimated that there was a minimum of 1.5 billion tonnes of ore with an average grade of 0.13% MoS_2. Although the terrain was rugged and road access needed to be built, conditions were very favourable for open pit mining and the market was buoyant.

Between 1970 and 1980 the average USA consumption of molybdenum had not increased dramatically, but the price had risen very rapidly in the late 1970s (Figure 28b). By 1982, a mine life of 70 years was proposed for Quartz Hill, commencing operation in 1987, at a capital cost estimated at $870 million. Access to the mine was achieved in 1983, and much of the pre-production construction had been completed by 1984. All of the environmental protection permits would have been obtained by the end of that year, but in April 1984 the company announced the indefinite postponement of the project because of the weak state of the molybdenum market (Figure 28a).

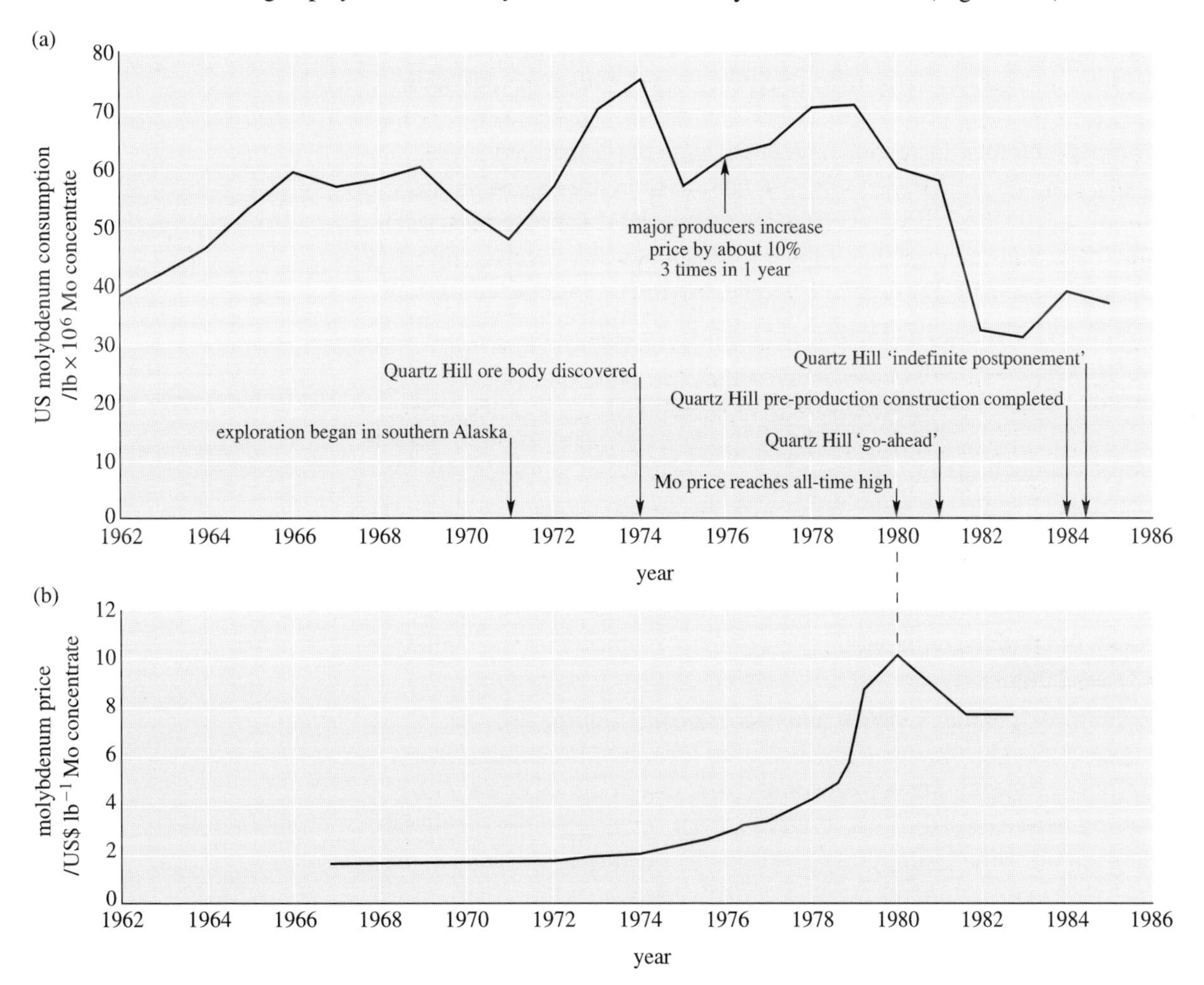

Figure 28 Molybdenum and Quartz Hill: (a) the Quartz Hill exploration program and USA consumption of molybdenum, 1962–85; (b) USA price of molybdenum, 1967–83.

2.8 Summary of Section 2

1 Exploration for ore deposits is essential in order to maintain profitable supplies of metals in the long term, and to identify deposits that are more accessible. All deposits eventually become worked out or uneconomic to mine and must be replaced by new supplies. The scheduling of activities must account for a period of exploration and lead time for evaluation and development before a newly found deposit becomes productive.

2 The decision to look for a particular type of deposit depends on world markets, supply and demand expectations, and company expertise. Regional targeting is initially based on desk studies involving the analysis and interpretation of available geophysical and remotely sensed data, mining records, and geological maps.

3 Historical methods of prospecting were based largely on surface observations sometimes supplemented by less tangible methods such as divining. Until diamond drilling was possible, trial diggings were the only means of proving deposits.

4 Modern exploration starts with rapid regional reconnaissance surveys at low cost per unit area, often involving airborne geophysics and sometimes regional geochemical surveys, designed to progressively narrow down the search area.

5 Localized, often field-based, geophysical and geochemical surveys provide higher resolution (or definition) of targets. They are more labour intensive and higher-cost than reconnaissance surveys. Financing at every stage of exploration is a high risk; returns are never guaranteed.

6 Geophysical techniques are used to detect buried bodies of rock with anomalous physical properties. They often record properties of accompanying rock formations rather than ore deposits themselves. Gravity and magnetic surveys rely on natural force fields; resistivity, induced polarization (IP) and electromagnetic (EM) surveys rely on applied and induced electrical fields; spontaneous polarization (SP) relies on natural electrical fields. While geophysical surveys indicate the presence of mineralization targets, geochemical studies are necessary to identify the nature of the mineralization.

7 Probably the most effective geophysical techniques for locating ore bodies are IP, EM and SP. Of these, EM and SP are appropriate only for massive conducting ore bodies and SP works only for sulphide ore bodies that straddle the water table. EM has the advantage that it can be undertaken from aircraft and responds to many types of oxide and sulphide ore bodies. IP, like SP, is ground-based but is suitable for both massive and disseminated ore bodies as it depends on chargeable surfaces of conductive mineral grains and not on the electrical continuity of the ore body.

8 Geochemical methods look for anomalous concentrations (that is, deviations from background concentration levels) of mineralizing or pathfinder elements. Surveys generally start on a regional scale with sampling of stream sediments or water, and progress to more localized soil sampling. Direct sampling of bedrock by drilling is normally necessary to prove mineralization at a likely target.

9 Geochemical sampling depends on the transfer of anomalous compositional characteristics from a mineral deposit to media that can be sampled, such as sediments, water, vegetation and soils. This process

involves geochemical dispersion of these anomalous characteristics: primary dispersion occurs at the time the deposit formed (as in porphyry deposits); secondary dispersion occurs long after mineralization and is due to near-surface groundwater movement and weathering processes.

10 Evaluation of a mineral deposit involves further high-cost drilling to delineate grades of ore and define the extent of the ore body, as well as determining if and how a deposit can be mined profitably. Assessing the cost of setting up the infrastructure to mine and process ore, and the wider political, economic, environmental, and social implications are all part of evaluation.

3 MINING, ORE PROCESSING AND METAL EXTRACTION

3.1 Mining

Mining for metals has been carried out on every continent except Antarctica and it is arguably one of the fundamental industries of civilization. Block 4 *Energy 1* introduced the concepts of surface and underground mining for coal and described problems associated with this type of mining (Block 4–1, Section 3.3). Many of these problems are relevant to metal mining, but there are significant differences.

- Mining methods employed in metal mines are more varied than those used for mining coal — why do you think that is?

- Coal forms from organic debris laid down in fairly regular sedimentary layers that are relatively easy to follow and mine — metalliferous deposits form in many different ways, have different geometries and reside within many different types of host rock.

The problems of waste disposal in metal mining are also different from those of coal mining because of the particular chemistry and mineralogy of the ore bodies and their associated gangue. In addition, the problems of waste disposal in metal mining are aggravated by the sheer bulk of the waste that may be produced. Many large metal mines such as Bingham (*Metals 1*, Figure 31) and Chuquicamata (Plate 59) work deposits where the grade of ore is about 1% copper, meaning that for every 100 tonnes mined, about 97 tonnes is gangue for which a disposal site must be found (notice that it takes about three tonnes of ore mineral concentrate (largely sulphides) to produce about one tonne of copper metal). The environmental implications of this are obvious. However, the scale of some metal mines that produce large tonnages every year is difficult to appreciate without being seen. For example, at Mount Tom Price — an iron ore mine established on Precambrian banded iron formation (BIF) in Western Australia — 46 million tonnes of ore are excavated per year (Plate 64 and box in *Metals 1*, Section 3.3.1). The ore is transported over 300 km to the coast by trains 2 km long; 9 such trains travel every day.

- If the iron ore has a density of $3.5\,\text{t}\,\text{m}^{-3}$, what volume is removed from Mount Tom Price each year?

- The volume $= 46 \times 10^6/3.5\,\text{m}^3$

  $= 13.1 \times 10^6\,\text{m}^3$

  That's roughly a 235 metre cube, or an amount of ore over 5 times the volume of the Cheops Pyramid (Block 2, Section 1.1).

3.1.1 Economics and mining strategy

The decision whether to mine a deposit at the surface, below ground, or not at all, is based on economics. When the decision is made, the project that began as an abstract exploration objective and proceeded through several phases of exploration to evaluation — with decreasing risk but increasing cost (Figure 10) — has still not earned any money. And, as we saw at Quartz Hill (Section 2.7), there is no guarantee that a mine will open up even after exploration, evaluation and development. By the time a mine is operating, 10 years or more might have passed, and tens or hundreds of millions of dollars might have been spent. The design of a mine and the associated processing operations must, therefore, aim to provide a rapid return on the investment. At the same time, it is important to ensure continuity of operation and flexibility of production to take account of changing metal prices and demand. The first consideration in deciding how an ore deposit will be worked is to compare the potential *value* of the product with the estimated *cost* of mining it.

Unit cost

The full cost of transforming *one tonne of ore* in the ground into a saleable commodity is termed the **unit cost** (C_{unit}). In a much simplified form, the unit cost is made up of:

C_{ore} = the cost of excavating and transporting one tonne of ore (including ore minerals and gangue);

C_{waste} = the cost of excavating, transporting and disposing of waste rock (overburden and waste from access shafts and tunnels) removed in order to obtain one tonne of ore;

C_{proc} = the cost of processing to transform one tonne of ore into a saleable product;

C_{fixed} = the fixed costs in setting up a mine and repayment of capital plus interest, per tonne of ore extracted per year.

So, the unit cost can be expressed as:

$$C_{unit} = C_{ore} + C_{waste} + C_{proc} + C_{fixed} \quad (3.1)$$

The first three items on the righthand-side of Equation 3.1 are mine operating costs, and are made up of wages, 'consumables' (for example, explosives, reagents, fuel), maintenance of equipment and spare parts. These are *variable costs* that depend on the amount of ore being mined; they include the separation of ore minerals from waste, disposal of waste, the transportation of concentrates and production of the refined metal. C_{ore} and C_{proc} depend on the type of ore, type of mining operation and the amount of ore produced — economies of scale generally operate. C_{waste} is determined by the form of the deposit and the type of mining operation. The *fixed costs* are those of setting up a mining operation and they include the costs of items such as long-lived fixtures and equipment, land, access roads, insurance, environmental restoration, and possibly an environmental 'bond' (Section 4.5); these are overheads, incurred whether or not the mine enters production. In most cases money will have been borrowed to pay for these items so the fixed costs also include the interest to be paid on the money borrowed. However, C_{fixed} is expressed as cost per tonne of ore extracted per year, obtained by dividing the *overall fixed costs* by the expected lifetime of the mine, and its expected annual output (in tonnes). It is important to appreciate that, while the overall fixed cost does not vary, the *contribution* of fixed cost to unit cost changes during the lifetime of a mine.

- What might cause the contribution of fixed cost to the unit cost to vary dramatically?

- If for some reason, such as a labour dispute or a fall in demand, a mine's output decreases, then its fixed costs *per tonne of ore*, and hence the contribution of fixed costs to unit cost, will increase. On the other hand, if productivity increases, fixed costs per tonne of ore, and the contribution of the fixed costs to the unit cost, will decrease.

Historical developments in mining

The easiest way to mine is at the surface, by picking up ore where it is found in outcrop. The earliest mining was as simple as that but was soon followed by the digging of small surface pits. However, the development and rise to dominance of true underground mining was inevitable for a number of reasons. First, only rich, high-grade ores were suitable for the early smelting techniques that extracted metals. Secondly, such ores generally occur as *confined deposits* forming narrow, sheet-like bodies, such as hydrothermal veins (*Metals 1*, Section 4); these usually have small surface outcrops (and hence limited surface pickings) and are more extensive below ground.

In Greek, Roman and medieval times, metal mining was an industry powered mainly by human, animal or water power, and early miners developed quite sophisticated mining methods within these limitations. However, the lack of earth-moving equipment other than picks, shovels and animals, meant that large volumes of rock could not be excavated. Underground mines following the intricacies of vein deposits were in operation during the period of the Roman Empire, but the depth of underground mining was limited by the level of the water table, below which water invaded excavations. Until simple pumps were devised, mines could not go any deeper. A further depth limitation, that imposed by ventilation problems, had to await the invention of a means to circulate air.

In England, the hilly topography of the Pennines was ideal for underground mining. Early miners drove horizontal tunnels called adits into the hillsides and used gravity flow to drain the mines. Pumping was not a great problem in the Pennines, but provision of drainage was essential for the deep tin mines of Cornwall. Where hand-pumps could not cope, pumping machinery was driven by waterwheels, which provided most of the industry's power. Because of the sulphide content of veins, and its oxidation on exposure to air and percolating solutions (*Metals 1*, Section 3.2.2, Equation 3.5), the water pumped from mines was often acidic. Large amounts of reddish-orange ochrous mud polluted streams when pumped water ran into them (see also Section 4.2.2).

Raising ore in deep mines was a problem. Manual winding by windlasses could lift only small loads over distances of about 15 m up vertical shafts, and required a series of lifting stages, each with one or two men operating a windlass at each level and one man to transfer the rock. So, mining at a depth of 70 m meant that over 10 workers were needed to clear the work of a single pickman at the working face. This explains why deep Cornish mines employed large labour forces, and why the deeper the mining, the less productive the operation per man. Horse-power could lift greater weights for longer distances, but it was not only ore that had to be raised. In deep metal mines, it was necessary to remove many tons of water to extract each ton of ore. Before the advent of steam power that was a problem. For example, a sixteenth-century mine in the Carpathian mountains required three separate teams of horses (two of which worked underground) to lift water more than 200 metres in three stages. In all, a total of 96 animals! Water power was used where it could be harnessed, sometimes in ingenious ways, as illustrated in Figure 29.

Figure 29 Sixteenth-century ingenuity from Agricola's *De re metallica*: a huge wooden waterwheel used for raising ores from deep mines. The water bag (M) is raised or lowered using a bidirectional waterwheel. The direction in which the wheel rotates is determined by which of the two rows of buckets (G and H) receive the water flow directed via chutes (E and F) by the operator (O) activating levers (C and D).

The Industrial Revolution, with its rapidly increasing demands for larger quantities and a greater variety of metals, triggered great technological developments in mining, and improvements in mine design.

- What were the major developments in (a) fuel usage and (b) power generation, which drove the Industrial Revolution?

- In (a), the use of coal (a concentrated form of energy), and in (b) the development of coal-fired steam engines. The first major application of the steam engine was in Cornish metal mines, where efficient pumping allowed veins to be followed to great depths, even under the sea (Figure 30).

Major advances in tunnelling were due first to the use of explosives (1670s), which increased the rate of tunnelling (although premature explosions often caused injury and death) and, much later, to the development of the safety fuse (1831), which made blasting much safer. Towards the end of the nineteenth century, the introduction of compressed air drills for mechanized boring of shot holes (for loading explosive charges), coupled with the use of high-explosives, further increased tunnelling speeds. At about the same time, development of earth-moving machinery enabled large surface excavations to be opened up quickly and cheaply. This transformed mineral deposits with much lower grades of ore — typically dispersed deposits — from mere geochemical anomalies into profitable and huge reserves which could be dug out cheaply from the surface. In the twentieth century, surface mining has rapidly overtaken underground mining as the dominant source of metals, but subsurface operations still play an important role, particularly for high-grade (confined) deposits.

Modern pumping and ventilation systems ensure that water levels and ventilation are not serious problems in today's mines. But there are still two important factors which limit the depth of mining — heat and pressure. The ultimate limits to mining are those imposed by explosive failure of rock under extremely high pressures, and by the increase in temperature with depth in the Earth. For instance, some South African gold mines exceed 4 km in depth. At these depths the rocks are under such pressures that they do not simply collapse as shallow workings might — they literally burst. Rock bursts are explosive phenomena that create minor seismic events and may cause buildings to vibrate at the surface. At great depths, rock temperatures can exceed 100 °C and once working temperature (that is, air temperature) is over about 45 °C, cooling is necessary. This is achieved by pumping refrigerated water but it is expensive in terms of energy and requires large quantities of water. To design an operating mine that is safe and adequately ventilated in such a harsh environment taxes the skills of the engineers and geologists.

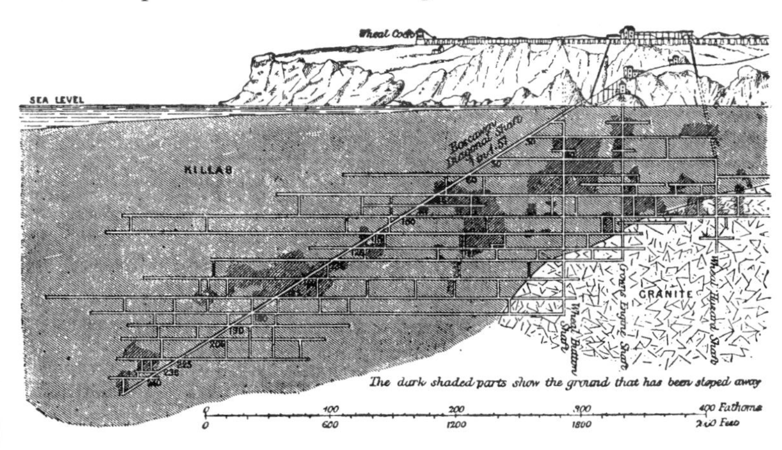

Figure 30 A section through a Cornish mine showing a network of horizontal adits and vertical shafts that reached as far as 300 m below sea level and required efficient pumping to prevent flooding.

Underground and surface mining clearly face different problems. As a result, there are two main economic differences between surface and underground mining.

1 Underground mining requires permanent constructions and long-lived equipment, including fixed systems of access shafts and underground railways, and provision of ventilation and drainage. Therefore, the fixed costs per tonne of ore, C_{fixed}, are significantly higher than those of surface mining, especially as the quantities of ore mined underground are usually smaller than at the surface. In a surface mine, access is often part and parcel of ore excavation, and drainage, though often necessary, is relatively inexpensive.

2 Costs of removing rock (both C_{ore} and C_{waste}) are much higher in underground mines than in surface mines. So much higher, that the ratio of C_{fixed} to (C_{ore} + C_{waste}), which compares long-term capital costs of mining with day-to-day running costs, is in fact usually lower in underground mines than in surface mines.

Unit value

The value of one tonne of ore, its **unit value**, is much simpler to estimate than the unit cost. The variables are the metal content of the ore — its *grade*, assuming complete recovery — and the market price of the metal. Thus:

$$\text{unit value} = \text{grade} \times \text{metal price} \qquad (3.2)$$

- If the grade of an ore is 2% copper, and the copper price is $\$2000\,t^{-1}$, what is its unit value?

- The unit value in this case is $2000 \times 2/100 = \$40\,t^{-1}$.

Mining cut-off

For any mine, whether surface or underground, there is a *break-even point* where unit cost *equals* unit value. This point, which separates working at a profit from working at a loss, defines the **mining cut-off**. For a stable metal price, the break-even point can be expressed in terms of the lowest grade of ore that can be mined at a profit, the *cut-off grade* (*Metals 1*, Section 1.3).

- Recalling from Section 1.3 of *Metals 1* that cut-off grade is defined in economic terms, what are the factors it depends on?

- It depends both on world economic conditions as reflected in the market price, and on local economic factors, such as the presence of valuable by-products, and the costs of environmental protection.

Cut-off grade also depends on the local geology — specifically the size, form and occurrence of the deposit — because the geology influences the design of the mining operation and the ratio of fixed to variable costs. For example, deeper mining incurs greater unit costs and therefore to be viable, demands a higher cut-off grade. For instance, we saw in *Metals 1* that nickel and chromium ores can be mined economically at lower grades from surface residual deposits than from underground magmatic segregation deposits.

Operating strategies

The profitability of a mine clearly depends on the difference between the unit value and the unit cost. But what can be done to improve the long-term and short-term profitability of a metal mine?

All managers of metal mines strive to keep their unit costs as low as possible. However, given the components of unit cost listed in Equation 3.1, mine managers have relatively little control over the long-term fixed costs, since these depend on the size of the operation (decided at the outset), and its form (whether it's a surface or an underground mine). Moreover, because borrowing money is expensive, there's a financial incentive for the operating company to repay money borrowed to finance exploration and to develop the mine and its infrastructure as quickly as possible, even if this reduces early profits (Section 1.1). The area where the mine managers have more control is in minimizing shorter-term costs (C_{ore}, C_{waste} and C_{proc}). In practice, many deposits contain rocks with a range of metal contents, so there is also a decision to be made on whether or not to mine only the higher-grade ore for a quicker return on the initial investment. This strategy is particularly tempting at times when the metal price is high, but, although very profitable in the short term, the removal of high-grade ore may be to the long-term detriment of the mine.

Rocks and ore bodies are very variable in terms of shape, ease of access, and ore grade, yet management is always striving for smooth and consistent production patterns. Any piece of equipment, such as a rock crushing mill or a processing plant, has a set of *optimum* operating conditions. Money can be lost if the throughput of material is too large, because that prevents maintenance and affects the reliability of the equipment; money can also be lost if the throughput is too small, because expensive machinery is standing idle. Common solutions are (a) to have a number of mines feeding material to a centralized processing plant and thus smoothing out variations in production from individual mines, and (b) to accumulate a stockpile.

Stockpiling happens to some extent in all mining operations, but it is particularly common at mines in dispersed deposits where there are likely to be large quantities of the resource at grades close to cut-off grade (Figure 31a). As cut-off grade varies with the price of metal on the world markets, a common strategy in porphyry copper mines, for example, is to extract ore at different grades, building up a stockpile to ensure constant feed to the mill when cut-off grade changes. Low-grade ore can still generate a profit when price falls, provided that the high proportion of unit costs in excavation has been recovered during periods of high price. Sometimes preservation or stockpiling of high-grade reserves serves the same purpose (i.e. to maintain long-term economic viability).

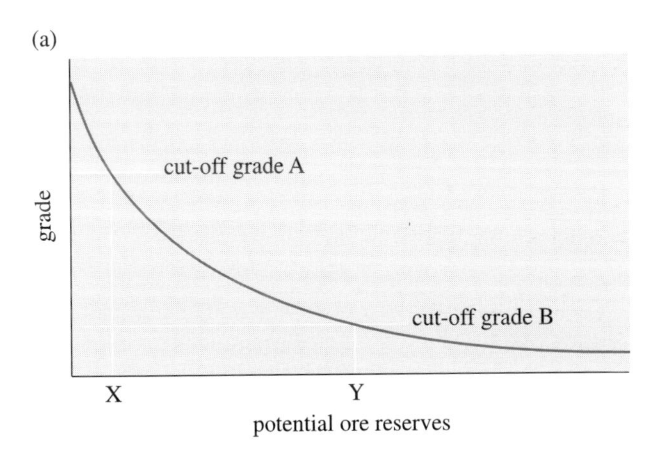

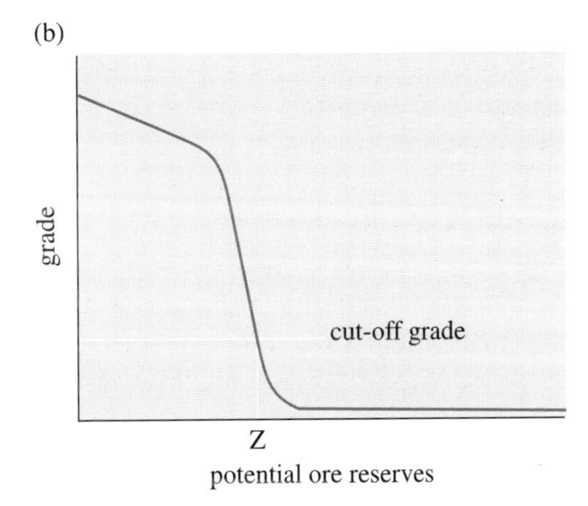

Figure 31 Idealized relationship between grade and tonnage of potential ore reserves: (a) for a dispersed deposit; (b) for a confined deposit — the sharp drop in grade represents the margins of the deposit. (See answer to Question 21 for a fuller explanation.)

Another way to achieve financial stability is to agree a price for your product in advance; this demands confidence that the price won't change significantly, at least in the short term. Thus, the products from a mine are rarely, if ever, sold at the daily *spot price* for a metal but are sold on the *futures market* where the price is fixed several months, even a year, ahead of supply. This enables mining companies to make stable economic plans. In many cases, it is not the pure metal itself that is sold, but ore mineral concentrates, sometimes in the form of a mixture of several ore minerals.

Do you recall which of the mines featured in case studies in *Metals 1* was especially dependant on long-term sales contracts?

It was Rössing, which could hardly remain profitable mining such low grades of ore at today's uranium price without a guaranteed return from long-term contracts negotiated when the price was high.

In *Metals 1*, Section 1.3 we considered how different types of deposit may be affected by changing market conditions. Here we reinforce that point through Question 21. When you compare Figure 31 with Figure 9 of *Metals 1*, you should note that despite their similarity, the horizontal axis in Figure 31 refers to potential reserves of ore, not reserves of metal, since this provides a more convenient description of the deposit for mining purposes.

Question 21

Use Figure 31 and Activity 3 of *Metals 1* to answer the following.

(a) How does the idealized relationship between grade and ore reserves in a confined deposit compare with that in a dispersed deposit?

(b) Are the reserves of a confined deposit more or less sensitive to economic fluctuations than those in a dispersed deposit?

The answer to Question 21 implies that unlike low-grade dispersed deposits, high-grade confined deposits can be mined continuously and profitably at constant rates even when costs and prices fluctuate dramatically. These are sometimes called 'bonanza' deposits. However, confined deposits come in all shapes and sizes, as shown in Figure 32, and they can occur at any depth. Consequently, the unit costs for each are different, and the cut-off grade for a particular metal varies from deposit to deposit.

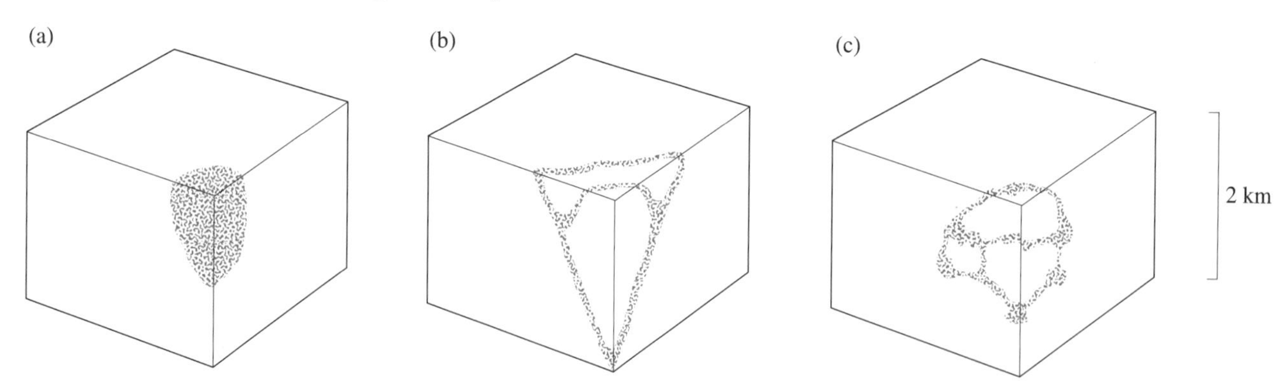

Figure 32 Idealized representation of confined deposits arranged in order of increasing unit cost: (a) a 'massive' deposit; (b) a simple vein deposit; (c) irregular vein deposits with large ore pockets. The density of the dots represents the ore grade.

Question 22

Examine Figure 32, which shows three different forms of confined deposit.

(a) Which of the three deposits could be worked at the surface and which would be most likely to require underground workings? What would be the implications for waste?

(b) Given the variation in unit cost (increasing from a to c) of the three deposits, how would you expect their cut-off grades to vary?

3.1.2 Surface or underground mining?

Advantages and disadvantages of surface and underground mining were discussed in connection with coal mining in Block 4 *Energy 1*. What were they? Why do underground coal mines remain in operation?

Surface mines are cheaper and easier to operate than underground mines especially as unforeseen geological circumstances are easier to accommodate, but they usually cover a large area and can have more impact on the surface environment than underground mines. Many underground coal mines stay in operation because they are mining high-value coal, for example, anthracite — a coal with a high level of purity that commands a high price.

Although there are various factors to consider, such as the availability of a skilled workforce and environmental legislation, the choice between surface and underground mining usually depends on economics, in particular the form of the deposit and the level of unit cost to work it. As noted earlier, the unit cost of surface mining is usually lower than those of underground operations, so surface working is generally favoured, because it tends to be more profitable.

The vast majority of *dispersed* ore deposits are low-grade and until (and unless) entirely new developments in subsurface metal extraction through leaching are made (Section 3.2.2), surface mining is the obvious and only choice for exploiting them. In the case of porphyry-type ore deposits, which occupy large volumes, almost the whole excavation can be made in ore. For *confined* deposits, however, there is a choice between underground and surface working.

Overburden ratio

Figure 33a shows a horizontal ore deposit covered by a thin layer of barren rock; such a layer is known as **overburden** in ore mining. This deposit can be mined from the surface in the same way that flat-lying sedimentary rocks are worked — limestone and shale for cement, clay for bricks, and coal for fuel — depending on the *overburden ratio* (Block 2, Section 3.3). This is the ratio of the thickness of the overburden to the thickness of the deposit. It reflects the relative cost of removing waste compared with the value of the ore deposit.

(a)

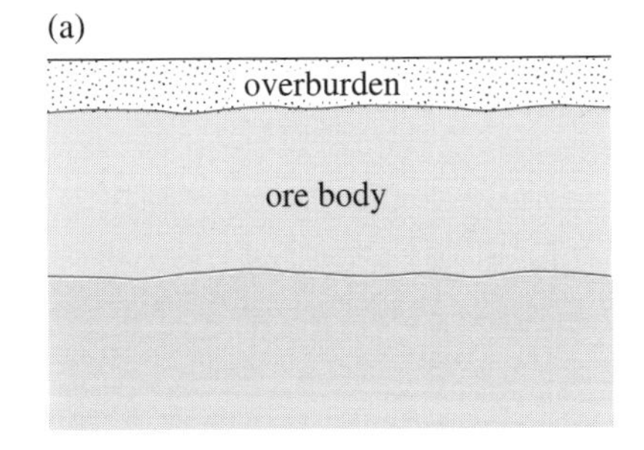

(b)

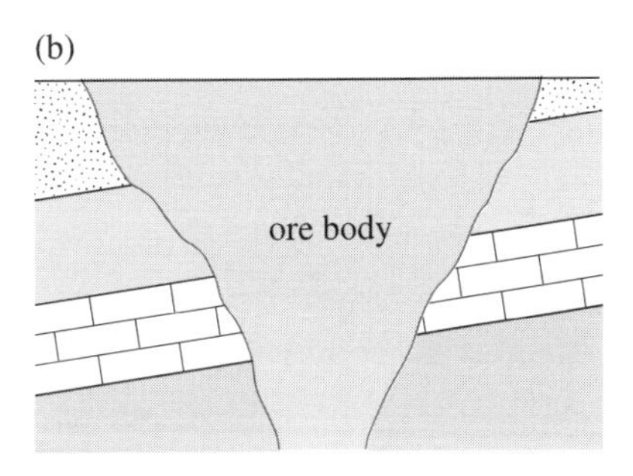

(c)

Figure 33 Different forms of ore deposit: (a) shallow layer; (b) inverted cone; (c) deep layer.

Figure 33b shows a confined ore deposit that reaches the surface — an obvious candidate for surface mining — but it also extends to deep levels. There will come a time when a decision has to be made to stop surface mining because it is more economic to mine underground in the deeper parts of the deposit. Plate 72 shows the effect of such a changeover in the Sudbury mining area — surface workings (open pits) have been abandoned and underground working (via shafts) has taken over.

Figure 33c shows a thin horizontal deposit beneath thick overburden. The decision here is between surface mining only, or underground mining only, depending on the value of the ore body and the cost of removing the overburden.

 Roughly what is the overburden ratio in Figure 33c?

 Approximately 4:1.

Stripping ratio

An overburden ratio of 4:1 is close to the economic limit of mining for low-value bulk materials. The limiting ratio may be even less for some low-grade ores, but it is much higher for high-grade ore deposits. However, quantifying the economics of surface mining requires a measure that is more generally applicable than the overburden ratio. The ratio used is that of the *mass of all rock waste* that must be removed during mining to *the mass of ore* that can be extracted; it is known as the **stripping ratio**. This is a better estimate of the relationship between the cost of waste removal and the potential income from extracting the ore, because many deep surface mines have the form of an inverted, truncated cone known as an **open pit**, as in the Bingham Canyon Mine (*Metals 1*, Figure 31). More overburden must be removed, other than that directly overlying the ore, because even very strong rocks will collapse if vertical faces are cut in them. To ensure stability of open pit walls, a series of benches are cut so that the pit sides are usually no steeper overall than about 45° to the horizontal. Activity 3 demonstrates how this affects the stripping ratio.

Activity 3 Calculation of stripping ratios

In the simplest case of mining a horizontal layer (Figure 34a), the excavation of a pit with walls at 45° involves the removal of overburden and ore. Figure 34a shows in cross-section the progressive development of an open pit in the type of

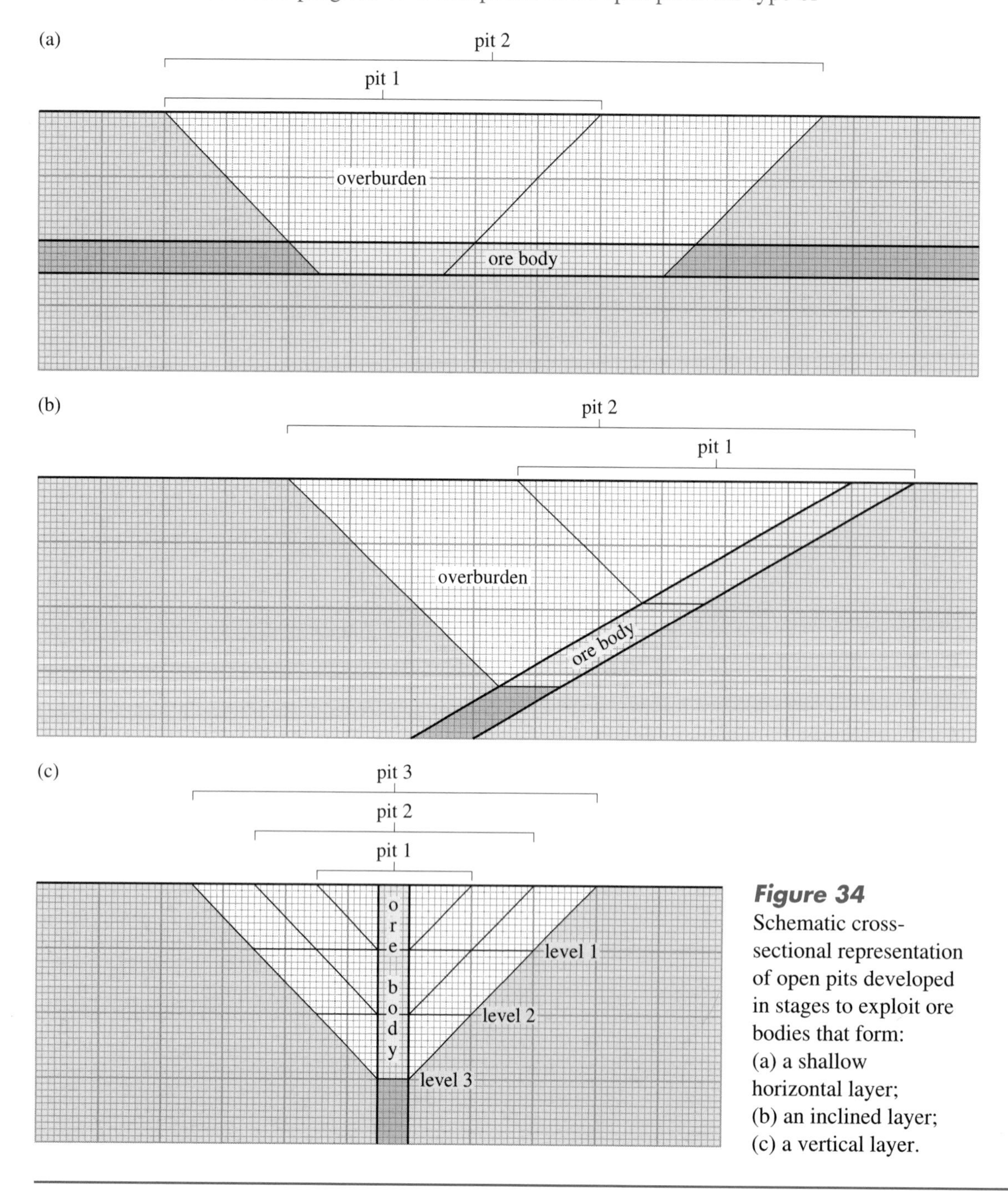

Figure 34 Schematic cross-sectional representation of open pits developed in stages to exploit ore bodies that form: (a) a shallow horizontal layer; (b) an inclined layer; (c) a vertical layer.

deposit shown in Figure 33c (the benches have been omitted for the sake of clarity). In the following discussion, assume *for simplicity* that the cross sectional areas shown in Figure 34 are proportional to volumes of rock in three dimensions (that is, assume the pits are linear rather than conical), and that the densities of the overburden and the ore are the same. Thus, the masses of overburden and ore are equivalent to their respective volumes.

Which is bigger for the open pits in Figure 34a, the overburden ratio or the stripping ratio?

The stripping ratio is larger, because it takes account of volumes rather than thicknesses and that includes the additional material removed to make benches, to ensure that the walls of the pit are at an angle of 45°.

For pit 2 in Figure 34a, the overburden ratio is 4:1 (thickness of the overburden = 20 squares, thickness of the ore body = 5 squares). However, the mass of ore is a total of 300 units (squares), and the mass of overburden that needs to be removed is 1700 units, so the stripping ratio is 1700/300, i.e. about 5.7:1.

As the pit in Figure 34a gets bigger, does the stripping ratio stay constant?

No, it decreases.
For pit 1 it is: 1000/125 = 8.
For pit 2 it is: 1700/300 = 5.7.

It is often preferable, in minimizing C_{waste}, to keep the stripping ratio low and expand an old pit rather than open a new one. In some cases the ore and the overburden will have significantly different densities and, since the stripping ratio is the ratio of the *masses* of the overburden to the ore, densities must be taken into account. In Figure 34a, if the ore has a density of 3.8 t m^{-3} and the overburden has a density of 2.6 t m^{-3}, the stripping ratio for pit 2 can be calculated as follows:

$$\text{stripping ratio} = \text{mass of waste / mass of ore} \qquad (3.3)$$

$$= \frac{\text{volume of waste} \times \text{density of waste}}{\text{volume of ore} \times \text{density of ore}}$$

$$= \frac{1700 \times 2.6}{300 \times 3.8}$$

$$= 3.9$$

Figures 34b and 34c respectively show inclined and vertical sheet-like deposits. Assume that the density of waste rock is 2.6 t m^{-3}, and that the density of ore is 3.8 t m^{-3}.

(a) Calculate the stripping ratios for pits 1 and 2 shown in Figure 34b. How does the stripping ratio change with depth of mining?

(b) How does the stripping ratio change when mining to levels 1, 2 and 3 in Figure 34c?

It may help you to know that the area of a triangle is calculated by:

$$\frac{\text{length of base}}{2} \times \text{height}$$

Clearly, from Activity 3, the stripping ratio generally increases with depth for most deposits, but the way in which it increases depends on the shape of the deposit. The stripping ratio increases much more rapidly with depth in the case of a deposit that narrows downwards than it does for a deposit that becomes wider at depth. At a certain depth, when the stripping ratio becomes so high that the unit cost (Equation 3.1) is dominated by C_{waste}, the unit cost will *exceed* the unit value. In these circumstances, the mine must either be abandoned or mining continued by underground methods for which C_{waste} will not be so large.

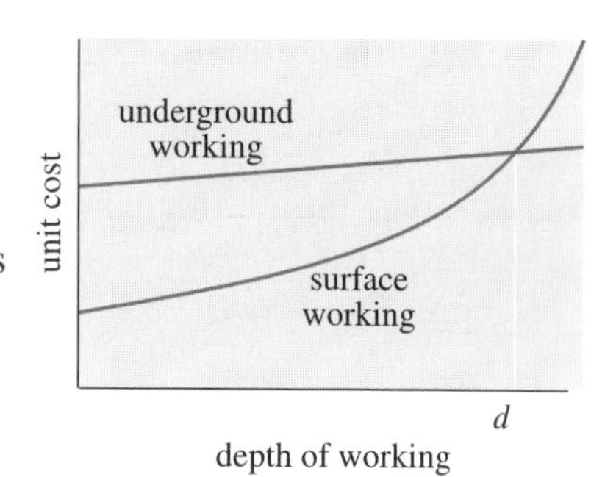

Figure 35 Schematic variation in unit cost of surface and underground mining with depth of working.

Although the unit cost of underground mining is generally higher than that of shallow surface mining, it tends to be less sensitive to the depth of operation. As underground mines go deeper, variable costs don't increase as markedly as they would for surface mining. Figure 35 shows, in a general way, how the unit cost of surface and of underground working vary with depth.

What is the significance of the depth marked '*d*' on Figure 35?

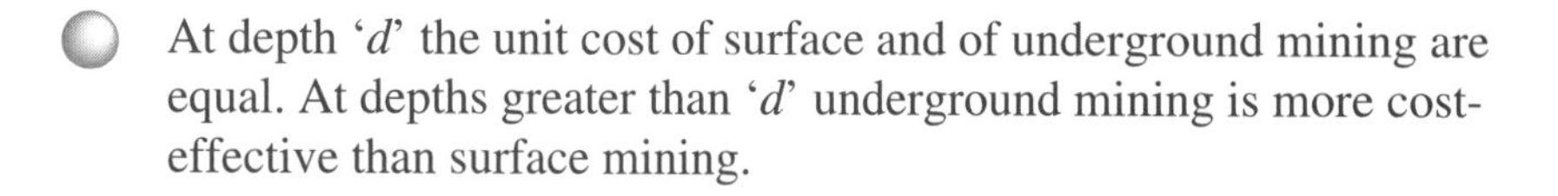

At depth '*d*' the unit cost of surface and of underground mining are equal. At depths greater than '*d*' underground mining is more cost-effective than surface mining.

It is important to remember that the unit cost of underground mining is high, so only ores with a high unit value are mined in this way. Ores with a low unit value are usually mined only in surface operations, and the depth of those mines is determined mainly by the value of the ore and the thickness of the overburden. Generally, less waste needs to be removed underground compared to an open pit, and in underground mining much of the waste can be returned to the mine.

3.1.3 Surface mining

There are few constraints on the space available for surface workings other than the size of the deposit and restrictions imposed by planning permission (especially important in more heavily populated or environmentally sensitive areas). Surface mining of a large deposit can benefit from economies of scale because large-capacity earth-moving equipment can be used with correspondingly higher productivity. This cuts down the unit cost so that low-grade deposits can be worked economically at high tonnages (*Metals 1*, Section 1.3, and above). In general, the larger the deposit, the more profitable it is likely to be — many large, low-grade porphyry copper deposits are more profitable than some small confined deposits. This is because mining a large dispersed deposit can be entirely within rock above the cut-off grade (there is no waste), whereas the need for stable pit walls in the case of confined deposits often requires waste to be removed to extract the ore (i.e. C_{waste} is high).

There are three main *designs* of surface mine, depending primarily on the form of the ore deposit.

1. Open pit (bench) mines are deep holes in the ground; they are the most common form of surface mining for metals. Open pits are appropriate for deposits that occur near to the surface and extend to some considerable depth, including large-scale dispersed deposits and steeply dipping confined deposits.
2. Opencast (strip) mines were discussed in the context of surface coal mining in Block 4 *Energy 1* and are similar to those used to quarry

limestone for cement at Dunbar featured in Video Band 5. They involve digging shallow, elongate pits, cutting into a rockface and backfilling the rear of the excavation. They are appropriate only where the ore body is at shallow depth and is laterally extensive.

3 Dredging is a suitable method of mining deposits in unconsolidated sediment, when it is waterlogged or under water (*Metals 1*, Figure 50).

From your knowledge of the form and occurrences of ore deposits from *Metals 1*, suggest at least one type of ore deposit that you think could be mined using each of these three types of surface mine design.

(i) Open pit mines are suitable for exploiting most porphyry ore deposits and inclined tabular deposits such as massive sulphides (*Metals 1*, Sections 2.4 and 4.2.2).

(ii) Opencast or strip mines are suitable only for horizontally extensive ore deposits that are close to the surface, such as residual deposits and some bedded iron ores (*Metals 1*, Sections 3.2.1 and 3.3.1).

(iii) Dredging can be used for alluvial or beach placer deposits (*Metals 1*, Section 3.4).

Open pit (bench) mining

The development of an open pit mine is quite simple. Overburden is stripped from the area of the final pit and downward excavation is by sideways enlargement as the floor is deepened (Figure 36b). The flanks of the working form a series of **benches** (Figure 36c and Plate 59). These benches serve three purposes. They improve stability of the pit walls; they act as traps for dislodged debris from higher levels; and they provide haulage access to the working floor. The height of each bench (5–20 m) and the angle of the faces depend partly on the need for stability (hence, on the mechanical properties of the rock), partly on the reach of excavating equipment, and partly on the maximum gradient for access by haulage vehicles. In the early days of bench mining — for example, at Bingham Canyon (*Metals 1*, Figure 31) — trains requiring low gradients were used. These have been superseded by gigantic trucks which can operate on gradients of up to 10%. In most cases, open pit excavations extend below the water table and water must be pumped to prevent flooding.

In open pit mining waste has to be removed and stored in spoil heaps. These must be well away from any likely extension of the pit so as not to cover up and hence impede access to ore which might be mined in the future. Spoil heaps can be huge and costly to landscape: restoration to the former state is impractical. Both opencast mining and dredging of surface deposits have the advantage that waste can be dumped in areas from which the ore has been removed. This practice also reduces transport costs, and allows continuous restoration, which avoids costly operations once mining is finished.

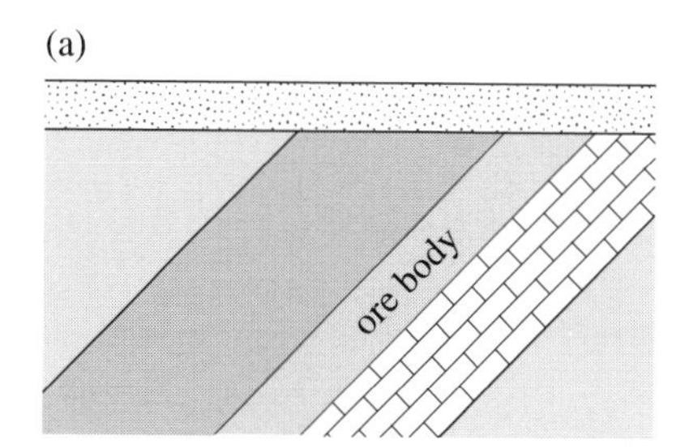

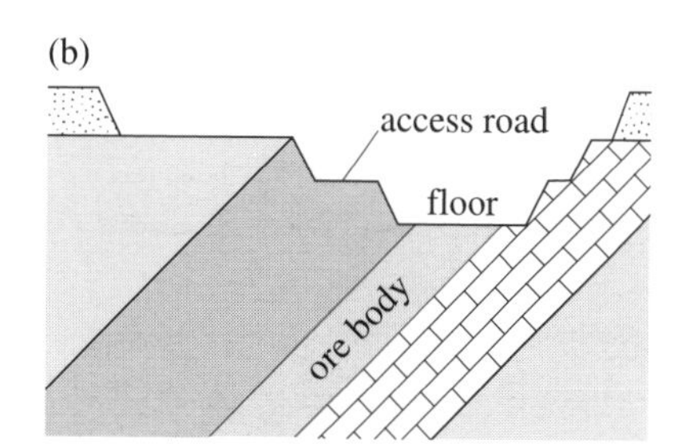

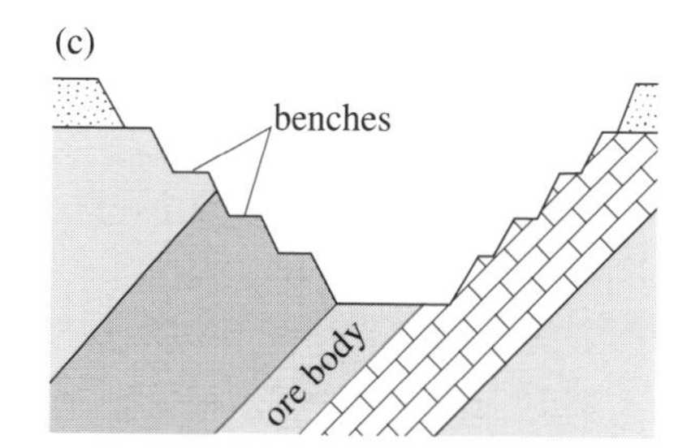

Figure 36 Development of an open pit to exploit a steeply dipping layer of ore: (a) before mining begins; (b) overburden has been stripped and the pit is on its second working floor; (c) pit sides are taken back to allow access to deeper levels, thus maintaining stability of pit walls and access via benches to the pit floor.

Figure 37 is an example of an open pit in the Sudbury magmatic sulphide deposit (Section 3.4). Where are the main spoil heap and the benches in Figure 37 and what is significant about the base of the pit?

The main spoil heap is beyond the open pit. Because the area is relatively uninhabited, it is possible to put the spoil heap wherever it is most convenient for the mine engineers. Old benches can be seen above the area of dark shadow in the left-hand wall of the pit. The important thing about the base of the pit is that it is flooded with water, and so pumping would be required if open pit mining were to proceed to greater depths.

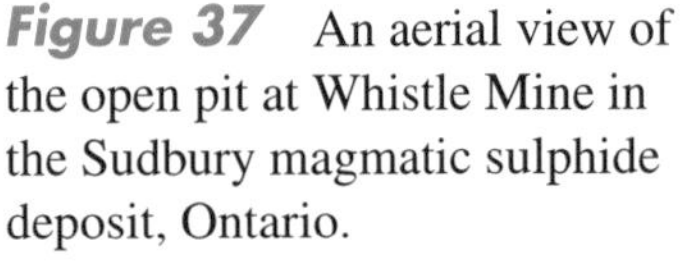

Figure 37 An aerial view of the open pit at Whistle Mine in the Sudbury magmatic sulphide deposit, Ontario.

This is a good time to view Video Band 17: *Pine Point: ore to metal*. It looks at mining operations at Pine Point, and at methods of ore processing and smelting, which is useful background material for the remainder of Section 3. Questions 23 and 24 will test your understanding of the first part of this video — read them through before viewing.

Video Band 17 Pine Point: ore to metal

Speakers

John Wright The Open University

Tom Healy Pine Point Mines

The first part of Video Band 17 concerns the development of a mine site from virgin land under which an ore deposit had been discovered by geophysical methods and evaluated by drilling (Video Band 16).

Question 23

(a) What was the lifetime of an individual pit at Pine Point? How does that compare with the lead time between discovery of a deposit and the start of mining?

(b) What preparation was necessary in the Pine Point area before mining could take place?

(c) Is it likely that mining a single deposit in the Pine Point area would be profitable? How does the presence of numerous deposits in the area affect the profitability of mining?

Question 24

(a) According to the video, what four factors were taken into consideration at Pine Point when evaluating a deposit for mining?

(b) How was the ore reserve evaluated at Pine Point?

(c) What was the importance of using large haulage trucks and maintaining continuity of operations at Pine Point?

The three main activities in open pit mining — drilling and blasting, stripping, and haulage — are well illustrated at Pine Point in Video Band 17.

Drilling and blasting loosens rock, whether overburden or ore. Vertical holes are drilled in patterns and charges inserted in the holes. Rock samples from the drill core can be analysed for the metals being mined, so that the distribution of ore and waste can continually be mapped. This information is used to decide which portions of the material blasted should be taken to the mill, stockpiled, or taken to spoil heaps.

- What are the three main environmental hazards from blasting?

- Dust, noise and shock waves.

These hazards are monitored and kept to a minimum. In the case of shockwaves, very tiny delays are programmed into the blast sequences so that the shock waves from successive holes cancel each other out. Blasts are sometimes videoed and replayed to view the sequential blasting and the amount of ground 'heave' generated. The objective is to blast the material so that it settles in a heap at the base of the working face. Too much explosive or a badly planned blast can result in fragments being flung out; such fragments could be costly to retrieve from other parts of the pit and dangerous to personnel and equipment.

Figure 38 Removing broken rock from an open pit.

Stripping is the excavation of loose ore and waste, and the loading of it onto haulage vehicles (Figure 38). It is important that the sizes of shovels and haulage vehicles are matched to ensure an efficient stripping process. About three shovel-loads should fill a truck.

Haulage of ore and waste from pit to processing plant and spoil heaps respectively is the most costly part of operations. To minimize costs through economies of scale, today's vehicles have capacities of up to 300 tonnes — their sizes and numbers tailored to planned rates of extraction and to ensure continuous stripping and loading. Haul roads have to be sufficiently shallow to allow fully laden trucks to ascend a maximum gradient of about 10%. In some mines, such as Rössing in Namibia (*Metals 1* Section 2.3), a 'trolley assist' system is used where diesel fuel and engine wear are saved as the trucks are drawn up the haul roads by cheap electrical power supplied through antennae mounted on the tops of the lorry cabs, rather like trolley buses. Continual maintenance of vehicles is required to ensure uninterrupted movement of materials. The huge weights of the vehicles and their loads necessitate continuous maintenance of roadways involving bulldozers, graders and water sprayers (to bind the surface and reduce dust).

3.1.4 Underground mining

Underground mining is a good deal less flexible than surface mining. The ore is deeper, so gaining access to the ore may take longer, and, once mining is underway, it is difficult to deviate much from the initial plans. The maximum output from any working face is usually much lower than in surface mining, and to achieve a high output several working faces are needed, rather than the single large working floor commonly encountered in opencast or open pit mining. It is, therefore, extremely important that an overall mine development plan is scheduled well in advance of actual operations. Consequently, the timescale from planning an underground mine to first income can be as long as 10 years, generally much longer than that for surface mines.

How does the timescale for developing the underground mine at Olympic Dam (Section 1.1) compare with that of surface gold mining in Nevada (Video Band 14)?

From starting work on site to production of ore took about 10 years at Olympic Dam, but less than 18 months at Lone Tree Mine in Nevada.

Design of an underground mine rests on three factors, all constrained by geology:

- how best to reach the ore;
- how to minimize extraction of waste;
- how to ensure safe operation.

All designs depend on the depth, form, and mechanical properties of the deposit and its host rocks.

One of the striking features of many of today's underground mines is the sheer scale of operations. These are not the mines of narrow tunnels with little room to stand upright that characterized early metals and coal mining in Britain (Block 4, *Energy 1*, Section 3.2). Rather, there are 40-tonne haulage trucks, front-end loaders, mechanized drilling rigs and maintenance crews moving around in small jeeps (Figure 39). Before extraction of ore can begin, means of access for workers and equipment, outlets for ore and drainage water, and ventilation must all be engineered (Figure 40). There are two options, either vertical shafts, or low-angled declines. Declines allow heavy wheeled equipment to enter and leave the mine under their own power. However, to maintain low gradients can mean extensive and complex, often spiral, tunnelling (Figure 40), particularly if deep ores are involved. Thus, at Sudbury, for example, the declines in some mines go down to 600 m, whereas vertical shafts go down to over 1200 m.

Although the use of declines is increasing as more heavy-wheeled equipment is used, most underground mines are still accessed by vertical shafts from which horizontal roadways branch out at different depths to reach the ore. Transport is either by conveyor, rail or small diesel vehicles.

If access is by vertical shafts, how do you think large pieces of equipment can be taken down to the deeper levels of the mine?

Quite simply, in parts. All large equipment must be taken below ground in kit form and then reassembled in place.

Although ore can be raised up a shaft, greater efficiency is possible with declines carrying conveyor belts. Recently, vertical conveyor systems have

(a)

(b)

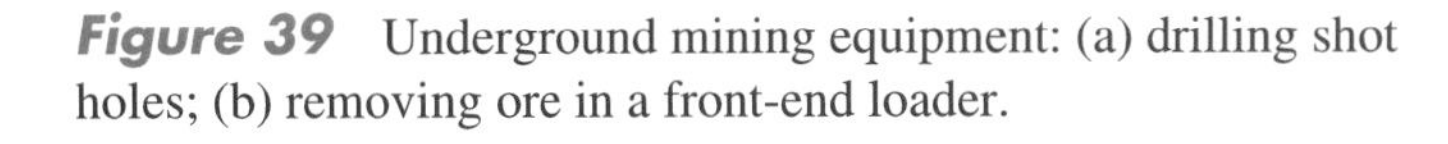

Figure 39 Underground mining equipment: (a) drilling shot holes; (b) removing ore in a front-end loader.

been introduced. In all mines, access routes must remain undisturbed by subsequent operations; it is important that they are located where future mining will not take place.

Mine design

In subsurface operations there are three main engineering requirements:

- the highest possible proportion of the excavation should be in ore above cut-off grade;
- gravity should be used wherever possible for ore transport and for ore breakage;
- the safety of workers, equipment and the excavations themselves must be ensured.

How might gravity be used for ore transport and ore breakage in the design of an underground mine?

Ore from a blasted face can be dropped down steep shafts to assist breakage before being picked up and transported to the surface (Figure 40).

Overall, the engineering requirements of a mine can be summed up in two main questions. Can the rock and ore support the mining excavations? Can gravity be exploited in the design?

The answers depend mainly on four geological factors.

1. The overall *shape of the deposit* affects the size of excavations and determines the kind of support necessary: a broad deposit tends to need more roof support that a narrow one. Tabular or vertical deposits, therefore, require a different basic mine design from more equidimensional ore bodies.
2. The *dip of the deposit* governs the inclination of excavations and the degree to which gravity can be exploited.

3 The *strength of the ore* determines the amount of support required for unworked ore, and whether or not the ore itself can be used to support the roof and walls.

4 The *strength of the host rocks* determines the stability of the roofs and walls of the excavation.

Ore deposits come in a bewildering variety of shapes and sizes, and both the ore and the enclosing country rock vary a great deal in their strength. Rock strength is also affected by the degree of water saturation and fracturing. So, unlike surface mines for which there are only three basic designs (Section 3.1.3), every underground mine is unique, but they fall into two main types.

1 Horizontally extensive deposits, such as tabular ore bodies with dips less than 10°, are worked by either *room and pillar* (also called *pillar and stall*) or *longwall* methods as widely used in coal mining (Block 4 *Energy 1*, Section 3.2.2). The method chosen depends on rock strength. Room and pillar operations require strong host rocks and strong ore. Where either is weak, organized collapse of the roof is achieved by longwall mining.

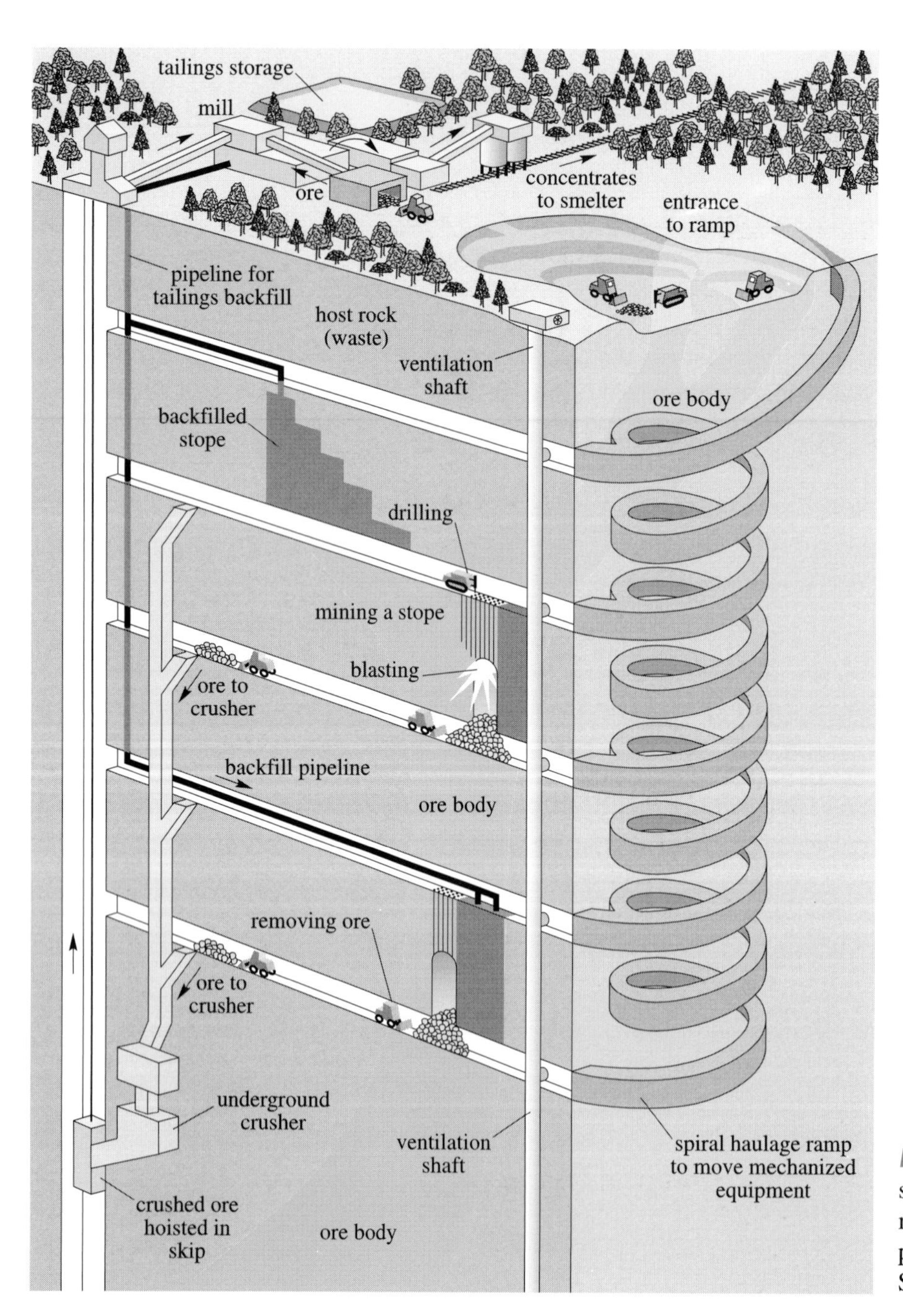

Figure 40 Schematic section through an underground mine associated with an open pit (after Ontario Geological Survey, 1989, p.15).

2 Vertically extensive deposits, such as pipe-shaped, conical and equidimensional deposits, steeply dipping tabular ores and vein-like hydrothermal or pegmatite deposits, are worked from horizontal tunnels, known as *levels*, with semi-permanent walls. Excavation of ore from the roofs and floors of levels is known as **stoping** and the regions mined are known as *stopes* (Figure 40). Where the host rock is strong, the walls need little support, but where it is weak, support is essential. A strong ore requires minimal roof support and can be left temporarily in place to support weak walls; a weak ore either needs much support or the use of a mining method where human and machine access to the excavation is minimized.

To excavate ores in vertically extensive deposits, a variety of underground mining methods have been devised. They may be conveniently grouped into supported methods and caving methods.

Supported methods require substantial amounts of artificial support to maintain stability in the workings. They are used when the volume of host rock being removed to get at the ore is relatively small, and as much as possible of the host rock is left in place. The more obvious, but usually more expensive, supports are steel jacks, arches and the like. However, a more satisfactory method is to use waste as backfill into areas previously excavated (Figure 40); this can stabilize the workings and support the overlying rock mass.

Caving methods are used if the deposit is large, almost all the rock is to be processed, and gravity can be harnessed. They are simple but potentially dangerous methods which involve inducing the ore to cave in, smashing itself in the process. Arguably the most dramatic is *block caving* in which large, often equidimensional deposits are mined, but this eventually leads to collapse of the surface, which can be environmentally damaging. Block caving was used at the San Manuel–Kalamazoo deposit in Arizona, one of the few porphyry copper deposits worked by underground mining methods.

Nearly all underground mines partly process the ore before it is transported to the surface, usually by jaw or cone crushers (Section 3.2.1) situated deep in the mine and to which ore may pass by gravity (Figure 40).

What are the advantages of doing some processing of the ore underground?

There is less environmental impact at the surface from noise and dust, gravity can be exploited to move and break up the ore, and the underground crusher produces small lumps of ore which are more easily carried to the mineral processing plant on the surface.

Question 25

Answer the following questions about the mining operation illustrated in Figure 40.

(a) What is the form of the ore body?

(b) How is the ore being mined?

(c) Where is the ore crushed?

(d) In what ways is the ore from underground transported in the various stages from blasting until it leaves the site?

(e) What use has the waste from mineral processing?

3.2 Ore processing

Most metal mining operations are partly concerned with the extraction of ore from the ground, and partly with ore processing — the separating out of ore minerals and preparation for the subsequent extraction of metals. A number of stages are involved, as outlined in Figure 41. The first is **liberation** — the breaking up of ore into fragments to *release* ore minerals from the gangue and from each other. The second is the *separation* of liberated fragments of ore minerals from fragments of gangue and other ore minerals, so reducing the volume and mass of the product: the **ore mineral concentrate**.

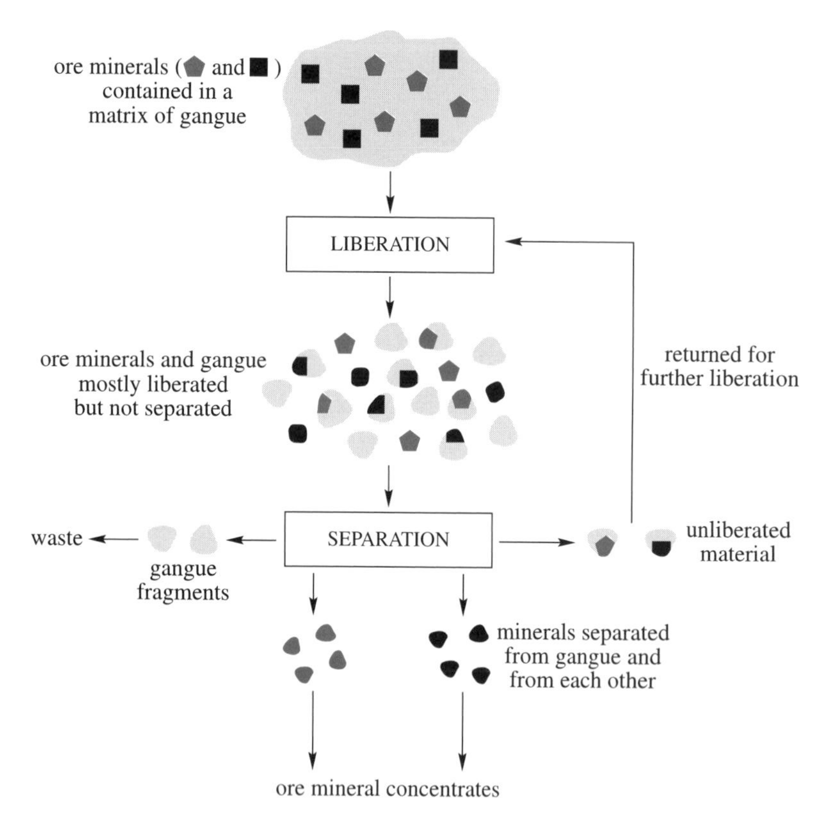

Figure 41 Schematic representation of the stages of ore processing.

Ores extracted by mining have the *same* grade as when they were in the ground. Low-grade ores, especially from dispersed deposits of copper, molybdenum and gold, may contain over 99% gangue, and even high-grade ores still contain a lot of gangue.

- Is the value of raw, untreated metal ores likely to be high or low, and what does that suggest about where the ores should be treated in relation to the mine?

- The value of untreated metal ores, especially low-grade ores, is low, often even lower than roadstone or building aggregates. So, it is uneconomic to transport them very far; they have a high place value. Consequently, mined ore must be processed as close as possible to the mine to remove worthless gangue and obtain an ore mineral concentrate.

Power and water are essential for ore processing; if not already available, they must be provided, as at Olympic Dam (Section 1.1). It is clearly an advantage to site the processing plant where there is access to these services, but they are generally more transportable than ore. An ore mineral concentrate has much greater value per tonne than untreated ore, and is a saleable commodity; it can be transported efficiently (has a low place value) and is ready for metal extraction, usually by smelting (Section 3.3).

Many of the ore processing operations described in this Section are featured in Video Band 17: *Pine Point: ore to metal.* If you have not viewed it already you should do so now. At the end of Section 3 you will be asked which forms of ore processing operate at Pine Point, and why they are appropriate for lead–zinc ores.

No two ore deposits contain precisely the same mineral assemblage, and the proportions, textures and grain sizes of minerals vary, even across the same ore body. To achieve optimum efficiency and profitability in mineral processing, procedures must be tailored to each ore body. Methods of liberation and separation never work perfectly, so rejected material is often recycled to earlier stages and processed again (Figure 41). Indeed, ore mineral *recovery* is never 100% (box 'Recovery from ores', Section 3.2.2), although modern processes are generally more efficient than those used in the past. Indeed, many old spoil heaps, containing material once regarded as waste, can now be mined economically, which helps to conserve remaining ore deposits.

3.2.1 Liberation

In ores, the ore minerals and gangue are generally intergrown, so before they can be separated they have to be liberated from one another. The easiest way of releasing minerals is to break up the ore into smaller and smaller pieces by crude mechanical methods, a process called **comminution**. Figure 42 shows how, after repeated fracturing to reduce grain size, ore minerals can be liberated; but many fragments still contain some gangue along with the ore minerals. Comminution is a process much like physical weathering, but achieved in minutes rather than over many years. However, the natural processes of weathering generally combine physical *and* chemical actions. The purely physical nature of comminution cannot exploit weaknesses in the rock as effectively as natural processes; fracturing tends to occur through mineral grains rather than along grain boundaries.

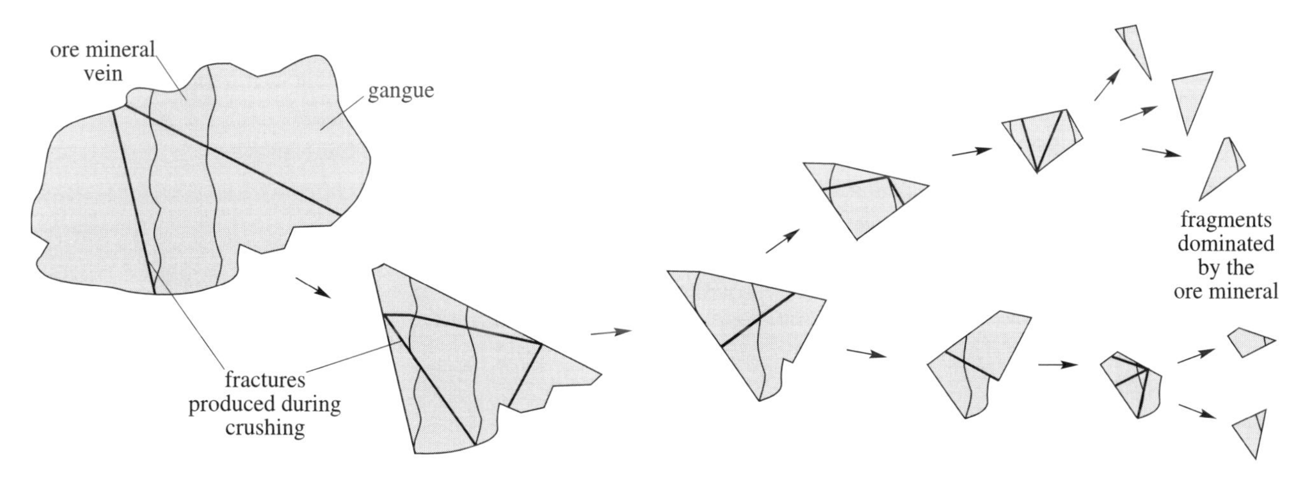

Figure 42 The effect of breakage along random lines on fragments of ore containing ore minerals and gangue. It takes repeated fracturing and reduction of grain size to produce fragments dominated by ore minerals. For efficient liberation, grains must generally be crushed smaller than the initial minimum dimension of the ore minerals.

Breaking rocks down to 1–2 cm diameter fragments is traditionally called **crushing**, whereas further reduction to smaller particle sizes is called **grinding**. Crushing and grinding the ore to release mineral grains is straightforward, but it cannot be achieved in a single operation. Equipment designed for coarse crushing, cannot produce fine powder, and equipment designed for fine grinding cannot handle large chunks of rock. Therefore, comminution is carried out in stages using a range of equipment such as that shown in Figure 43. Primary crushing involving heavy duty equipment often uses a jaw crusher or a cone crusher (Figure 43a and b) which can take blocks a metre or more across, to produce rock fragments of about 5–10 cm diameter. Secondary crushing with similar but scaled-down equipment

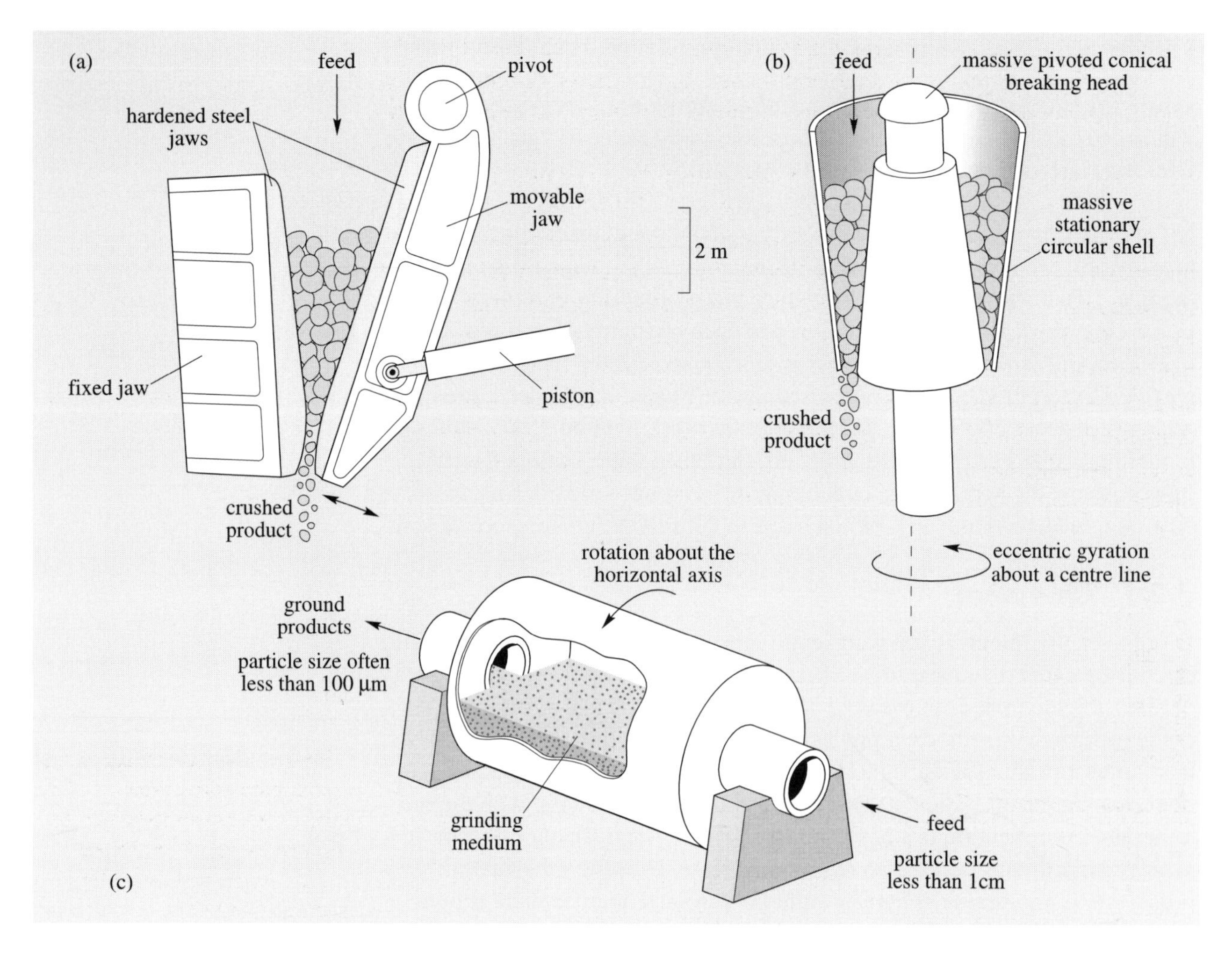

Figure 43 Methods of crushing and grinding:
(a) jaw crusher;
(b) cone crusher;
(c) ball mill with balls as the grinding medium.
Note scale.

reduces rock fragments to about 1–2 cm diameter. In any one crusher, the average size reduction is by a ratio of about 4:1. Grinding involves rod mills (Video Band 17), for coarser material, and ball mills (Figure 43c) for finer material, to reduce grain sizes down to less than a millimetre, and even to tens of microns.

For effective liberation, crushed fragments must be ground smaller than the ore mineral grains, so complete liberation of fine-grained ore minerals can be achieved only if the rock is broken into very small fragments. However, excessive grinding may be undesirable because it causes further breakage of already liberated grains and produces too many **fines**. Fines are a problem because physical methods of mineral separation don't work well with very fine-grained material, and so fines become waste. Excessive grinding is therefore inefficient; it wastes energy and increases processing costs. Because each stage of comminution does not produce fragments of uniform size, but a wide range of sizes, it improves efficiency if particles already at the required size are removed from the system as soon as possible, usually by large sieves or screens, before they are broken further. This procedure of size separation is known as **classification**.

Liberation of ore minerals can represent half the cost of ore processing so it is important to use energy-efficient comminution methods and to minimize wear and tear on the equipment. In the case of unconsolidated placer deposits such as tin river gravels and ilmenite beach sands, natural processes have already liberated mineral grains and ore processing is relatively easy.

- What properties of an ore would you think are most likely to affect energy consumption during comminution?

- The size of the ore mineral grains determines how much crushing and grinding is required for its liberation, and the hardness, or more strictly, the crushing strength of the ore determines how easy it is to break down.

The *crushing strength* of an ore can be determined in the laboratory. It is expressed as an index which represents the work in kWh t^{-1} required to reduce blocks of rock of infinite size to a particle size of 100 microns. Given this 'work' index for a particular rock type, the electrical energy requirement for reducing a given feed size to a required product size can be estimated. Figure 44 shows how the estimated energy requirement for grinding soft and hard ores differs, and how the requirement increases with decreasing grain size of the product. For product sizes below 100 microns energy costs rise dramatically. A balance must therefore be struck in order to minimize energy costs, maximize ore mineral liberation, minimize fines, and produce an optimum grain size for subsequent separation procedures.

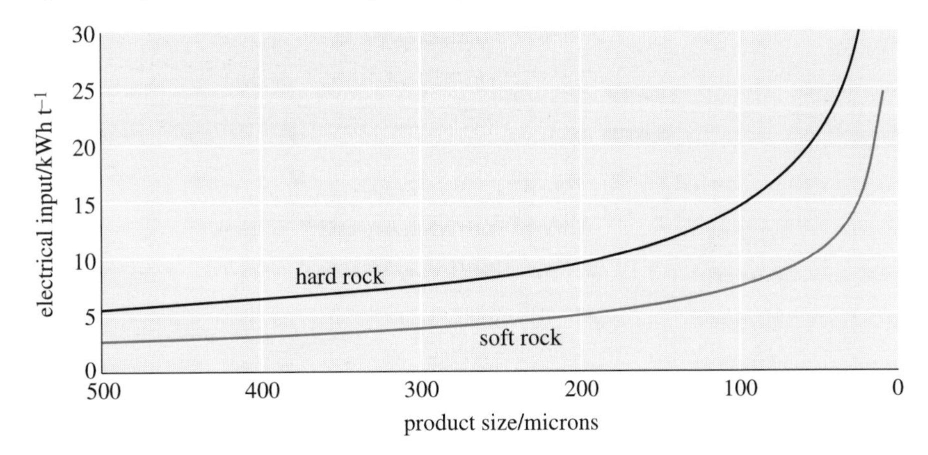

Figure 44 Electrical power requirements to produce products of varying grain size from a hard rock, and a soft rock. Curves shown are for a feed size of 1 cm.

Question 26

In the case of (a) an ore from a hydrothermal vein deposit and (b) an ore from a magmatic segregation deposit, which do you think would require less energy to liberate the ore minerals? Why?

3.2.2 Separation

Even after crushing and grinding to liberate ore minerals, the concentration of metals in a liberated ore remains the *same* as in the original rock. The next stage is to *separate* the valuable ore minerals from the gangue as cheaply and efficiently as possible. Separation usually involves *sorting* liberated ore mineral grains into groups by exploiting their physical or chemical properties. Separation of the ore minerals from gangue and especially from each other is often difficult; the success of separation is described in terms of **recovery**, the proportion of contained metal or ore mineral in the product, relative to that in the ore. As demonstrated in the box 'Recovery from ores', complete recovery of an ore mineral is never achieved.

- What physical properties form the basis of a separation technique?

- Density is perhaps the most obvious, as many ore minerals (such as oxides, sulphides) are denser than the gangue minerals (such as silicates, carbonates). Other properties with a potential for use in separation include simple physical properties such as grain shape and colour, electromagnetic properties (the ability to be magnetized or to retain an electrical charge), and chemical properties such as selective solubility in chemical reagents.

Recovery from ores

In producing an ore mineral concentrate, it would be ideal if all ore minerals could be separated from the ore. However, to liberate completely an ore mineral from most ores would require extremely fine grinding (Figure 42), and to separate all of it would require repeated recycling and reprocessing of waste to minimize losses (as separation is never 100% efficient). Such complex procedures would not only lead to reduced throughput (because very fine grains are difficult to separate), but would also consume large amounts of energy (Section 3.2.1). Therefore complete (100%) recovery is neither an economic nor a practical proposition.

Nevertheless, to minimize transport costs and to provide the smelter with a feed that is most favourable for smelting, a high grade of concentrate is required. However, in ore ground as fine as is economic and practical, there will always be some mixed grains, and to obtain a 100% ore mineral concentrate, all mixed grains must be rejected—even those with a high ore mineral content. This effect is illustrated in Figure 45, a typical *grade–recovery curve*, showing that the higher the grade of concentrate produced, the lower the recovery of contained metal (because it is lost through the rejection of mixed grains). It is difficult to quantify this relationship precisely because the shape of the curve varies depending on the nature of the ore and the efficiency of particular separation processes. As a rough guide, obtaining a 90% concentrate might entail the loss of 20–30% of the ore mineral, whereas perhaps only 10% might be lost in achieving a 70% concentrate.

There is clearly a balance to be achieved in maximizing recovery, while maintaining a high quality concentrate, and at the same time, minimizing processing costs. Optimum recovery is determined not only by the initial form of the ore and the purity required by the smelting process, but by a range of economic factors, including processing costs, transport costs, and metal price.

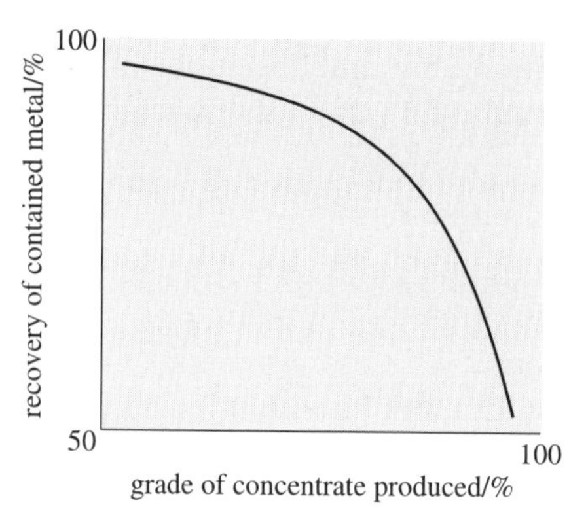

Figure 45 Typical grade–recovery curve for concentrates produced by ore processing.

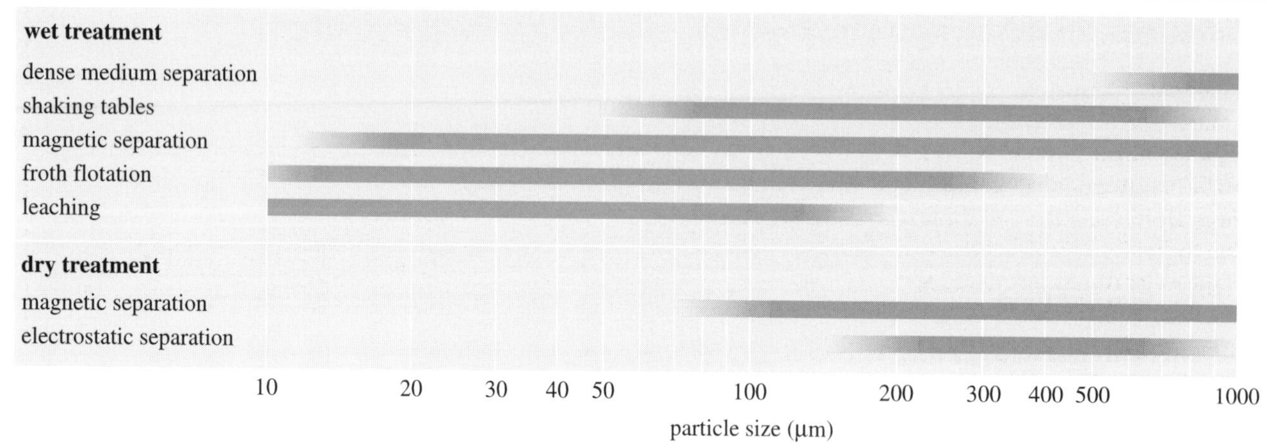

Figure 46 Ranges of particle size appropriate for some mineral separation processes.

Figure 46 summarizes the particle size ranges appropriate for several physical methods of separation. You will see that wet or dry treatments may be involved. Dry processes usually use less energy because there is no water to be pumped around and the concentrates recovered don't have to be dried. However, wet processes are often used because water aids dispersion of small particles that would tend to stick together electrostatically when dry, and it also acts as a lubricant to assist movement of larger particles. The choice of a wet or dry process depends partly on the grain sizes to be separated and partly on the properties of the minerals and the method of separation to be used. If crude separation can be achieved efficiently on large particles, separation can take place after crushing and before grinding to save energy, but this strategy would be suitable only for ores that contain large masses of ore minerals, more typical of confined deposits.

Density separation methods

Dense medium separation In the same way that sawdust can be separated from sand by floating it off in water, mineral grains can be separated into different density fractions using a liquid of intermediate density. This is the basis for the *float–sink* method. Water is not a particularly useful medium because it has a much lower density than all ore minerals. Dense organic liquids such as bromoform (used for separating minerals in the laboratory) are too expensive and too toxic for industrial use. A cunning approach involves mixing a very finely ground, heavy material in water to form a slurry. Magnetite and an iron–silicon alloy called ferrosilicon have been used as they are cheap. As the effective density of the slurry can be adjusted by varying its water content, it is possible to separate different ore minerals from each other and from gangue minerals. The process is usually referred to as **dense medium separation**. Both magnetite and ferrosilicon are highly magnetic, so they can be recovered from the slurry by magnets and recycled for future use.

Panning Roasted peanuts, rather unexpectedly perhaps, can serve to illustrate the principle of **panning**. Roasting peanuts in a pan generally results in many being burnt on one side, but vendors can avoid this by mixing the peanuts with hot sand to give an even roast. To separate the sand from the nuts, they simply shake the container and the peanuts rise to the surface. The sand is a dry dense medium and, when agitated, the low-density nuts float to the surface. Panning uses the same principle: shaking a slurry of mainly low-density grains causes the higher-density ones to *sink* to the bottom of the pan. A gold panner (Block 1, Figure 63) would separate the gold grains from the remaining waste by swirling the slurry around the pan and allowing the lighter grains to spill over while the heavier grains remain trapped in the pan. This method also exploits the ability of flowing water to separate minerals.

Separation of mineral grains in a flowing film of water

Figure 47a shows small mineral grains in a film of water that is flowing down a shallow inclined surface. At the point of contact with the surface, the water tends to stick due to friction. Hence, the velocity of the water film varies significantly across its thickness, increasing away from the contact area (as shown by the velocity profile in Figure 47a).

Large grains are little affected by the water flow — they just sit there, through *inertia* (resistance to motion) — they would roll under gravity only if the slope were steep. Very small grains are carried away in suspension. However, grains of intermediate size roll under the influence of the flowing water. The larger of these grains move faster than the smaller ones because they are acted on by the fastest water flow (Figure 47a). In addition, lower-density grains tend to be moved further than those with higher densities (because they have less inertia), and rounded grains move more easily by rolling than flatter ones do by sliding. Figure 47b shows the idealized result when grains of different sizes and densities are subjected to a water flow down an inclined surface.

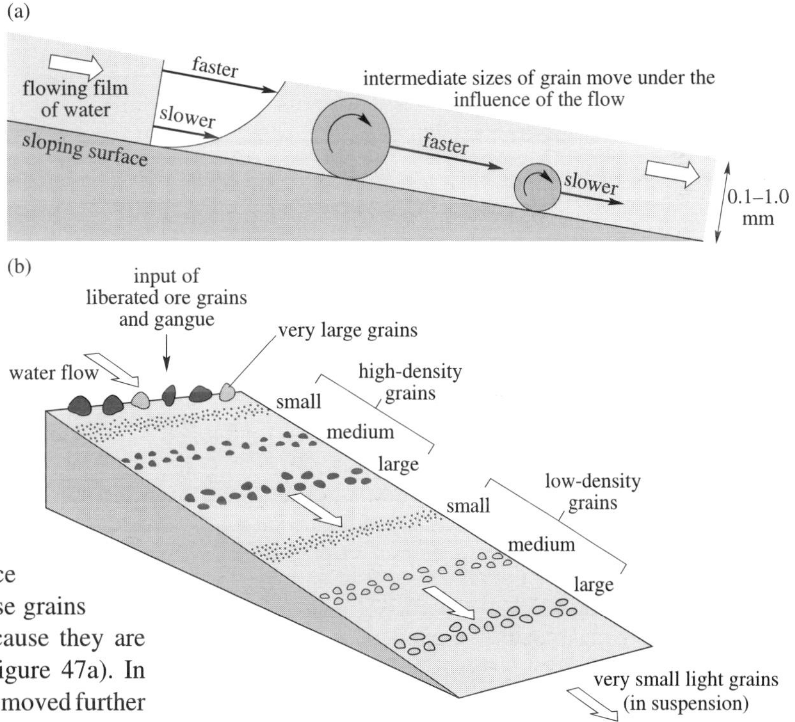

Figure 47 Using a flowing film of water to separate mineral grains: (a) velocity profile and movement of grains under the influence of flowing water; (b) separation of grains of varying size and density by a flowing film of water.

Shaking table A shaking table is a separating device that utilizes, in enhanced form, the principles of grain separation in a flowing film of water. Shown in Figure 48, it consists of a sloping surface down which a film of water flows and across which are rib-like barriers (riffles). The movement of the water down the slope is interrupted by the riffles which trap denser grains. The table is shaken to-and-fro with a horizontal action along the length of the riffles and at right-angles to the water flow in a manner such that motion is slow in one direction and then rapid in reverse. Effectively the table is pulled from under the denser grains (that have the greater inertia) so they advance along the riffles. Lighter grains progress across the riffles. Eventually an equilibrium is established by adjusting the flow rate, tilt angles and shaking frequency, so that grains of different densities are separated into narrow bands. Shaking tables work with grain sizes between 50 μm and 1 mm.

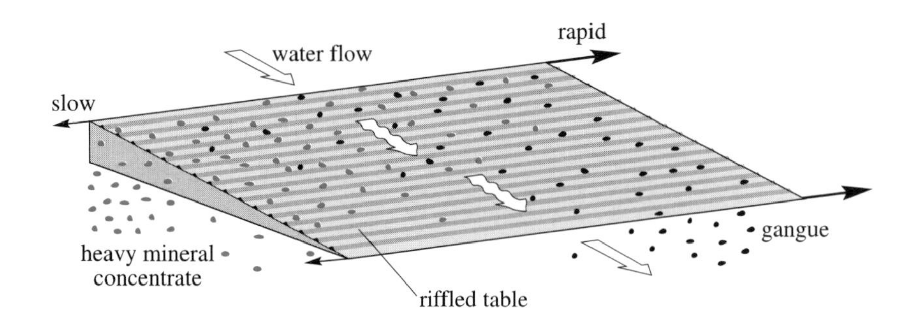

Figure 48 How a shaking table works: grains for separation are fed along the top edge with the water flow; the inertia of the denser grains in relation to both the shaking action and the water flow is the basis of separation.

Density separation using panning or shaking tables is *inefficient* for very fine particles and it relies on high density contrasts. The **density contrast ratio** is expressed as:

$$\frac{D_H - D_W}{D_L - D_W} \tag{3.4}$$

where D_H, D_L and D_W are densities of the heavy ore mineral, the light gangue mineral and water respectively. An empirical criterion for good separation is that the density contrast ratio must be greater than 1.25 and preferably greater than 2.5.

Question 27

Can a shaking table employing water be used to separate the following ore minerals:

(a) Cassiterite (SnO_2, density 6.9 t m^{-3}) from quartz (SiO_2, density 2.65 t m^{-3})?

(b) Chromite ($FeCr_2O_4$, density 4.6 t m^{-3}) from magnetite (Fe_3O_4, density 5.2 t m^{-3})?

(c) Galena (PbS, density 7.5 t m^{-3}) from sphalerite (ZnS, density 4.1 t m^{-3})?

In arid areas, a variant of the shaking table uses an air blower. This is called *dry blowing*; it produces huge clouds of dust.

- The density of air is very low, so would the density contrast ratio for two minerals be higher or lower if air rather than water were the separating medium? What is the implication for minerals to be separated?

- The density contrast ratio between heavy and light minerals in air is much less than in water. Thus, good separation can be achieved only for minerals with a very high density contrast. In practice, dry blowing is used only for separating gold and platinum from silicate minerals.

Historical methods of ore processing

Many early forms of ore processing followed similar principles to those of today, even if the types of ore that could be processed and the technology and resources available to do the job were limited. It was just as important to obtain an ore mineral concentrate from the ore. The manual procedures used were commonly known as *dressing*. Early forms of dressing were particularly labour intensive, giving work to women, old men and boys. It was done near the mines, often in exposed places, largely as an outdoor operation which was at the mercy of the weather. Daylight and water supplies were essential.

On leaving the mine, the largest lumps of ore were broken up using sledge-hammers. Ore fragments were sorted according to their size, using either a grating of parallel bars, about 25 mm (1 inch) apart, or a hand sieve with a 25 mm mesh. Over-sized ore was further crushed by hand. Crushing was the first process to be mechanized, with either horses or waterwheels providing the power. Stamp mills were available by the sixteenth century as illustrated in Agricola's *De re metallica* (Figure 49), but in the UK their use was mainly confined to Cornwall and Devon for crushing tin and copper ores.

When powered machinery became more widely available during the nineteenth century, it was possible to crush large amounts of ore quickly. Mechanical crushing also reduced costs so much that it became possible to work those parts of veins that had previously been left because the ore was too finely intermixed with gangue minerals. These developments meant that larger quantities of ore had to be handled and finer material processed. Therefore dressing also had to be mechanized.

Dressing had been mainly by gravity separation in water, and relied on the different densities of the ore minerals and gangue. When a mixture of *equal sized* fragments of ordinary rock and dense minerals are agitated in water, and then allowed to settle, a crude separation occurs. The heaviest fragments, usually of ore minerals, form a layer at the bottom, on top of which there is a layer of heavy rock fragments with ore minerals attached to them. The topmost layer, of the lightest rock fragments, is waste. For this process to work efficiently, it was essential for the crushed material to be *classified* into fractions according to size. Very fine material was difficult to process in this way.

The fine ore and mud produced by mechanical crushing had to be processed differently and a mechanized version of another form of dressing was developed. This was the buddle. In its basic form, a buddle is a wooden trough, with a slight slope along its length, along which water flows. When feed of uniform size is introduced at the top, grains are deposited from the flowing water and distributed, according to their density, along the length of the buddle, in a similar way to the separation shown in Figure 47b. The gradient and length of buddles varied according to the grain size and density of the material being treated — a finer feed needed a shallower slope, a longer channel and less water to facilitate separation. The process was used to separate ore into 'heads' — dominantly ore minerals; 'middles' — fragments of ore mineral and gangue; and 'tails' — mainly gangue. The 'heads' were sent for smelting: the 'middles' were reground and reprocessed: the 'tails' were dumped.

Figure 49 A sixteenth-century stamp mill. Four vertical stamp rods (D) are lifted in turn by the axle of the water wheel and then allowed to fall. The ore is shovelled in and crushed under the iron shoes of the stamp rods (E).

To make the process more efficient, a circular buddle fed from the centre (Figure 50) was developed in the mid-nineteenth century. The heavy ore minerals were deposited first, nearest the centre, while lighter materials continued towards the perimeter. Enrichment of ore minerals was to about 40% on the first treatment and to 70–75% on the second. Similar equipment used in northern England enabled about 20 tons of material to be processed in a day and its lead content raised from 20% to 60%. As a result, larger tonnages of material could be treated, and mechanization made savings in the amount of labour employed. Broadly similar techniques were used for dressing lead and copper ores, but tin ores had to be ground much finer and needed more elaborate procedures to trap ore minerals.

Ore processing has long given rise to environmental problems, especially in the nineteenth century. Buddling produced large quantities of contaminated water and its use by lead miners in Derbyshire caused 'vexation and annoyance' among farmers and other users of streams. The River Derwent, at Matlock Bath, was described by an early nineteenth-century writer as 'made as thick and yellow as a strong solution of gumbouge [a soup], and so continue for hours'.

Even though dirty water from dressing was allowed to settle in lagoons before being returned to the rivers, a government commissioner said: 'After all that can be done to get all the lead from the ore, many particles are carried down in the muddy water of the river, or burn, and no man allows himself or his cattle for many miles below a washing-place to take the poisonous draught.'

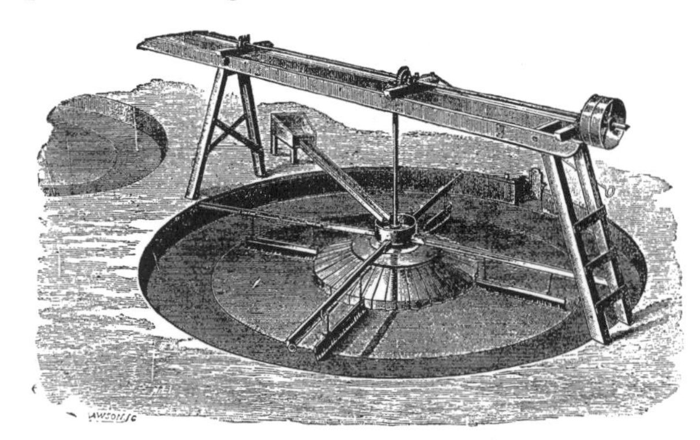

Figure 50 A mid-nineteenth-century round buddle. Built in a shallow pit, about 300 mm deep and 6–7 m in diameter, it is basically a wooden floor in the form of a shallow cone. A slurry (fine solids and water) is fed by a wooden trough to the centre of the buddle, so it flows outwards down the slope. Light brushes, on rotating arms, sweep the slurry round the buddle preventing it from settling unevenly and forming channels.

Electrical and magnetic separation

If a mineral can be magnetized or if it can accept an electrical charge, its behaviour, when passed through a magnetic or an electrical field, will be different from that of a mineral that is not easily magnetized or electrostatically charged. Magnetic separation can work on wet or dry materials, but the electrostatic method works only on dry material (Figure 46). Very similar designs are employed in the two kinds of separator (Figure 51).

(a)

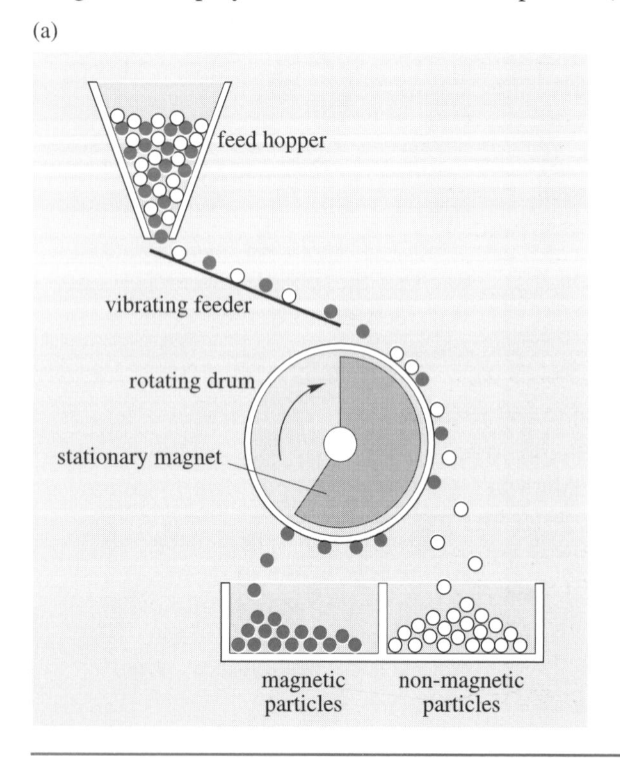

(b)

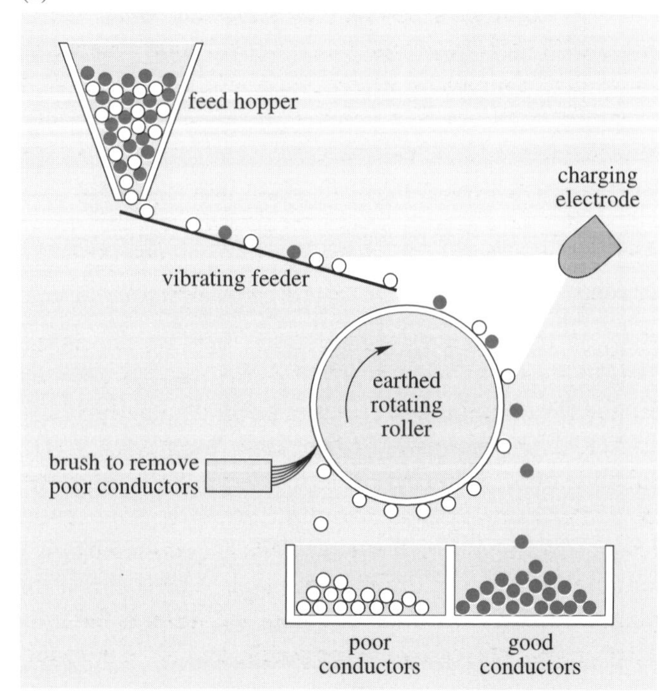

Figure 51 Schematic forms of: (a) magnetic separator; (b) electrostatic separator.

In *magnetic separation*, a stream of grains, ideally a layer only one grain thick, is fed through a strong magnetic field. The magnetic grains are attracted by the field and collected separately from the non-magnetic grains (Figure 51a).

Electrostatic separation is based on the attraction of electrically charged particles to neutral surfaces where opposite charges are induced locally. This is rather like picking up small pieces of paper using a charged plastic comb; you can charge a comb sufficiently just by combing dry hair. Mineral grains are charged by an electrode as they are fed onto an earthed metal roller (Figure 51b). The grains stick to the roller for as long as they hold their electrical charge. Some grains lose their charge quickly, and so fall from the roller. Other grains tend to retain their charges, stick to the roller for longer, and follow a different trajectory as they fall.

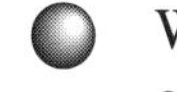

Which minerals hold an electrostatic charge well, good or poor conductors?

Poor conductors retain their charge better than good conductors. Good conductors allow their charge to flow away easily.

Electrostatic separation is often used to recover naturally liberated conducting minerals such as iron–titanium oxides from unconsolidated beach placer deposits and works best for grains of 0.2–1 mm in diameter.

Froth flotation

A rather unexpected form of separation process (featured in Video Band 17) had its origins in a domestic setting. Washing the grimy and greasy clothes of lead miners produced very dark soapsuds. It was noticed that the suds were covered with tiny grains of galena. This was rather surprising because galena is dense and would be expected to sink in water rather than float. In fact, the galena was coated in grease and the grease caused the galena grains to become attached to the bubbles. The phenomenon is the basis of a method called **froth flotation** that has been an important industrial separation process since the beginning of the twentieth century.

Froth flotation relies on the preferential attachment of particular mineral grains to air bubbles, so that they are carried to the surface of a frothing liquid while other mineral grains remain submerged in the liquid. Only grains that *repel* water, behaving rather like the non-wettable greasy surface of an oily cloth, become attached to the bubbles. With the addition of suitable chemicals, usually organic compounds, it is often possible to coat mineral grains selectively with a thin film of a substance that reduces their wettability (as did the grease from the miners' clothes). The 'non-wetted' mineral grains become attached to bubbles when the mixture is aerated, whereas 'wetted' grains remain in the water.

Many of the chemicals used in froth flotation for coating grains have been found by trial and error. They allow, for example, the separation of sulphides from non-sulphides, and different sulphide minerals from each other. The maximum size of a particle that can be 'floated' depends on its density. Sulphide minerals with a density of the order of $5\,\mathrm{t\,m^{-3}}$ can be floated only if the particles are less than about $200\,\mu\mathrm{m}$ diameter. Figure 52 shows the basic design of a single flotation cell. Cells are commonly grouped in a circuit to separate a number of different minerals. The slurry of fine-grained minerals, gangue minerals, chemical reagents and water is fed into the bottom of the flotation cell, stirred by a large paddle and air is introduced. The bubbles rise, with the non-wetted ore mineral grains selectively attached, to accumulate as froth at the top. The froth is scraped off, while the wetted grains pass to disposal as waste or to another flotation line where they are separated using different chemicals. As well as being selective, flotation is capable of separating grains between 5 μm and 200 μm.

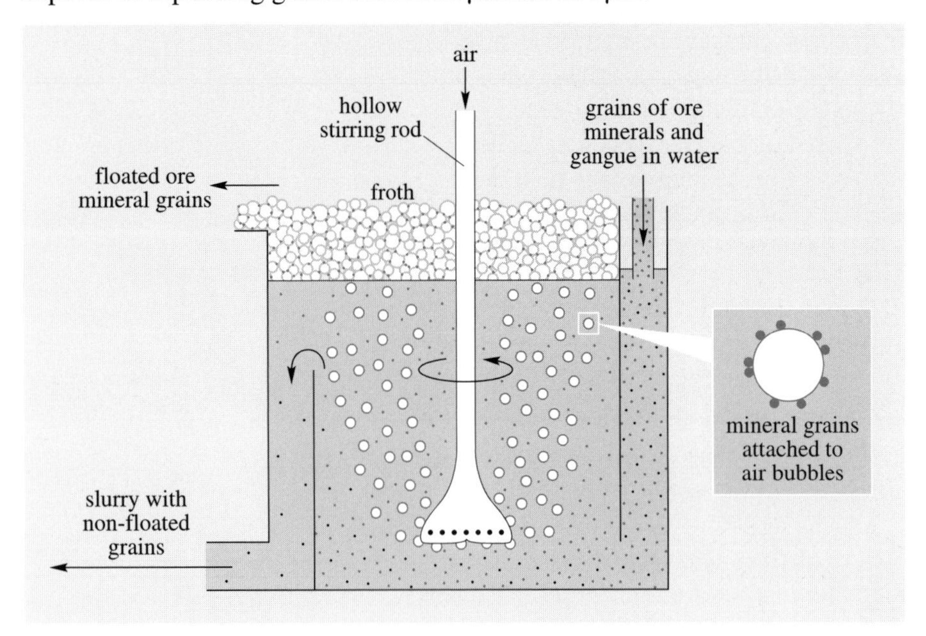

Figure 52 Schematic form of froth flotation cell.

Froth flotation can be used to separate fine ore mineral grains from almost any low-grade dispersed deposit, but it is widely used for the separation of fine-grained metal sulphides. Froth flotation made the processing of porphyry copper ores possible, and helped to make deposits such as Bingham Canyon, Utah, economic to mine (*Metals 1*, Section 2.4).

Leaching

The **leaching** of ore with chemical solutions is a form of ore processing that allows direct metal extraction. It depends on the creation of conditions in which ore minerals can engage in chemical reactions that release the metals they contain into solution. It has several advantages, the most important being that complete liberation is unnecessary as the grains need only be partly exposed to enter into chemical reaction. Very low-grade ores can be treated, sometimes *in situ* but more often in what would otherwise be waste heaps.

- What do you think might happen to chalcopyrite ($CuFeS_2$) in a waste heap that is wet and aerated?

- In *Metals 1*, Section 3.2.2 you encountered the oxidizing reaction that occurs naturally to break down chalcopyrite:

$$\underset{\text{chalcopyrite}}{4CuFeS_2(s)} + \underbrace{10H_2O(l) + 17O_2(aq)}_{\text{rainwater}} = \underset{\text{iron(III) hydroxide}}{4Fe(OH)_3(s)} + \underbrace{4Cu^{2+}(aq) + 8SO_4^{2-}(aq) + 8H^+(aq)}_{\text{soluble ions}} \quad (3.5)$$

This reaction allows copper to enter solution as Cu^{2+} ions together with H^+ and SO_4^{2-} ions. In other words, an acidic copper sulphate solution develops. Such oxidizing reactions are assisted by the bacterium *Thiobacillus ferrooxidans* which thrives in acidic solutions especially under warm conditions.

The process just described has often caused metal pollution in streams below copper mines. Copper-rich solutions emanate from the Parys Mountain Mine in Anglesey, as shown in Video Band 2. An iron key, placed in the water, emerged with a coating of copper. The same principle has been used to reclaim copper from copper sulphate solution leaking out of waste from porphyry copper mines. Scrap iron is thrown into the water, and copper, having a higher electronegativity than iron, precipitates onto the iron while iron enters solution. This helps to solve two problems — the wastage of copper and the effects of copper pollution. Copper can be reclaimed electrolytically from the scrap, and iron in solution is far less toxic than copper. In an oxidizing environment, dissolved iron is precipitated as iron(III) hydroxide slime that can be filtered from the water by sand beds. Nowadays, the copper sulphate solutions emerging from ores below cut-off grade are often collected for direct electrolytic refining to extract the copper.

Not many ore minerals respond to natural leaching; generally, chemical reagents must be added. Video Band 14 contains a sequence on a heap leaching process that enables very low-grade gold ores with submicroscopic gold grains to be processed profitably. Blasting and primary crushing of the ore is sufficient preparation. Crushed ore is piled onto bitumen or plastic-lined impermeable pads for leaching by sodium cyanide which dissolves gold to form a solution containing a gold cyanyl complex (Equation 3.6). The gold in the solution is then concentrated by chemical processes and precipitated electrolytically.

$$\underset{\text{sodium cyanide}}{8NaCN} + \underset{\text{gold}}{4Au} + O_2 + 2H_2O = \underset{\text{gold cyanyl complex}}{4[Au(CN)_2]^-} + 8Na^+ + 4OH^- \tag{3.6}$$

Sodium cyanide might seem to be an alarming chemical to use, since cyanides are well known for their toxicity. However, it is rapidly biodegraded in sunlight and, as the eventual solution carries valuable gold, every attempt is made to ensure none is lost. Heap leaching is possible only for highly fractured, porous rocks, where the sulphide ores have already been oxidized, because sulphides would actually destroy the cyanide before any reaction could proceed. Therefore, sulphide-bearing gold ores are roasted to oxidize the sulphides, prior to leaching. For hard, non-porous fossil placer deposits of gold (*Metals 1*, Section 3.4) and many vein-type hydrothermal gold deposits, the ore is ground finely to liberate gold grains and then leached by sodium cyanide in reaction vessels.

Until the cyanide leaching process was developed, low-grade or fine-grained gold ores that could not be processed by simple density separation were treated using mercury. Mercury is liquid and takes gold into solution making a very high density liquid alloy called an amalgam. After recovery of the amalgam, roasting volatizes the mercury and leaves molten gold. Although the mercury vapour was recycled in condensers, much escaped both as liquid and as vapour, and since mercury is highly toxic and persists indefinitely, this process has been abandoned by large mines because of the hazards to both personnel and the environment. However, many gold prospectors in underdeveloped countries still use the mercury process, thereby continuing a grave threat to both health and the environment (Section 4.3.2).

The latest direction which leaching methods are taking is to use *in situ* reactions with ore, thus keeping mining to a minimum. Underground blasting of ore is used to create permeability, and absence of air precludes any chemical oxidation reactions. Bacteria that use particular chemicals as an energy source are then introduced. *Thiobacillus ferrooxidans* is one such bacterium which thrives on pyrite and chalcopyrite. Genetic engineering experiments are proceeding to create new strains of bacteria specific to particular sulphides. Though not yet implemented, *in situ* bioleaching could extract metals from an ore deposit without the need to remove or process the ore (other than by fracturing), and the metal-rich solution could be collected and refined electrolytically. Such procedures have the potential to reduce both energy consumption and environmental damage.

Video Band 17: *Pine Point: ore to metal* features many of the ore-processing operations you have been reading about. If you have not already viewed it, you should do so before attempting Question 28.

Question 28

What forms of mineral processing are used to liberate and separate sulphide ore minerals at Pine Point? Why are they appropriate for sphalerite and galena?

3.3 Metal extraction

Extracting metal from ore minerals that have been mined, liberated and concentrated can take several forms. Block 1 Section 1.3 and Video Band 1 introduced the *smelting* of iron ore, which is smelting in the traditional sense: the roasting of ore minerals, often with other substances, such as carbon (in the form of charcoal, coal or methane) to *reduce* ore minerals to their contained metal. After traditional smelting, metal products often require **refining** to improve their purity. Another way in which metals may be extracted from their ore minerals is by *electrolysis*: either of a molten ore mineral, or of a solution produced by leaching. Electrolysis involves electrical energy rather than heat energy, but in the metals and mining industry it is seen as a form of smelting.

The procedure used for smelting depends on the chemistry of the ore mineral, especially whether it is an oxide, or a sulphide, and the ease with which bonds can be broken to liberate the metal. It was noted in connection with electronegativity (*Metals 1*, Section 1.2), that highly electronegative metals, such as copper and nickel, tend to form sulphide ore minerals. However, oxides are more suitable to smelt, so sulphides are usually converted to oxides by roasting in air. Oxides of the more electronegative metals, such as copper and mercury, can be decomposed simply by heating, whereas oxides of rather less electronegative metals, lead and zinc for example, do not decompose directly but can be reduced by carbon, in a similar way to the smelting of iron ore.

Ore mineral concentrates cannot be produced without gangue, often comprising silicate minerals, and there are also likely to be impurities in the ore minerals themselves. To remove many of these unwanted substances during smelting, a *flux* is added, which combines with gangue minerals to form a silicate melt called *slag*. The slag, in which many impurities are dissolved, is lighter than molten metal and can be tapped off (Block 1, Figure 10). Limestone is a commonly used flux that combines with silica (from quartz or silicate minerals) in the gangue to form a silicate slag as follows:

$$\underset{\text{limestone}}{CaCO_3} + \underset{\substack{\text{silica}\\\text{(silicate)}}}{SiO_2} = \underset{\text{slag}}{CaSiO_3} + \underset{\substack{\text{carbon}\\\text{dioxide}}}{CO_2} \qquad (3.7)$$

Reduction reactions between oxides and carbon also release carbon dioxide, as illustrated by the reduction of haematite:

$$\underset{\text{haematite}}{2Fe_2O_3} + \underset{\text{carbon}}{3C} = \underset{\text{iron}}{4Fe} + \underset{\substack{\text{carbon}\\\text{dioxide}}}{3CO_2} \qquad (3.8)$$

Although carbon dioxide is not a serious pollutant, it does contribute to the *greenhouse effect* (Block 4 *Energy 1,* Section 5.4). More serious is the release of sulphur dioxide when sulphide ore minerals are roasted. Sulphur dioxide is a major pollutant, a respiratory irritant and a cause of acid rain (Block 4 *Energy 1*, Section 5.4.1). Environmental consequences of its release include the destruction of plant habitats, especially forests on soils that cannot neutralize the enhanced acidity (Sections 3.4.3 and 4.3.3).

The final part of Video Band 17: *Pine Point: ore to metal* featured the smelting of the zinc ore concentrate, sphalerite.

What stages were involved in converting the sphalerite concentrate to zinc?

(i) Sphalerite concentrate was roasted in air to drive off sulphur.

(ii) The product (zinc oxide) was taken into solution with sulphuric acid.

(iii) The pH of the solution was adjusted with lime (to neutralize excess acid).

(iv) The solution was electrolysed: zinc was deposited on the electrodes.

(v) Pure zinc from the electrode plates was melted and poured into moulds.

Before electrolytic methods became available, carbon reduction was the main form of smelting. But for some metals (such as titanium and aluminium) that are very strongly bound in their oxides, a more powerful form of reduction was required. This usually involved the reaction of one of the salts of the metal, often a chloride, with a more highly reactive metal, such as sodium (Equation 3.9).

$$AlCl_3 + 3Na = Al + 3NaCl \qquad (3.9)$$

$AlCl_3$		$3Na$		Al		$3NaCl$
aluminium chloride		sodium metal		aluminium metal		sodium chloride

In the nineteenth century, aluminium was produced this way and was available only in small quantities; hence it was highly priced. It was regarded, rather like silver and gold, as a precious metal. Titanium is still produced in a similar way, which accounts for its high price (*Metals 1*, Table 1).

With the availability of electricity in the late nineteenth century, a new process was discovered which allowed the extraction of aluminium by dissolving alumina (Al_2O_3) from bauxite in a molten mixture of cryolite (Na_3AlF_6) and fluorite (CaF_2) and then passing an electric current through the melt. Molten aluminium collects at the cathode while the anode burns away as oxygen is liberated from the melt. However, it wasn't until the mid-twentieth century that the process could be scaled-up to produce sufficient aluminium to reduce its price and allow its widespread use.

Today, extraction of metals takes place by a variety of procedures and sometimes occurs close to a mine site to minimize transport costs, given high enough tonnages for the operation to be economic. At Olympic Dam, for example, a range of processing and refining activities are carried out on site, including the leaching of low-grade ore followed by electrolytic recovery of copper, which is carried out alongside more traditional smelting of higher-grade ore. Copper that has been smelted to 99.5% purity is often subsequently refined electrolytically to improve its purity to 99.99%.

Question 29

Iron pyrites is commonly found in sulphide deposits. Why is it less suitable as an iron ore mineral than haematite?

Nineteenth-century lead smelting

Nineteenth century dressing of lead ores produced lead ore mineral (galena) concentrates containing 70% lead; the remainder was sulphur, other metal sulphides (often iron and zinc) and gangue. The concentrate was smelted in two stages. First, it was roasted in an oxidizing atmosphere, which enabled recovery of 40–75% of the metal but left a lead-rich 'grey slag', containing lead oxide and lead sulphate, that required a second stage of smelting. This second stage took place in a reducing atmosphere containing carbon monoxide produced by burning coke or charcoal. The resultant molten slag and metal were tapped off as liquids; the molten lead was cast into ingots, and the slag formed a more-or-less black glass which was often reprocessed.

Before the nineteenth century, fumes from smelting were vented into the atmosphere from chimneys directly over the furnaces. This meant that sulphur dioxide from decomposition of sulphide minerals, metallic dust from lead volatilization at high temperatures, and sometimes arsenic from impurities spread across and contaminated the adjoining land.

In the early nineteenth century, however, flues were added to smelting vents which took the fumes to a remote chimney, often on poorer land. At first, many flues were around 100 m long, but they were extended (often considerably and in one case to around 5 km) after it was discovered that valuable amounts of metallic dust condensed in them and could be recovered. Nevertheless, pollution was still a problem and a government commissioner wrote, after visiting the North Pennine Orefield:

> In going across from Stanhope to the Derwent Company's mines and smelting mills on the river Derwent, I saw at the top of a hill a tall white circular turret rising up out of the ground, and a cloud of white smoke issuing from the summit. The road came to within the distance of a quarter of a mile from it, and the smoke, as we passed through it, was disagreeable. The ling, or common heather, had its blossom and leaves entirely destroyed. This chimney was a mile from the smelting mills.

3.4 One of the world's major mining areas: Sudbury, Ontario

Northern Ontario is a land of wilderness, lakes and low hills with forests of pine and birch that is very popular with hunters and tourists. It is also an important mining area, and much of the mining is associated with the Sudbury Igneous Complex, a large layered igneous intrusion that measures approximately 25 × 60 km at the surface, and thought to contain a staggering 23% of the world's nickel reserves. The total value of the metals mined from the Sudbury area from 1888 to 1991 is estimated to be of the order of C$120 billion at 1991 prices: a breakdown of which is given in Table 5. Indeed, Sudbury mining contributed over C$6.5 billion to the regional Ontario economy in 1993 alone. These are large sums, and many people's livelihoods are closely linked to the success, or failure, of the mining and ore processing industry. Thus, instability of world metal markets and restrictions on mining or mineral processing for environmental or other reasons would be critical to the local economy.

Table 5 Summary of metals production in the Sudbury area, 1888–1991.

Metal	Production tonnes	Value (1991 prices) C$ × 10^6
nickel	8 400 000	80 000
copper	8 200 000	22 000
cobalt	4800	1400
palladium	260	900
platinum	255	3900
gold	91	1200
rhodium	31	4700

The development of mining in the area was closely linked to the opening of the railways in the 1880s. Regional surveys in 1856 had noted areas of unusual magnetization, but the magnetic nature of some of the sulphides in the ore bodies was not established until later. The mineralization at Sudbury was actually discovered during the construction of the railway in 1883, because iron sulphides were weathering to a distinctive rust-coloured gossan on the surface. Subsequently, similar occurrences became targets for further exploration.

Although Sudbury is important for both nickel and copper, nickel is the most valuable (Table 5) and the deposit represents one of the world's major nickel resources (Figure 53). In fact, the Sudbury deposits produce over a sixth of the world's nickel. About two-thirds of the world's nickel resources are in laterites in which nickel has been concentrated by leaching and subsequent precipitation of secondary nickel minerals by percolating solutions in deeply weathered soil horizons on peridotite bedrock (Metals *1*, Section 3.2.1). About one-third is in magmatic sulphide deposits, most of which occur in layered igneous complexes (*Metals 1*, Section 2.2.2). The mines of the Sudbury Igneous Complex in Canada, and of the Noril'sk and Talnakh intrusions in the low Arctic of Russia, are the largest producers of combined nickel, copper, and platinum group metals (PGM — platinum, palladium, rhodium, ruthenium, osmium, iridium).

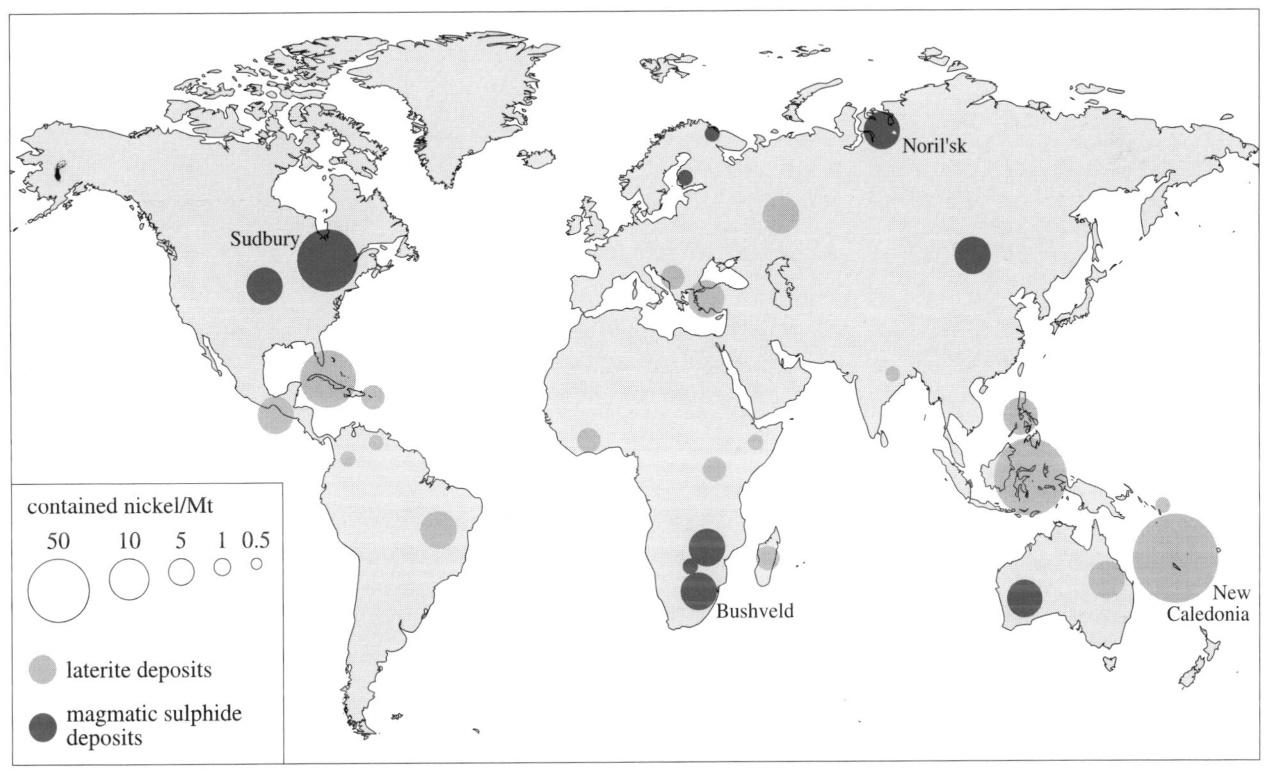

Figure 53 The global distribution of nickel deposits.

Nickel is in considerable demand. About 922 000 t was mined worldwide in 1992, at a value of about US\$7000 t^{-1}. Yet nickel occurs only in low concentrations (110 ppm on average) in the rocks of the Earth's crust. In layered igneous complexes of basaltic composition, nickel, like copper, is commonly concentrated in sulphide ore minerals — they are both metals with high electronegativity (*Metals 1*, Figure 6a). An exploitable grade of nickel is 1–1.5%, so it is only when natural processes concentrate nickel in the Earth's crust by a factor of over 100 that it becomes economic to mine.

- Based on an average grade of 1% nickel, how much nickel ore would have been processed worldwide in order to supply the 922 000 t of nickel produced in 1992?

- 922 000 × 100 t = 92.2 Mt of nickel ore.

This is a minimum figure, because recovery of nickel during separation and extraction is not 100% (Section 3.2.2). Also, for every tonne of nickel ore that is mined, a substantial amount, perhaps as much as 5 tonnes, of barren rock has to be removed in order to get at the ore. Thus, the total amount of rock that was removed during nickel mining operations in 1992 could have been of the order of $6 \times 92.2 \approx 550$ million tonnes.

- If the average density of the rock removed was 3 t m^{-3}, what would be the volume of 550 Mt?

- $(550 \times 10^6)/3 = 183 \times 10^6$ m^3 — or the volume of some 300 football pitches dug out to a depth of 100 m — in just one year.

This should give you some idea of the scale of the mining, processing and smelting operation required to supply the world's nickel market. In addition, processing nickel sulphide ores, it has been estimated, has the potential to release 8–10 tonnes of sulphur for every tonne of nickel produced, so there is a high potential for environmental pollution.

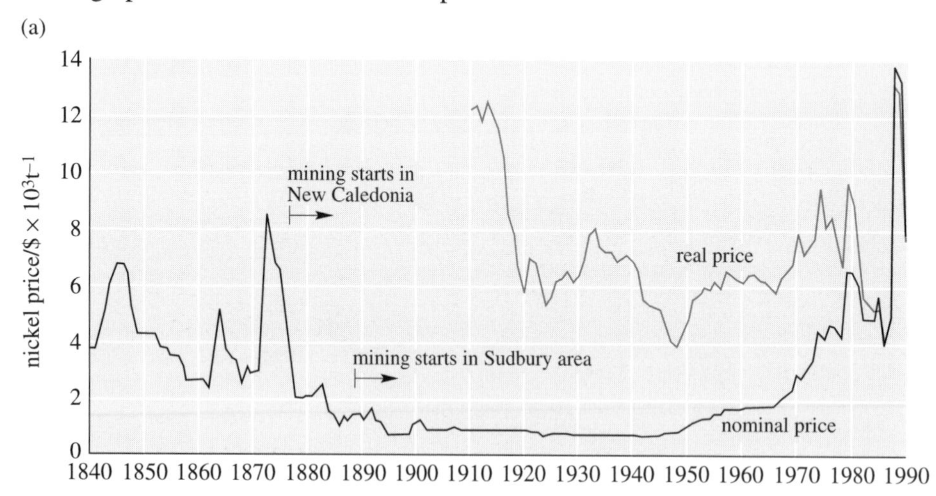

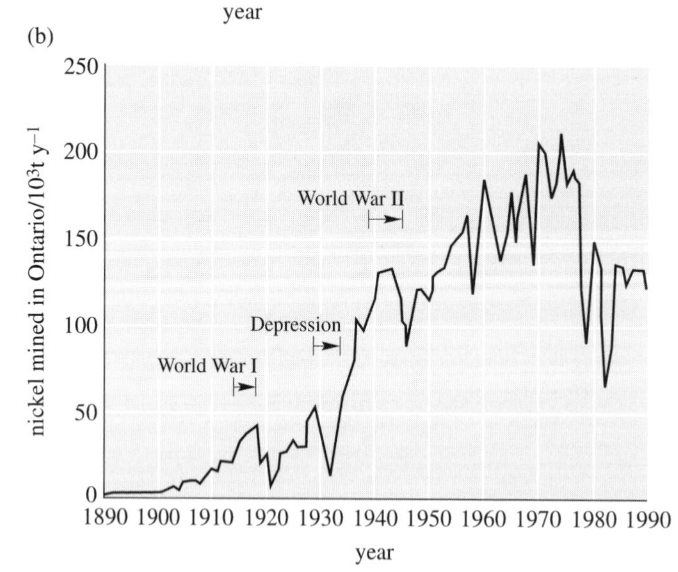

Figure 54 Nickel in the nineteenth and twentieth centuries: (a) variations in the annual average nominal price of nickel since 1840 and the annual average real price since 1910 (note that the real price is set to equal the nominal price in 1985); (b) variations in the volume of nickel mined in Ontario during the twentieth century.

Question 30

Examine Figure 54(a and b) to help you answer the following:

(a) What explanation can you give for the nominal price of nickel being lower between 1890 and 1950 than it was between 1840 and 1890?

(b) The amount of nickel produced in Ontario started to increase early in the twentieth century. This was some 30–40 years *before* the start of increased aluminium production worldwide (Figure 5). How does the use of nickel differ from aluminium (Section 1.2), and why did its level of production start to increase significantly before that of aluminium? (Hint: bear in mind the comments on aluminium production in Section 3.3.)

(c) Look at the graph of changing nickel production in Ontario over the twentieth century. How and why did the two World Wars affect nickel production?

3.4.1 Occurrence of the Sudbury ores

Most of the rocks in Northern Ontario are ancient, having been formed 2–3 billion years ago. Just to the north of Lake Huron near Sudbury there is an unusual basin-like structure called the Sudbury Basin that contains both igneous and sedimentary rocks that form an elliptical outcrop pattern (Figure 55a). This structure lies on top of the older metamorphic and igneous rocks which are known as *basement*. The form of the structure underground is still under investigation, but the rocks of the southern margin dip more steeply than those of the northern margin, as shown (much simplified) in Figure 55b.

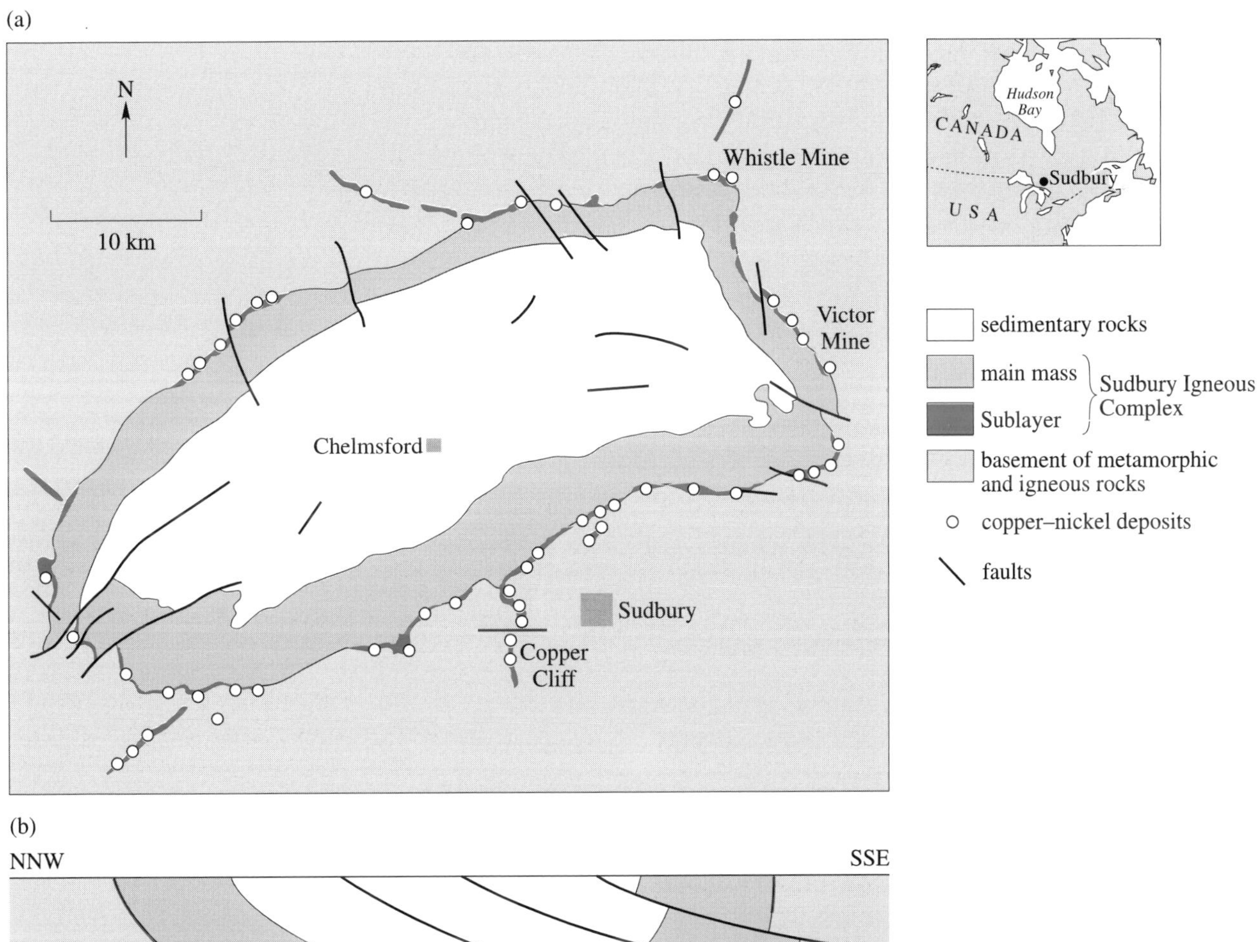

Figure 55 The Sudbury Basin: (a) simplified geological map with mine locations; (b) schematic cross-section, NNW to SSE.

How do the mines shown in Figure 55a relate to the Sudbury Basin?

They occur around the margins of the basin at the base of the Sudbury Igneous Complex.

The most important feature of the Sudbury Basin is the layered igneous complex, which crystallized from basaltic magma about 1850 Ma ago. At the base of the complex there is a unit of gabbro called the Sublayer, which contains most of the mineralization and is the target for almost all of the mines shown on Figure 55a. Above the Sublayer, the complex is made up of more gabbros, and granophyre (a type of fine-grained granitic rock). These units contain little or no sulphide mineralization. The overall thickness of the complex is 2–3 km, and the total volume of igneous rock is estimated to be in excess of 8000 km^3. Above the igneous rocks, in the middle of the elliptical basin-like structure seen in Figure 55a, there is a thick sequence of younger sedimentary rocks.

There are some broad similarities between the Sudbury Igneous Complex and the Bushveld Complex in Southern Africa (*Metals 1*, Section 2.2). Both are large bodies of layered basaltic igneous rocks, and they contain very rich metal deposits. However, Sudbury is much smaller overall, and it lacks the regular layers of ore minerals associated with the Bushveld, where individual layers, sometimes only a few centimetres thick, can be traced for many kilometres. At Sudbury, the mineralization is within the gabbros of the Sublayer, which has highly complicated geology. In many areas, the rocks of the Sublayer are highly broken up (brecciated) and they often contain fragments of other rocks from beneath the complex. The thickness of the Sublayer varies greatly from nothing to about 700 m. It also extends into the basement as narrow breccia zones which are often associated with dyke-like igneous intrusions (Figure 55a). These zones are particularly rich in sulphide mineralization.

Considering the form of the Sublayer, which contains most of the Sudbury deposits, what problems can you envisage when it comes to designing a mine and what would the implications be?

The Sublayer is highly irregular in form, in contrast to the continuous and regular layers of the Bushveld Complex. Following irregular ore bodies underground can be difficult and expensive. Therefore, individual mines have large drilling programmes in order to map out these highly irregular bodies prior to extraction.

The principal ore minerals that contain nickel in the Sudbury Igneous Complex are pentlandite ($(Ni,Fe)_9S_8$), millerite (NiS), pyrrhotite (FeS); copper is found mainly in chalcopyrite ($CuFeS_2$). A typical example of the sulphide ore is shown in Colour Plate 55. Pentlandite is the most important nickel mineral; it contains 25–41% nickel and accounts for 90% of the nickel mined from the sulphide ores. Pyrrhotite invariably accompanies pentlandite and is commonly the most abundant sulphide mineral, but only contains up to 1.5% nickel. Only 10% of the nickel in the Sudbury ores is in pyrrhotite. There are two main types of pyrrhotite, one is magnetic and the other is not. The latter contains twice as much nickel at Sudbury, which is an important consideration when designing mineral processing systems.

Origin of the Sudbury Igneous Complex and the sulphide mineralization

The origin of the Sudbury Complex is still controversial. The large volume of igneous rocks indicates a major geological melting event. This may have been due to a mantle hot spot — similar to those responsible for the basalt magmatism in ocean basins (*Metals 1*, Figure 20b) — or to a meteorite impact that pierced the crust and caused melting of the mantle beneath. There is compelling evidence that a meteorite did strike the Sudbury area at about the right time, because very distinctive impact shock features are observed in the surrounding rocks. Other evidence consistent with a meteorite impact includes the shape of the Sudbury Basin and the presence of sediments in the basin that might represent fall-back debris after the impact.

Whichever of these models is correct for Sudbury, most of the sulphide ore minerals in the layered igneous complex crystallized from magmas formed by partial melting of the mantle. Thus, the Earth's mantle was the probably the main source of sulphur, nickel, copper and PGM; whether any nickel in the Sudbury Complex has a meteoritic origin is a matter of speculation.

Immiscible (iron-rich) sulphide liquids separate from basaltic magmas when there is too much sulphur for it to be accommodated in the silicate melt (*Metals 1*, Section 2.2.2). This can occur either when the silica content of the melt increases (so reducing the *solubility* of sulphur in the melt), or when the sulphur *content* of the melt increases through crystallization of silicate minerals. In either case, when the sulphur content exceeds its level of saturation, a sulphide liquid separates. The igneous complex has a relatively high average silica content for a mantle melt, suggesting that it may contain a large amount of melt derived from the crust. Mixing of high-silica crustal melt and basaltic magma may have triggered the formation of immiscible sulphide liquids, but the sulphides still had to be concentrated locally. As sulphide droplets are denser than the silicate liquid in which they formed, they would have settled out to form concentrations of sulphide liquid near the base of the complex. This explains why the sulphide ores at Sudbury are concentrated at the base of the intrusion (Figure 55).

The scavenging of nickel, copper and PGM from the magma by the iron-rich sulphide liquid, together with gravitational settling, are thought to be the main processes responsible for the formation of the magmatic nickel, copper and PGM deposits.

3.4.2 Mining and processing of the Sudbury ores

Sulphide ores are mined from a number of sites around the margins of the Sudbury Basin (Figure 55a). Individual ore bodies range from a few million tonnes to over 200 million tonnes of ore. With the exception of the Whistle Mine open pit illustrated in Figure 37 at the north-eastern corner of the complex (Figure 55a), the other modern operations are all underground mines (Plate 72). Underground mining involves lengthy and costly exploration. It may cost almost CAN$300 million to locate, evaluate, and open up a new deposit, and this process can take over 10 years. It is often more economic to explore from existing mines and discover additional reserves than it is to explore for a new deposit. Exploration involves a combination of field-based geological mapping, geophysical surveys, and drilling (Section 2).

The ore bodies are concentrated around the margins of the Basin and tend to be steeply dipping. A number of the mines go down to 1500 m and mining methods must take account of the steep dip of the ores. Shallower deposits can be accessed by driving down fairly steep inclines, but below about 750 m access is by vertical shafts which transport equipment, fuel and personnel, as well as bringing the ore to the surface. Typically, it is necessary to blast and remove 5 tonnes of barren rock for every tonne of ore. Once the ore has been reached, charges can be set from above and below, and blasting makes the ore collapse onto the lower level (Figure 40). Continuous loaders and conveyors can remove 1000 tonnes of ore from the face in an hour. In recent years advances in technology and automation have improved safety, increased productivity and reduced manpower, as demonstrated in Figure 56.

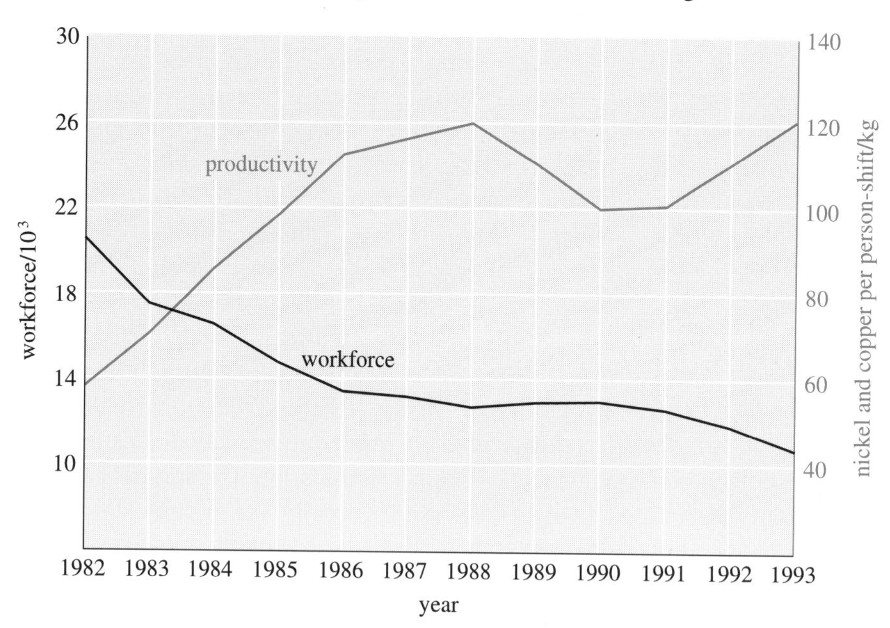

Figure 56 Sudbury's increased mining productivity coincides with a reduction in personnel through automation in recent years.

At the surface, sulphide ores are transported by conveyor to crushers (Plate 72) where processing starts. Figure 57 schematically represents the stages involved in recovering nickel and copper from the ores. First, the ore is crushed, partially ground, and magnetic separation is used to remove pyrrhotite. Froth flotation (Section 3.2.2) separates sulphide ore minerals from silicate gangue. The concentrate is filtered and dried before being transported to the smelter.

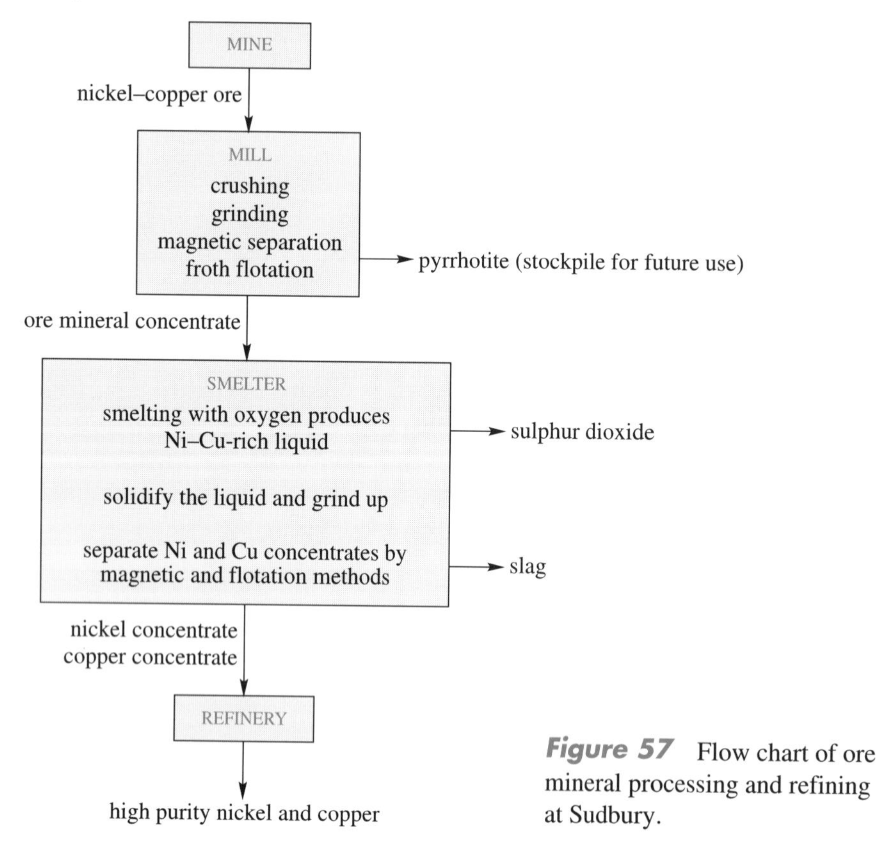

Figure 57 Flow chart of ore mineral processing and refining at Sudbury.

At the smelter, the bulk sulphide ore concentrate is smelted using pure oxygen to produce a molten metal-rich concentrate, known as *matte*, with slag and sulphur dioxide as by-products (Figure 57). The slag is stored for building and road construction. Modern technology enables much of the sulphur dioxide to be fixed for the production of sulphuric acid for the petrochemical industry. The matte is cast, then ground so that magnetic separation and flotation methods can be used to produce separate copper and nickel concentrates.

The copper concentrate is smelted further to produce impure 'blister' copper which is then electrolytically refined to produce high purity copper. The by-product slimes of the electro-refining are also processed to extract gold, silver, selenium, tellurium and PGM concentrates.

The nickel concentrate is roasted to produce nickel oxides from which a variety of nickel products are produced — nickel oxide, nickel powder, coinage strips, nickel pellets, and ferro-nickel plates. Much of the metal mined in Sudbury is refined in the UK: nickel (to high purity) at Clydach in Wales, and PGM at Acton in London. PGM are widely used in electronics, in jewellery, and as catalysts.

3.4.3 Environmental considerations

The production of sulphide ores, their subsequent processing, with the release of sulphur dioxide in particular, and the resulting acid rain, have had a profound environmental impact in the region surrounding Sudbury. Remember that for every one part of nickel produced from the ore, there is the potential for eight parts of sulphur to be released: clearly it is important for this sulphur to be contained if the emissions that give rise to acid rain are to be avoided.

Sudbury has a history of nickel production going back over 100 years, and the environmental consequences were increased by particularly destructive stripping of indigenous pine by lumber companies in the nineteenth century. Once, open-bed roasting was part of the smelting process. This was extremely damaging to the environment for two reasons: it released vast quantities of sulphur dioxide pollution at ground level, and necessitated the cutting of timber for fuel. By the 1920s, this process was contained in factories, and the emissions were vented through chimneys. In the late 1940s, technology was developed to improve the separation of pyrrhotite using large magnetic separators, and in the 1960s processing steps were introduced to remove some of the SO_2.

- Why was it an advantage to remove pyrrhotite?

- Although pyrrhotite contains nickel, it is in relatively small amounts compared to that in pentlandite, the main nickel ore mineral (Section 3.4.1). Therefore, as pyrrhotite is the most abundant sulphide mineral, reducing the pyrrhotite content of the concentrate reduces greatly the amount of sulphur released per tonne of nickel produced.

In 1972, the 387 m 'Superstack' was built (Figure 58); it has significantly improved the air quality and vegetation growth around Sudbury. Although the Superstack has allowed the rehabilitation of local environments, the pollutants discharged from it have had unforeseen impacts elsewhere. Some 60 km downwind is the Killarney Provincial Park. The water bodies there (on quartzite rock) were alkaline to neutral, but have been tipped over into acidity by acid rain from the plume of sulphur dioxide. The recognition of this problem in the 1970s led to intensive monitoring of ecosystems. In recent years, increased effort and investment has been put into clean-up and ore processing technologies, both to improve productivity and to mitigate the environmental impact associated with traditional processing methods. The development of new smelting technologies has resulted in a reduction of emissions, and the conversion of waste products into marketable sulphuric acid. Another significant step was the further reduction of the proportion of pyrrhotite fed into the smelter through improved efficiency of separation from pentlandite. Sulphur dioxide emissions were down to 265 000 tonnes a year by 1994—only 12% of the 1965 level and a drop of 60% on the 1980 level. However, a consequence of more efficient mineral separation is that sizeable amounts of nickel are now residing in waste tips awaiting the technological advances that will permit the clean extraction of nickel from pyrrhotite at a reasonable price.

Figure 58 The Sudbury 'Superstack'.

Reclamation of waste tips and tailings areas in the Sudbury Basin has established habitats for wildlife and restored much of the devastated landscape. Rehabilitation programs have demonstrated the feasibility of using grasses and clovers, which grow on the toxic acidic soil with the aid of fertilizers and lime, to establish a humus layer. Colonization by small local plants follows, along with the growth of poplars and birches. Black locust, pine and spruce trees have been planted in groups specifically as sources of seed for future tree cover.

3.4.4 The future of mining at Sudbury

Mining in Canada as a whole has seen a 50% decline in capital investment between 1981 and 1991. There has also been a significant decline in Canadian mineral production: from C$19.6 billion in 1990 to less than C$16.3 billion in 1992. Sudbury remains the world's largest nickel mining area, although there is a trend for major multinational companies to shut down their Canadian operations in favour of cheaper alternatives in countries where deposits can be exploited more easily by open pit or bulk mining methods, taxation levels are commensurate with the contribution made to the country's economy, labour costs are lower, and environmental regulations are less restrictive. It is well known that the reserves of nickel, copper, and PGM could take mining in the Sudbury area well beyond the twenty-first century. Whether or not the Sudbury mining area will survive, hinges on the economics of mining in Canada and its worldwide competitiveness.

Question 31

(a) What principal factors are likely to influence the future prosperity of a major mining area such as Sudbury?

(b) What implications does protecting the environment have for the future of mining in such an area?

3.5 Summary of Section 3

1. Mining may be carried out at the surface or underground, depending on the location and form of the deposit, and on the economics of mining, which can be described in terms of unit cost and unit value per tonne of ore. Unit cost includes the cost of extracting ore, processing ore, and handling waste, and the capital tied up in permanent constructions and provision of infrastructure. Unit value depends on the grade of ore and metal price.
2. With increasing depth of surface mining, stripping ratios usually become greater because waste must be removed and benches must be cut in barren rock to provide access and maintain stability. Consequently, costs rise and it may become more economic to move to underground mining. The unit cost of mining underground is high; it is only economic to mine ores with a high unit value in this way.
3. Open pit mining is the most commonly used type of surface mining for ore deposits, but it requires surface storage of waste. Opencast mining can be used only for extensive deposits near to the surface and involves backfilling excavations with waste. Dredging can be used where a deposit is unconsolidated and waterlogged.
4. Underground mine design depends on the strength and structure of the host rock as well as the form of the deposit. Underground mining has the advantage of being out of sight and the workings can be backfilled with waste.
5. Ore processing generally involves the liberation of an ore mineral and its separation from gangue to produce an ore mineral concentrate suitable for processing to extract the metal.
6. Liberation demands comminution of ore to a grain size fine enough to release ore minerals yet coarse enough for separation to be efficient. An economic balance has to be struck between the energy costs of crushing, grinding and separation, the grade of concentrate produced and metal recovery.
7. Separation frequently exploits physical properties of ore minerals, for example, density, magnetization, and electrical conductivity. Separation by froth flotation and leaching are particularly appropriate for low-grade deposits. Leaching may reduce the need for fine comminution, and in the future may even be carried out *in situ*.

8 Metals are extracted from ore mineral concentrates by various methods. Smelting traditionally involves roasting of ore, often with a flux and a reducing agent, to produce molten metal that separates from molten slag containing the gangue and impurities. Modern smelting may involve electrolytic decomposition of molten ore concentrates (as in the case of aluminium), and electrolysis may be used both to extract metals (for example, copper) from leachate solutions as well as to refine metals (for example, zinc) to a high degree of purity.

9 Sudbury is a major mining area on the world scene, and a leading producer of nickel, along with copper and PGM. Nickel and copper sulphide ores at Sudbury are located in an irregularly shaped layer at the base of the basin-like structure of the Sudbury Igneous Complex. Retrieval of nickel and copper from the ore involves decomposition of sulphides and there is the potential to release large quantities of sulphur dioxide into the atmosphere. The area has suffered severe effects of acid rain in the past. As a result of various strategies to reduce emissions, pollution is now much reduced.

4 ENVIRONMENTAL IMPACT OF METALS EXTRACTION

Historically, the effects of metals extraction on the environment were mainly localized until the Industrial Revolution, when development of mechanized mining and ore processing enlarged the scale of working. Even then, during the eighteenth and nineteenth centuries, environmental effects were largely tolerated or ignored unless they directly influenced mining operations or had a drastic impact on miners and local communities. Yet, even in the sixteenth century, Agricola was reporting concerns about the effects of mining:

> ...the strongest argument of the detractors is that the fields are devastated by mining operations, ...that the woods and groves are cut down, for there is need of an endless amount of wood for timbers, machines, and the smelting of metals. And when the woods and groves are felled, then are exterminated the beasts and birds, very many of which furnish a pleasant and agreeable food for man. Further, when the ores are washed, the water which has been used poisons the brooks and streams, and either destroys the fish or drives them away. Therefore the inhabitants of these regions, on account of the devastation of their fields, woods, groves, brooks and rivers, find great difficulty in procuring the necessaries of life, and by reason of the destruction of the timber they are forced to greater expense in erecting buildings. Thus it is said, it is clear to all that there is greater detriment from mining than the value of the metals which the mining produces.

Since the Industrial Revolution, and particularly in the twentieth century, global expansion of industry, technological developments and rising populations have greatly increased the demand for metals. Metals extraction has spread from centres in Europe and parts of North and South America to locations worldwide, often in remote, undeveloped areas. With the increasing scale of operations, greater mechanization and improved efficiency, even very low grades of ore can be worked, resulting in very large mines and the need to dispose of vast amounts of waste material. Wherever extraction of metals occurs, there is the potential to damage the natural environment and that potential is now of worldwide extent with increasingly serious implications for land, water, air and life.

Today, with increasing national and local government controls to protect the environment, careful planning is necessary when siting and constructing metal mining and processing industries, as is environmental monitoring during operation. Greater awareness of environmental problems in recent years has led individuals, international organizations, governments and mining companies to increase their efforts to protect the environment from the adverse impacts of resource exploitation.

4.1 Physical effects of mining

Because of their visibility, the physical effects of any mining activity are often the most obvious, although the chemical effects of mining and metals extraction are frequently the more damaging, especially where living organisms are concerned. This section considers the physical impacts of mining. In later sections, we examine the chemical effects of mining and ore processing activities, including metal smelting.

4.1.1 Visual impact

The visual intrusion of mining on the landscape varies with the type, location and scale of mining. The biggest open pit metal mines are exceedingly large holes, often much bigger than opencast coal mines (compare Plate 37 with Plates 59 and 64, for example). However, open pit excavations may be very conspicuous from the air, but can be almost invisible from the ground away from the hole itself. The Bingham Canyon copper mine, Utah (*Metals 1*, Figure 31), is the largest man-made hole on Earth, around 2.5 km across and almost 1 km deep, but this gigantic hole is visible only from above or from close range. Small underground mines, in contrast, may be little more than holes in a hillside, just a few metres in diameter, or steel shafts smaller than a grain elevator. Open pits at the edge of raised topography can be highly visible — one way to minimize visual impact is to leave intact the margins of the hillside and to excavate the area behind using 'keyhole' access via a narrow chasm or even a tunnel.

In addition to the land taken for the mine itself, every large mine site requires an infrastructure of roads and power lines, perhaps a rail link, and possibly a water pipeline (cf. Olympic Dam, Section 1.1). These constructions can often be more extensive and conspicuous than the mine itself. Buildings and equipment associated with moving, crushing and processing of ore are also likely to be visible (Figure 59) but can sometimes be hidden from view in an open pit. They are likely to be more conspicuous above an underground mine, and actually housing them underground adds to the cost.

For every large hole dug for ore, especially for low-grade ore, there is a huge amount of waste rock, and, unless its distribution is well managed, it is likely to have a much larger visual impact than the mine itself, as we saw for Cornish china clay waste tips (Block 2). Waste originates not only from ore processing, but also from the removal of overburden to create a pit shaped for optimum production and safety (Section 3.1.2). Whether rock is classified as ore or waste may depend on the prevailing price of the product. Often, rock that has to be mined so as to get at the ore has a sub-economic mineral content, and could be valuable if the metal price increased. Such material is often separated from barren rock and stockpiled for possible future use, so it must remain accessible, and is usually visible.

The movement of waste is a major cost and has no immediate return, so waste rock is usually stored in large piles near the mine to minimize transport costs and use of land. Such piles are often major visual intrusions on the landscape around mine sites (Figure 59). Thus, although the massive Bingham mine itself is not as visible as might be expected, its waste dumps are over 300 m high and can be seen from the edge of Salt Lake City, some 20 km away, despite having been constructed so as not to break the skyline. Tips may also pose a hazard through slope failure. Much can be done to landscape and vegetate tips to reduce visual intrusion and potential instability. When mining is underground, worked-out parts of the mine can be back-filled (Section 3.1.4), so helping to solve the waste disposal problem. In open pit mines, filling with waste may not be an option until the mine is closed.

Figure 59 Visual impact of mining: ore processing plant and waste tips beyond.

The volume of ore minerals extracted and processed from *low-grade* deposits in open pits is inevitably very small in relation to the amount of waste, which commonly occupies a larger volume than the hole from which it was extracted.

- Bearing in mind what is involved in processing ore from just about any kind of mining operation, can you suggest why this increase in volume occurs?

- When rocks have been fragmented initially by blasting and then by crushing, the resulting volume of crushed rock is not just that of the rock itself but also of the spaces between the fragments.

Because of this effect, if you put all the waste from an open pit back into the hole from which it came, the final ground level would be higher than when you started. For the same reason, back-filling of underground mines cannot accommodate all the waste produced either.

4.1.2 Noise and dust

Other obvious local impacts of mining are noise and dust. Noise is a major problem for large open pit mines; it is created intermittently by blasting and continuously by crushing equipment, drills, shovels and dump trucks. In underground mining, noise from ventilation fans and rock dumping can be a problem. Noise is generally localized but can be a nuisance to inhabitants living within a kilometre or so, as mining operations often continue throughout the night. Blasting can often be heard several kilometres away and vibrations from underground blasts can be felt in houses within several hundred metres. These effects, however, are short-lived and their consequences are not normally severe enough to crack plaster. The effects of blasts and noise can be sharply reduced by building strong fences or planting trees around the mine site.

Dust is often a more serious problem, particularly in arid areas. It originates from blasting, from waste tips, from the movement of vehicles, and especially from the removal of crushed ore from stockpiles. The problem is usually controlled by spraying roads and rock faces with water (Figure 60), and enclosing stockpiles behind fences or walls.

Figure 60 Spraying water to damp down dust.

Health of miners

Mining is traditionally regarded as a dangerous occupation and underground mining remains hazardous although modern methods have greatly improved safety. Apart from the problem of underground rock-falls, the major hazards to miners are dust and gas. Inhalation of dust — fine-grained mineral particles — over long periods of time is a major problem responsible for the death of many miners by lung disease, in particular silicosis caused by silica dust (quartz). Dust can be controlled by spraying working areas with water (Figure 60), and the state of miners' lungs can be monitored by chest X-rays. Exposure to crocidolite asbestos, which occurs naturally in some peridotite-hosted mineral deposits and in banded iron formations has also been responsible for many deaths from lung cancer (asbestosis).

A major hazard in areas where uranium concentrations are high is radon gas, produced by the natural radioactive decay of uranium (Block 4 *Energy 2*). Radon gas is itself radioactive and, when inhaled, a small amount decays to form radioactive particles which stay in the lungs, emitting alpha particles. These radioactive emissions can initiate lung cancer.

Question 32

Compare the dust and gas hazards in an underground mine working lead–zinc ores in a limestone host rock, with one working tin deposits from veins in a uranium-rich, quartz-bearing granite.

4.1.3 Mining subsidence

The effect of underground mining on the stability of overlying rocks was considered in relation to coal mining in Block 4 *Energy 1* (Section 3.5). Underground metal mines can cause environmental damage through two types of subsidence: continuous and discontinuous.

Continuous subsidence is generally more predictable, less disastrous and is more or less limited to the lifetime of a mine. This type of subsidence is associated with the removal of thin, shallow-dipping or horizontal ore bodies overlain by weak strata. After the extraction of ore, the roof is allowed to collapse, as in longwall coal mining (Block 4 *Energy 1*, Section 3.3.2) and in the underground mining of evaporites such as halite and gypsum (Block 2, Section 6).

Discontinuous subsidence is usually less predictable and is often associated with large surface displacements over restricted surface areas. A number of mining methods can cause this type of ground failure. Old deserted mine workings may degrade, and pillars or timbers left for support can decay and collapse. Left unsupported, a mine cavity may propagate towards the surface as blocks from the roof repeatedly cave-in — rather like the limestone mines of Bath (Block 2, Section 2.9). The mining method known as *block caving* (Section 3.1.4) is designed to draw ore from above down into the mine; in so doing it draws overlying waste rock behind it and this in turn may eventually cause subsidence at the surface. 'Chimney caving' is the term applied to the progressive upward migration through weak overlying rock of an unsupported mining cavity of fairly restricted lateral extent. Such chimneys have been known to extend upward for many hundreds of metres.

Subsidence through chimney caving occurred at the Mufulira mine in Zambia in 1970. The Mufulira mine is one of a group of large copper mines established on the Zambian Copper Belt. On 25 September that year, a cave-in which had propagated upward about 500 m broke the surface under the mine tailings pond. Approximately 450 000 m^3 of water-saturated mud

Mining subsidence in Cornwall, England

In the UK prior to 1876, mines were not required to keep accurate survey plans, and mining in the early days was sometimes continued upward (by stoping) almost to 'grass root' level; in addition, shafts, when abandoned, were generally capped by timbers and covered with soil. Where no records of shafts exist, or where they are not accurately marked on old maps, modern housing developments, schools or roads may have been built over them. Indeed, shafts may only come to light years later when timbers decompose and the surface fill collapses down the mine shaft. Subsidence can occur rapidly and without warning; it is potentially damaging to property and injurious to inhabitants, as demonstrated by the 'near miss' shown in Figure 61. Fluctuation or lowering of water tables through drought or nearby pumping of groundwater allows saturated timbers to dry out, which causes them to weaken and exacerbate the problem.

- Considering the ways in which ore deposits are detected (Section 2), what kind of surveys could be carried out to detect old mine workings and reduce the danger of subsidence in old mining areas?

- Surveys that can 'see' underground and look for continuity of rock formations, i.e. geophysical surveys and drilling, as used in mineral exploration (Section 2).

Geophysical surveys are much cheaper than drilling, but drilling may be necessary for confirmation when a 'target' is found. Once found, the action taken may be simply to avoid the unsafe area, possibly to fill the shaft or to cap it securely. A cap may either be a concrete raft much bigger than the hole or a plug. However, to be secure, plugging should be done only in bedrock.

Figure 61 An example of unexpected subsidence from long-abandoned mine workings in Cornwall.

poured down the chimney and flooded part of the mine. Eighty-nine men were killed in this disastrous event and a large section of the mine was rendered inaccessible and subsequently had to be isolated between concrete bulkheads. This illustrates that discontinuous subsistence is a hazard not only to surface activity but to mining itself, especially below surface water or tailings areas.

The potential for catastrophic, though localized, subsidence in populated areas overlying mine workings is obvious, and such problems arise in old mining areas, as described in the box 'Mining subsidence in Cornwall'.

4.2 Mine water and drainage

The physical presence of water is a potential problem in mining because groundwater saturates rocks below the water table. It is also a resource in its own right (Block 3) and may be in demand for use in the mine itself or as a community water supply. The ability of water to take into solution metals released by mining may lead to problems of water quality.

4.2.1 Water—too much or too little?

In order to reach deposits below the water table in safety, it is necessary to remove water from the working area of a mine. This is normally done by pumping—first from surface boreholes to draw down the water table, then from within the workings. Lowering the local water table may have serious side-effects on surface drainage; it may cause gradual subsidence through shrinkage of dewatered rock formations, and may even trigger localized roof collapse into caverns.

In limestone areas, pumping to remove water may increase circulation of groundwater and enhance solution effects, leading to roof collapse, and sinkholes may be formed. These are steep-sided, often rounded, depressions. Such problems occurred in South Africa where the gold-bearing conglomerates of the Witwatersrand Basin are overlain by dolomitic limestones. Sinkholes in the dolomitic limestones to the west of Johannesburg were responsible for the subsidence of roads and houses, and one sinkhole even swallowed the crusher at West Driefontein mine in 1962. In addition, systematic dewatering of these dolomitic limestones for mine drainage has reduced their potential for industrial and domestic water supply in the Johannesburg area. Sheets of impermeable intrusive igneous rock separate the dolomitic limestones into 'compartments', and extreme care has to be taken during mining, as breaking into a new 'compartment' can flood underground workings. This happened at West Driefontein in 1968, but fortunately no lives were lost and the mine was saved by inserting concrete plugs underground.

- Excess water is clearly a problem in mining, but water is also in demand at many mines. Why is it needed?

- Large quantities of water are often required to operate the ore processing plant, to reduce dust at the surface, and to cool rock and air in deep underground mines.

The lack of water in arid areas is a major problem and can cause conflict with other potential users. Large mines are very 'thirsty'. It has been estimated that the South African gold mines consume more water than the inhabitants of Greater London. If a mining area is drought-prone, then an adequate water supply must be ensured, usually by tapping groundwater. For example, the Orapa diamond mine in Botswana, one of the largest in the world, is currently supplied by groundwater. Its only alternative supply, fortunately not needed as yet, is from the Okavango Delta. This huge 'inland delta' is one of the major wildlife reserves in Africa and would be destroyed if the amounts of water needed for the diamond mines were to be extracted from it.

4.2.2 Acid mine drainage

One of the major impacts of most metal and many coal mines is the occurrence of **acid mine drainage** (AMD). This is the formation of acidic water, i.e. water with low pH, and is due to the oxidation of sulphide minerals in the rock, particularly pyrite. At nearly neutral pH, pyrite oxidation by groundwater proceeds only slowly, often with assistance from natural bacterial action (Equation 4.1). However, the hydrogen ions produced by this reaction then reduce the pH, which increases the solubility of iron(II). Although iron(II) may be transported briefly as soluble Fe^{2+} ions in acid solution, it is often oxidized to precipitate insoluble hydrated iron(III) oxides (Equation 4.2).

$$\underbrace{2FeS_2(s)}_{\text{pyrite}} + \underbrace{7O_2 + 2H_2O}_{\text{oxygenated water}} = \underbrace{2Fe^{2+}(aq) + 4SO_4^{2-}(aq) + 4H^+}_{\text{soluble ions}} \quad (4.1)$$

$$\underbrace{4Fe^{2+}(aq)}_{\text{iron(II) ions}} + \underbrace{O_2 + 10H_2O}_{\text{oxygenated water}} = \underbrace{4Fe(OH)_3(s)}_{\text{hydrated iron(III) oxide}} + 8H^+ \quad (4.2)$$

Formation of acidic groundwaters with properties comparable to AMD occurs naturally where unmined sulphide deposits have been oxidized and leached by percolating surface waters, as described in the production of secondary enrichment deposits (*Metals 1*, Section 3.2.2). The surface leaching and oxidation of pyrite-bearing deposits forms colourful iron(III) oxide cappings — gossans. In mining, this natural process is enhanced because groundwater is drained through the sub-surface and air is present, so oxygenating the water. Therefore, large surface areas of rock containing sulphide minerals are exposed to oxidation. The sulphides decompose and, as a result, the water becomes acidified and contaminated with metals. In addition, sulphides are finely ground during ore processing (Section 3.2.1). The waste sulphides, often largely pyrite, are then discarded on waste tips and are liable to oxidation and leaching by acidic rainwater with consequent formation of AMD.

Although all mineral deposits that contain iron sulphides have the potential to form AMD, a number of other factors may be important. The rate of the oxidation is controlled by temperature, ease of access of oxygenated water to sulphide grains, and the nature of the host rock. If the sulphides are hosted by limestone, for example, then the acidity generated by sulphide oxidation is rapidly neutralized.

- How might neutralization of acidity occur in limestone rocks? What is the chemical reaction that neutralizes the hydrogen ions produced by sulphide oxidation?

- The hydrogen ions (H^+), produced by oxidation of sulphides, would react with the limestone ($CaCO_3$) as follows:

  $$CaCO_3(s) + H^+ = Ca^{2+}(aq) + HCO_3^- \quad (4.3)$$

  Removing H^+ ions by the formation of HCO_3^- ions increases the pH and neutralizes the solution.

The acidity (low pH) of AMD is a major problem in itself, causing distress or even death to aquatic organisms. At the same time, the oxidation of iron(II) in solution leads to the precipitation of red-brown hydrated iron(III) oxides, to form coatings on the beds of drainage channels that can stop fish and other organisms feeding (Plate 73). However, the names of rivers in major mining areas, for example the Rio Tinto in southern Spain and the Red River in Cornwall, suggest that this is not a new phenomenon but one that may have occurred naturally prior to mining. Plate 68 shows the accumulated effect that even a concentration of only 1 mg l^{-1} (1 ppm) of iron in solution can have.

The change in pH of groundwater caused by oxidation of pyrite also affects the solubility of many trace elements, notably metals such as copper and zinc. In ore deposits, these metals are often held in sulphide and oxide minerals that are stable at neutral pH. In oxidizing (acidic) solutions, especially at pH less than 5, they form soluble cations such as Cu^{2+} and Zn^{2+}. Elements from associated minerals (for example, arsenic from arsenopyrite) form soluble anion complexes, such as the arsenate ion, AsO_4^{3-}, which is transported in solution until precipitation occurs by reaction with other ions or with particles in the water or sediment. The arsenate ion is attracted to particles with a positive surface charge, the most abundant of which are hydrated iron(III) oxides. Arsenate ions are adsorbed onto these surfaces, which may already coat sedimentary particles, and the arsenic is then transported as part of these composite particles rather than in solution.

The pollutants in mine water largely depend on the elemental composition of the mineral deposit, the supply of water, its pH, and access to air. The seriousness of the hazard depends on the toxicity of the pollutants. For example, the trace element cadmium is often only a minor component of sphalerite in zinc deposits. If it were released during oxidation of the sphalerite, it could prove hazardous, whereas the zinc itself is less harmful.

When an active mine is being pumped, the water is likely to be contaminated by AMD and contain soluble metal ions because it has percolated through mineralized rock where oxidation reactions occur. However, these reactions are generally slow and the AMD is diluted as long as there is a continual flushing through of fresh, meteoric water by pumping. Also, as water percolates through cavities, it evaporates, and metals in solution may be precipitated as encrustations — like the calcite encrustations in limestone caverns where stalactites and stalagmites can be so spectacular. In an abandoned mine, on the other hand, when there is no continual flushing of the system, concentrations of metals and acidity can build up dramatically. When mine levels containing previously oxidized minerals are flooded, more metals are released into solution. Therefore, levels of metals and acidity from an abandoned mine are often greatly in excess of those from an active mine. However, once flooded and once the groundwater becomes more reducing, further oxidation reactions are less likely to occur, but minerals produced as encrustations earlier may be redissolved and add to the supply of toxic metals. In addition, the pumping of an active mine is likely to be controlled and procedures can be set in place for decontamination, whereas at an abandoned mine there may be no systems in place for treatment, and discharges are more likely to be irregular and unpredictable, depending on groundwater levels and rainfall. Problems of AMD from abandoned mines are illustrated in the case study 'AMD at Wheal Jane Mine in Cornwall'.

AMD at Wheal Jane Mine in Cornwall

Events in the early 1990s at Wheal Jane, an abandoned tin–copper mine in Cornwall, provide an example of the impact of AMD. Modern, large-scale underground mining began in 1970, although there had been mines in the area for several hundred years. The aim of the new mine was to exploit a large ore deposit in which the main metal of interest was tin (as cassiterite), although other metals were also of value, notably copper and zinc. Ore minerals were separated using gravity to concentrate coarse grains of high-density cassiterite, and flotation for fine cassiterite and sulphides. The wastes from mineral separation were mainly pyritic fines, which were fed into a tailings pond (Figure 62a and b).

Mining proceeded under the ownership of Consolidated Gold Fields until 1978. It was less profitable than anticipated because of difficulties with cassiterite separation and large inflows of water through extensive underground workings that intensified when a nearby mine was closed. Wheal Jane itself was also closed for a short period, until the UK-based multi-national mining company RTZ was persuaded to open a larger, more efficient mine based on the two closed mines. Environmental concerns had not been of overwhelming importance when the 'new' Wheal Jane Mine had been opened in 1970, and planning permission to re-commence operations a decade later was obtained without

(a)

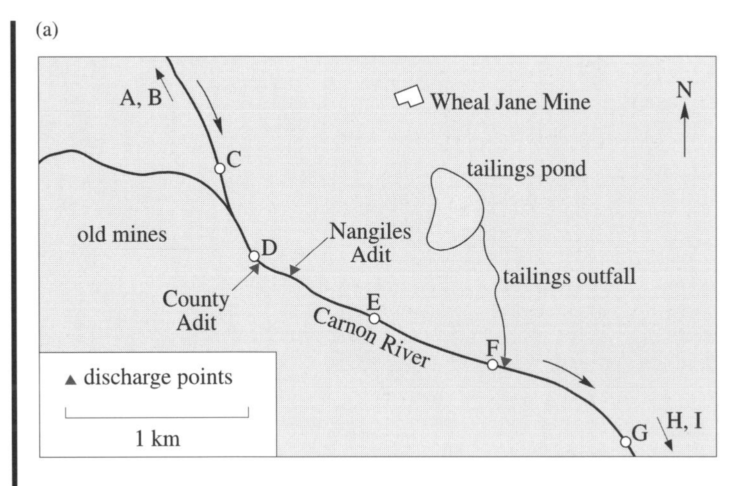

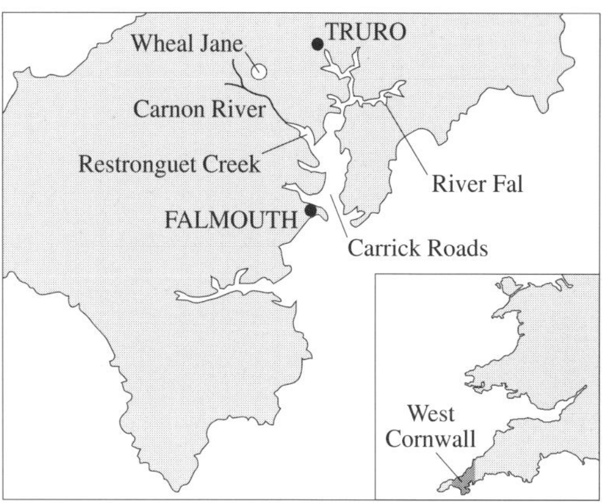

(b)

Figure 62 Wheal Jane Mine: (a) sketch map of the mine area showing sampling sites (Figure 64) and discharges into the Carnon River at the County Adit, the Nangiles Adit, and the tailings outfall; (b) aerial view, looking north, of the tailings pond at Wheal Jane.

difficulty. Improved underground productivity and more efficient recovery of tin at the mill enabled the mine to extend to a depth of 520 m and to continue profitable working until the world tin price collapsed in the mid-1980s. Economic difficulties led to a management buy-out in 1988, but the continued low price of tin eventually forced the new company, Carnon Consolidated, to close the mine in 1991.

The acidic nature of the mine water was a major problem during mining; it accounted for about 12% of operating costs and necessitated frequent changes of pipework. It was controlled by pumping and by allowing some settling. The Carnon River into which any overflow was pumped was already badly contaminated from a mine drainage network dating from the mid-eighteenth century, and did not support any fish. About 3 km downstream from Wheal Jane, the Carnon River flows into an estuary, the Carrick Roads, which contains a shell fishery and is a popular recreational area.

When the mine finally closed, it was allowed to flood and water quality was monitored by the National Rivers Authority (NRA) which warned that measures taken by the last operating company were inadequate. In order to control the water quality, the NRA implemented interim treatment measures: the main drainage adit was blocked off and water was pumped out from the main shaft and into the tailings pond. Here it was treated with lime to precipitate metals and reduce the acidity before being allowed to flow into the Carnon River. However, in January 1992, when the water levels in the mine were high, pumping was stopped as a result of stormy weather and because the tailings dam was approaching full capacity. This caused a build up of pressure in the mine, bursting the plug in the drainage adit. Many millions of litres (1 million litres = 10^3 m^3) of metal-rich water were released into the Carnon River and eventually mixed with the seawater of the Carrick Roads. Figure 63 shows how the level of cadmium in the Carnon River rose following this incident. Previously, the average background level of cadmium was 6 μg l^{-1}, even then considerably above the NRA quality standard of 1 μg l^{-1} (1 ppb).

According to Figure 63, what level did the cadmium concentration reach in the river after the 'burst' incident? How does that compare with the background level of cadmium in the Carnon River?

It reached at least 600 μg l^{-1} Cd (in fact, it reached 605 μg l^{-1} Cd), over a hundred times above the background level.

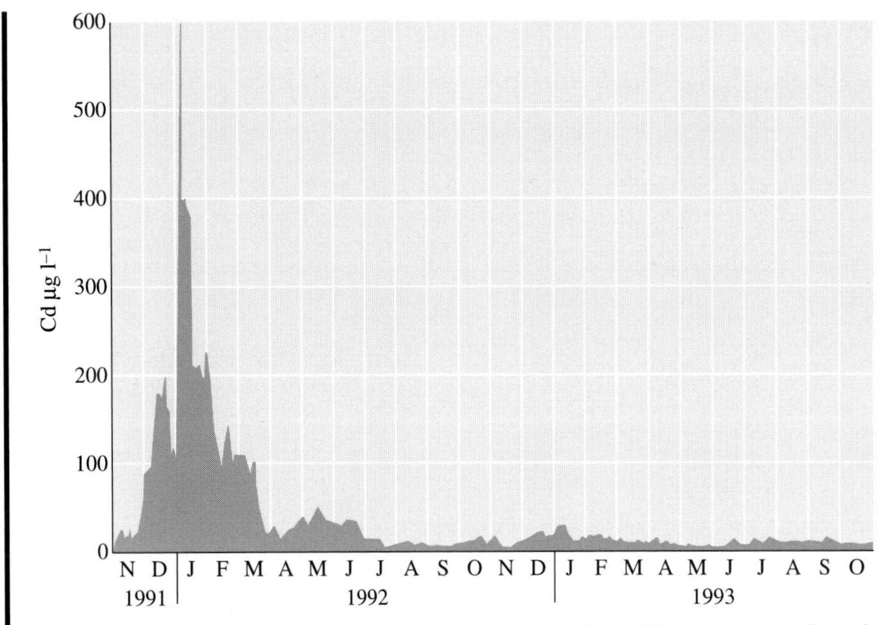

Figure 63 Variation of cadmium concentration in the Carnon River, 1991–93.

After pumping was resumed and the capacity for treatment increased, it took about 3 months to bring the situation under control (Figure 63).

Looking at Figure 63, would you say that by October 1993 the cadmium concentration complied with the NRA standard?

No. The NRA standard of 1 $\mu g\, l^{-1}$ is undetectable on the scale of Figure 63 which shows the level as lying consistently between about 5 and 15 $\mu g\, l^{-1}$. In any case, with a background concentration of 6 $\mu g\, l^{-1}$ Cd, the level measured could not comply with the NRA standard.

The company that abandoned Wheal Jane was under no obligation to carry out corrective measures because the original mining activities pre-dated planning requirements. Therefore, it was the NRA with its responsibility for water quality that had to take control. At the end of 1992, the Department of the Environment approved funding to set up a pilot scheme to provide a long-term solution to the Wheal Jane problem. This involved pumping to prevent sudden discharge of water, use of limestone to treat the water, and vegetation (reed beds) to settle particles and to absorb and fix metals at low operating cost.

Some of the consequences of the Carnon River pollution are described in the box 'Consequences of AMD at Wheal Jane', but first complete Activity 4 which looks in more detail at sources of contamination.

Activity 4 Contamination of the Carnon River

Much of this activity is based on analytical data obtained from sediments and water from the Carnon River. It is similar to the investigations that are performed during geochemical exploration for ore deposits (Section 2.3), but here the principles are being applied to pollution monitoring.

Figure 62a shows the Wheal Jane mine, the tailings pond, the Carnon River, a tributary which drains an area of old mining, and the locations of discharges into the river. Mine drainage is from the County Adit, which dates from the eighteenth century and drains several old mines west of the river, and the Nangiles Adit, which carries the main drainage from Wheal Jane. The overflow from the tailings pond also drains into the river. Figure 64 shows some analytical data for water at a number of points along the Carnon River. Water samples were filtered to separate particulate from dissolved components so that they could be recorded separately.

Use Figure 64 to answer questions (a), (b) and (c).

(a) At which sites would data represent the approximate background concentrations of arsenic and copper in the Carnon River? What are those concentrations? What is the background pH?

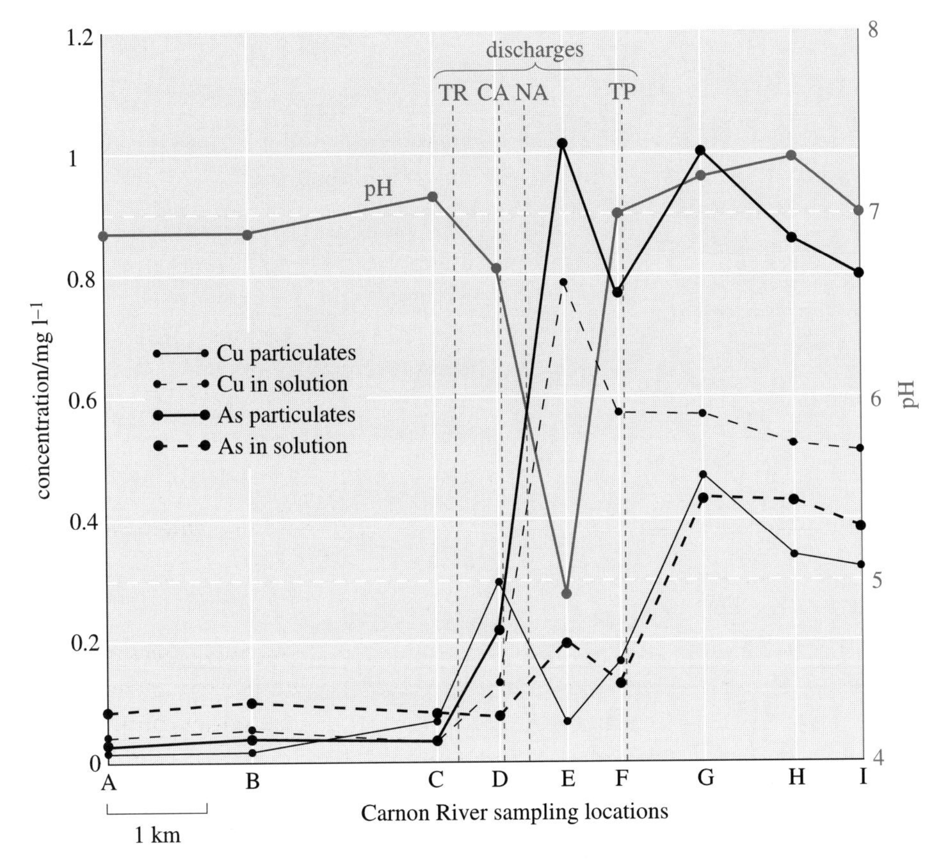

Figure 64 Analytical data from water sampled at points A to I along the Carnon River for dissolved and particulate arsenic and copper (all in mg l^{-1}, i.e. ppm), and acidity (pH). The discharge points from the two adits and from the tailings pond (see Figure 62a for locations) are also shown: CA = County Adit, NA = Nangiles Adit, TP = tailings pond. A tributary joins the river at TR.

(b) How do the locations of the three mine discharge points relate to (i) the highest concentrations of dissolved and particulate arsenic and copper and (ii) the most acidic waters?

(c) Downstream of the County Adit, which of the two river contaminants is the more abundant in dissolved form and which is the more abundant in particulate form? How does this match up with information about arsenic presented earlier in Section 4.2.2?

Table 6 provides data on the concentrations of copper and arsenic from all three sources and their discharge flow rates. Particulate and dissolved contents are combined.

Table 6 Copper and arsenic contamination from mine discharges into the Carnon River

Location of discharges	Concn of Cu/ mg l^{-1}	Flow rate/ l s^{-1}	Flux of Cu/ g s^{-1}	% of total flux	Concn of As/ mg l^{-1}	Flow rate/ l s^{-1}	Flux of As/ g s^{-1}	% of total flux
County Adit	1.08	330	0.356	...	0.21	330	0.069	...
Nangiles Adit	2.71	4	...	...	14.70	4	...	...
tailings pond	1.24	30	...	...	2.61	30	...	...
total flux			...				...	

(d) Why are the concentration levels of copper and arsenic so much greater from mine discharges in Table 6 than those at sampling sites in Figure 64?

(e) Calculate the flux of both copper and arsenic from each of the three mine discharges. The flux (the amount of contaminant passing per second) is simply the concentration of the contaminant in the water multiplied by the flow rate. Enter the values in Table 6. Then calculate the percentage contribution made by each discharge to the total of the three discharges and complete the table.

(f) According to your calculations, which of the three discharges is responsible for most of (i) the copper and (ii) the arsenic pollution?

Consequences of AMD at Wheal Jane

Prior to the discharges of 1992, there had been little aquatic life in the Carnon River because of the high background levels of metals, and even in the tidal waters of Restronguet Creek only a few metal-tolerant species thrived. Shortly after the discharge, surveys revealed only minimal impact on the biological community.

By the mid-1990s, the effects of metals from mine waters were still visible in the Carnon River (Plate 73). Some sources, like the following press report, believe that the contamination of 1992 has longer-term consequences.

> Animal experts believe that the swans on the Fal estuary in Cornwall are dying from the effects of a chemical cocktail released when the abandoned Wheal Jane tin mine flooded two years ago. A quarter of them are thought to have died in 18 months.
>
> The pollution followed the rising of the water level in the mine when its pumps were switched off after it ceased production. *The Sunday Telegraph* revealed in January 1992 that the Government had ignored pollution warnings when it refused to give financial assistance to the Carnon Consolidated mining company to keep the mine working.
>
> A mineshaft collapsed and 10 million gallons of a solution laced with arsenic, cadmium, copper, iron and zinc overflowed into the River Carnon, through Restronguet Creek and into the Fal estuary. River water turned a bright orange, and householders using boreholes were told to boil their water supplies.
>
> Ironically, an experiment was officially launched last week to treat the minewater by organic methods, using newly planted reedbeds, straw, gravel, sawdust and cattle slurry in shallow lagoons over an 11 acre site.
>
> The low-cost project is designed to replace a temporary chemical treatment plant installed immediately after the disaster.
>
> The Government is funding the clean-up operation to the tune of £8 million through to March 1996, and the National Rivers Authority will use the results of the pilot tests to provide options for long-term treatment.
>
> As a result, the water now running into the Carnon is probably cleaner than at any time since mining began in the area – but the suffering of the Fal swans continues. RSPCA inspectors began rescuing listless emaciated birds from the river in January 1993. At first it was thought they were starving, but autopsies on 20 bodies at the Ministry of Agriculture's Veterinary Investigation Unit in Truro established a different cause.
>
> Vic Simpson, RSPCA veterinary officer, said: 'Zinc poisoning causes the same symptoms as starvation. By June this year, we'd shown that virtually all the swans coming in from that area had zinc levels up to 15 times higher than normal.'
>
> Mr Simpson believes that when the first catastrophic flood burst from Wheal Jane and met the chemically neutral waters of Restronguet Creek, the subsequent reaction dumped a huge concentration of heavy metals on to the mudflats where the swans normally feed.
>
> As the toxic cocktail flowed further downstream, it was quickly diluted by the vast volume of water in the estuary. This might explain why other wildlife, notably the Fal oysters, have shown no signs of contamination.
>
> There are fears, however, that there may be more, less obvious, victims. Rex Harper, warden of RSPCA's Perranporth Animal Centre, where many of the swans have been treated, said 'Birds such as waders feed there as they pass through on migration. There is no way of telling how badly they might be affected.'
>
> The NRA is unwilling to pin blame without more proof, but Les Sutton, the RSPCA's Chief Inspector for Cornwall, said: 'We have periodically found birds suffering from lead poisoning, but we had no problems of this volume prior to the Wheal Jane spill. Logically it has to have something to do with what happened then.
>
> *Sunday Telegraph 11.12.94*

Question 33

With the background of the Wheal Jane discharges, how do you think such environmental problems occurring after mine abandonment could have been avoided?

4.3 Ore processing and smelting

As you know from Section 3, most metals are extracted from their ores in several stages by:

- liberating ore minerals by crushing and grinding the ore;
- separating ore minerals from waste by physical processes;
- extracting metals by smelting ore mineral concentrates or chemically extracting metals from crushed ore.

Most of these activities produce wastes of various kinds and have the potential to affect the environment.

4.3.1 Physical wastes from ore processing

Fine crushing (grinding or milling) of ore to liberate ore minerals for separation causes two main environmental problems. First, large quantities of fine-grained waste are produced. This waste can cause problems of visual impact, dust and acid mine drainage. Second, large amounts of energy are used in the crushing process; in most cases, the energy consumption exacerbates the depletion of fossil fuels and adds to the build-up of carbon dioxide in the atmosphere.

Typical low-grade metal ores may contain only a few ppm of metal (for example, gold) or a small percentage of metal (for example, many sulphide deposits). As mentioned earlier, a large, low-grade copper deposit may generate 97 tonnes of waste for 3 tonnes of copper sulphide concentrate, and that may contain only 1 tonne of copper. At the very low grades that are economic for mining gold, there may be up to 1 million tonnes of waste to be disposed of from the production of a tonne of gold — about enough waste to completely fill Wembley stadium (see also Video Band 14: *Gold Rush in the 1990s*).

The waste from wet separation of ore minerals forms a slurry that must be stored in containment areas to allow the solids to settle out. Such materials can be contained in several ways: ponded in depressions, held behind a dam (as at Wheal Jane, Figure 62b), or accumulated as heaps of thickened slurry. Ponding or damming has the advantage that immersion in stagnant water prevents access of oxygen to the tailings, inhibiting the oxidation and acidification that would form AMD (Section 4.2.2). Tailings ponds must be impermeable, of course, and should not be allowed to overflow, so their containment requires constant monitoring. A collapse can be catastrophic as it was at Merriespruit, South Africa, in the spring of 1994, when gold tailings from a large dam flowed into a small town after a rain storm, killing 17 people. The mining company and their consulting engineers have paid out vast sums (R20 million) in compensation since the event. Clearly, it is in a company's best interests to manage its operations well.

Tailings ponds must not be allowed to dry out, as tailings are fine grained and are extremely susceptible to wind dispersion, unless the material has been stabilized by vegetation cover. Coarser tailings can be used to back-fill underground mines, where they set like cement and reduce the incidence of rock failure. In the area to the south and west of Johannesburg (also known as Egoli — the City of Gold) about 120 million tonnes of rock are mined annually and there are more than 450 waste tips. Virtually all the sand and slimes tips have been vegetated to prevent dust and erosion by run-off. Rapidly growing grasses are planted until indigenous plants can establish themselves. Residual acidity from decomposition of pyrite is overcome by liming, and the addition of nitrates improves the fertility of the soil.

4.3.2 Chemical wastes from ore processing

Most physical methods of concentrating ore minerals (using density or magnetic properties, for example) produce wastes dominated by finely ground gangue, essentially as rock powder or slurry. Some concentration methods require the use of chemical reagents. For example, froth flotation makes use of inorganic and organic chemicals, including oils. Leaching of metals generally employs acids. Some of the chemical reagents in use are harmless but others are highly toxic. Wastes from many of these separating procedures are likely to be contaminated and pose risks to the environment.

There are many different chemicals used in ore mineral separation. Rather than provide a catalogue of them and all their possible side-effects, we shall consider two different forms of gold ore processing to illustrate the sorts of problem that are associated with chemical reagents.

Crude chemical separation (amalgamation) of gold

Small-scale gold mining is often carried out by operators with very limited capital. A prime example of the environmental problems caused by small-scale mining is the impact of primitive *garimpo* gold mining on the Amazon basin of Brazil (Figures 65 and 67). The miners or *garimpeiros*, who numbered at least 500 000 in the 1980s, are mainly young men, many the sons of farmers. They use mercury to extract gold from alluvial placer deposits. The sediment is first hosed to wash away light minerals and mud, then the remaining gold-bearing sand is concentrated by panning or riffling (Section 3.2.2). The concentrate is mixed with mercury which extracts gold by forming a dense amalgam (effectively a solution) that settles out and can be drained off. The gold is recovered from the mercury–gold amalgam by roasting to vaporize the mercury, which boils off at 357 °C.

Figure 65 Garimpeiros in the Brazilian Amazon basin. These men are using high pressure hoses to loosen unconsolidated sediment and remove mud before separating out heavy minerals. This form of mining often causes devastation of the region. Many miners suffer from malaria, and deaths by shooting are commonplace.

Workers inhaling mercury vapour often suffer from mercury poisoning, but they can recover after terminating their exposure to mercury. The mercury that ends up in rivers is a more serious problem. More than 1 kg of mercury is used to recover 1 kg of gold and it is estimated that 100 t of mercury have been released into the Madeira River of the SW Amazon Basin. The mercury settles to the river beds and enters the food chain, eventually accumulating in fish that are the basic diet of the native Indians. Mercury is transformed into toxic methyl-mercury that can accumulate in humans.

Advanced chemical separation (heap leaching) of gold

The revival of gold mining in the western United States illustrated in Video Band 14: *Gold Rush in the 1990s* is based on low-grade ore deposits, mechanized open pit mining, and the use of heap leaching.

- What is the chemical basis for heap leaching of gold and how is it used?

- Sodium cyanide solution dissolves gold by forming the soluble gold cyanyl complex ion, $Au(CN)_2^-$ (Section 3.2.2). The ore needs only to be crushed to allow the solution access to the fine gold grains. Crushed ore is piled into heaps on an impermeable membrane and sprayed with sodium cyanide solution.

  The gold-laden cyanide solution from heap leach pads is collected into ponds and pumped to a recovery plant where the gold is removed by reaction with zinc or, more usually, with adsorbent carbon. Although recovery of gold may only be 70%, it is more efficient to crudely crush the low-grade ore and accept low yields, than to use more energy to grind it finer and increase recovery to 95%.

The environmental problems in this process are due to the toxicity of cyanide, which is lethal to humans, even in small amounts, and is particularly easily absorbed as hydrogen cyanide gas. Fortunately, the cyanide is rapidly oxidized by exposure to sunlight and hydrogen cyanide gas is generated only at low pH (i.e. in acid conditions). Control of the cyanide in the process is important, however, and is achieved by lining the leach pads with plastic and monitoring for any leaks. Some state regulatory authorities in the US insist on triple-lined pads and sophisticated leak detection. Although humans generally avoid taking drinking water from collection ponds, migratory birds are unable to distinguish them from more ordinary water holes. The death of birds was a problem in Nevada but has been cured by mechanical bird-scarers and the imposition on companies of severe fines by the US Environmental Protection Agency. One company was fined $25 000 for each visiting duck found dead.

4.3.3 Emissions from smelting

The final stage in the metals extraction process is the conversion of ore minerals into metals through smelting. Smelting of ores poses particular problems as the process may release metal oxide dust, sulphur oxides and volatized metal into the atmosphere. Through rainfall, these pollutants accumulate in soils, in surface waters and groundwaters. Pollutants are not confined to the metals sought; volatile elements present in smelting fluxes and minor constituents of ore minerals may also be released and may be toxic. For example, many electrolytic aluminium smelters have polluted surrounding areas with fluorine released from the fluxes used to dissolve the aluminium ore (Section 3.3). Smelting pollution is not new: pollution from nineteenth-century UK lead smelters was mentioned in Section 3.3. In most countries today, there are greater environmental safeguards and regular monitoring is obligatory to ensure lower emission levels, but worldwide, the amount of metal smelted is vastly greater today than in the past (Section 1.2). Without changes in practices and improvements in technology (for example, as described for Sudbury in Section 3.4.3), total emissions of pollutants would be much higher.

The impact of individual smelters can be more serious than that of individual mines, although smelters are fewer in number. So let's consider where they occur.

 Is the distribution of smelters likely to be the same as mines?

 No, it's not the same because smelters are traditionally sited where there are energy supplies, often near to consumers. For example, Europe mines only 10% of world lead production but smelts 25% of the total.

Due to increases in energy prices in the 1970s, many modern smelters have been sited in areas of cheap energy. For example the largest aluminium smelters in the world are based on the hydroelectric plants of the major rivers of central Siberia. Markets and expertise are also important in locating smelting operations. Indeed, in Section 1.3 we saw how lead ore continued to be imported to Britain for smelting in the late nineteenth century even though the UK lead mining industry was declining.

Not all smelters have a good history of environmental control, despite the fact that public awareness and legislation in industrialized countries have led to considerable improvements in recent years. But such improvements have financial consequences: clean-up costs in the US lead smelting industry have been estimated at 9–12% of net production costs. The two main forms of fallout from smelters are toxic metals and acid rain.

Bioavailability — lead

The effects of metal pollution on wildlife (as described in the box 'Consequences of AMD at Wheal Jane') depend on the bioavailability of toxic metals. **Bioavailability** is the extent to which metals can be absorbed by organisms, and depends on the chemical form in which they occur. Metals are released in different forms by the mining, processing, and smelting of ores. As you read in *Metals 1*, Section 1.4, small amounts of many metals are *essential* to the health of humans and other organisms, but large amounts can be toxic, causing health problems, even death; many metals are toxic even in small amounts.

The bioavailability of lead has been investigated in detail because lead is a neurotoxin, and it has been claimed to have a particular impact on young children, causing impaired intelligence and slowed reaction times. Studies have demonstrated that children take up lead from a number of sources, mainly by ingestion of dust from hand contact, but the amount of lead taken up biologically depends on the chemical form in which it occurs.

Studies of contaminated soils from areas of mining and smelting have shown that although galena (lead sulphide) is the dominant mineral in lead ore deposits, it is not the main lead mineral found in soils. Soils from areas of mining are dominated by complex lead oxides with lesser amounts of lead sulphates and phosphates. In areas of lead smelting on the other hand, the main lead minerals are simple oxides. The only part of the mining process where sulphides dominate is in areas contaminated by dust from ore loading.

The bioavailability of lead to humans is dependent on the solubility of minerals during the few hours that they pass through the gastro-intestinal tract. Lead is taken into the blood system by absorption of fluids through the wall of the small intestine after dissolution in very acidic stomach fluid (pH around 1.4). In the stomach, galena is the most soluble of the lead minerals found in mine soils, but only sparingly so. The complex oxides and phosphates that are more common there are much less soluble. The simple lead oxides that are found in soils near smelting operations are readily soluble and much more easily absorbed into the body than lead minerals from mining.

Toxic metals

The smelting of lead and zinc poses special problems because of the toxicity of lead and the presence of the toxic metals arsenic, cadmium, mercury and thallium as trace constituents in the ore mineral concentrates. Cadmium is of special concern in zinc smelting as it commonly occurs as a minor constituent of the main zinc ore mineral, sphalerite. It has been responsible for health problems and even deaths in Japan, where high levels of cadmium released from smelters into the atmosphere have contaminated soils used for rice growing in the immediate area. Rice is the staple diet in Japan and cadmium-contaminated rice has caused Itai-Itai disease, which destroys bone structure. Whereas background levels of cadmium in rice were less than 0.1 ppm, plants within 0.5 km of one smelter contained 18 ppm, and the soil contained over 30 ppm. The discovery of the extent to which plants and soil processes were capable of concentrating cadmium led to the recognition that it was a major pollutant.

The largest lead–zinc smelter in the UK is at Avonmouth, near Bristol, which has been producing metal from a variety of imported lead–zinc ores for many years. The sulphide ores are first roasted to form an oxide sinter which is transferred with coke to a blast furnace where reduction of the sinter to metals occurs. Molten lead accumulates with the slag but zinc, having a lower boiling temperature, is vaporized. The zinc vapour is condensed *in* molten lead on which liquid zinc floats and can be separated. Toxic volatile constituents such as sulphur and mercury oxides are removed from waste gases. Cadmium is released (and collected) mainly in the final stages of zinc refining. Considerable amounts of liquid effluent are also generated during smelting, mainly from cleaning of waste gases and treatment of slag.

In times past, smelting methods were dirtier. Cadmium was not collected from stack emissions and was released into the atmosphere. Soil surveys around the Avonmouth smelter indicate that surface soils are contaminated with lead and cadmium for almost 5 km from the smelter, and are quite heavily contaminated within 2 km of the smelter (Figure 66).

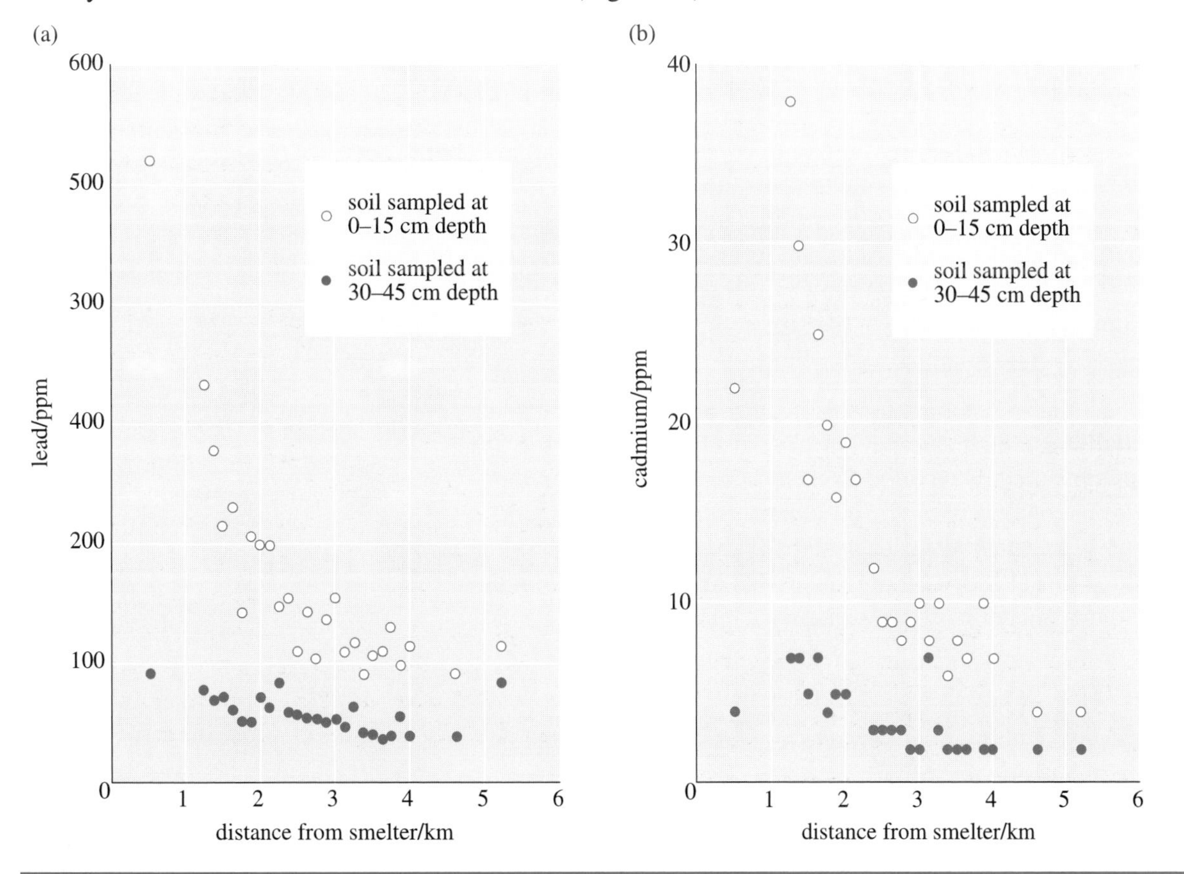

Figure 66 Contamination in soils along a traverse downwind for 5 km from the Avonmouth smelter: (a) concentrations of lead; (b) concentrations of cadmium.

Question 34

Examine Figure 66a and answer the following.

(a) In general, is the cadmium concentration in the soil at Avonmouth greater or less than in the Carnon River (Figure 63)? Give reasons why this might be so.

(b) Around the Avonmouth smelter, what is the difference in the concentration of lead compared with cadmium — is it likely to represent a corresponding difference in levels of toxicity to the environment?

(c) What reason can you give for the fact that the concentrations of lead and cadmium below the surface of the soil are less than at the surface?

Nowadays stack gases are cleaned by filtering after sulphur dioxide has been extracted for the production of sulphuric acid. Filtering removes dust (originating from material handling and ventilation systems) that would otherwise escape to the atmosphere. Emissions from smelter stacks in the UK today must be within limits laid down by the Environment Agency (formerly HM Inspectorate for Pollution). Discharges of effluent from the smelter into the Avon estuary are also controlled by the Environment Agency (formerly the National Rivers Authority). Before discharge, metals are removed by liming and the settling of precipitates.

Slag disposal is a major problem for smelters. Around 90 000 t of slag per year are produced at Avonmouth and, having no market, it has to be stored on site. Slag is about 12% base metal and long-term stores may be susceptible to leaching by ground and surface water. Besides pollution of the surrounding area, lead smelting is potentially hazardous to workers within the plant: their exposure to lead is monitored by regular blood sampling.

Acid rain

Emission of sulphur dioxide produced by the oxidation of sulphide minerals in copper and nickel smelters has made major contributions to acid rain in some parts of the world. The two largest nickel smelters, at Sudbury in northern Ontario, Canada (Section 3.4), and Noril'sk in northern Siberia, Russia, have been among the largest single emitters of sulphur dioxide. If vented into the atmosphere, sulphur dioxide is converted into sulphuric acid by reaction with water and leads to acid rain. An additional problem at both Sudbury and Noril'sk is that both smelters are surrounded by crystalline rocks with limited soil cover — this means that the immediate environment is unable to neutralize the acid rain. Acid rain leaches from soils elements that are normally stable, such as aluminium which is soluble at pH levels below 4 (*Metals 1*, Figure 41). Thus, lakes in the area can become polluted by the leachate, and the fish population is wiped out.

As noted in Section 3.4, an attempt was made at Sudbury to reduce the problem by building a high chimney, the 387 m superstack (Figure 58). Unfortunately, this merely exported the acid rain further afield. More recently, Inco (the owners of the main Sudbury smelter), have spent C$500 million in an attempt to reduce sulphur emissions. The problem at Noril'sk had not been tackled by the mid-1990s and a substantial area of tundra around the smelter has been seriously damaged.

Question 35

Why do you think smelting might present a greater environmental threat than mining or ore processing operations?

4.4 Social impacts of mining

Mining has often been responsible for bringing large numbers of people into sparsely inhabited areas. Mount Isa in Queensland, Australia, is now a substantial town that would not have existed but for discovery of rich copper ores there in the 1920s. Another example is Noril'sk in Northern Siberia, which, with a population of 180 000, is one of only three large towns north of the Arctic Circle and would not exist without nickel mining and smelting. In the past, those immigrants not forced to live in Arctic Siberia were provided with state inducements to stay in this inhospitable area.

The economic benefits of mining are more questionable when significant changes in the lives of indigenous people are caused. For example, the 1849 gold rush in California was one of the main factors that encouraged the settlement of the American west coast, and led to the development of rail links and the opening up of the mid-west. Some would argue that this was progress and a benefit, but the local American Indian population would no doubt have disagreed. Today, in a modern frontier mining area in New Guinea, the hiring of young men for mining has disrupted the traditional values of the society by introducing a cash economy and changing traditional ideas of seniority and common ownership. This situation is not uncommon in developing countries.

The transformation from small-scale traditional mining to modern large-scale mechanized methods also has major social consequences. At Potosi, in Bolivia, many thousands of individuals have mined low-grade silver ore underground for many centuries. Although working conditions are poor, and the life expectancy of miners is only 35–40 years, the mines support a sizeable community. Recent interest by large mining companies in what could be the largest known reserve of silver in the world has caused great concern. Although the operation would be highly profitable using large-scale opencast mining methods and heap leaching, the miners fear for their livelihood, the disruption of their society and its traditions.

Major mineral development projects that have opened up in recent years in sparsely populated regions include the Baikal Amur Railway (BAM) in north-east Siberia, mine developments in Papua New Guinea, and development projects in the Amazon region as described in the box 'Mining-led development at Carajás in the Amazon Basin'.

One way to minimize social impact is the use of fly-in/fly-out workforces, as at remote mines in Australia and Canada. This avoids the necessity of building houses and facilities for families and also minimizes the need for roads. In the case of the mines in northern Saskatchewan, labour is rotated on a two-week-on/two-week-off basis from the southern settled part of province. The staff live in spacious hotel-type conditions for their two weeks on and work long hours each day. During the two weeks off they are able to live with their families; many run small farms and live in rural areas.

In many countries, particularly the more developed ones, the potential of mining to have undesirable effects that outweigh the economic advantages leads to questions of whether or not mining should be permitted — this applies especially in *national parks* as described in the box 'National parks and wilderness areas'.

Mining-led development at Carajás in the Amazon Basin

The Carajás project is a mining project that was designed to act as a focus for regional development. The Carajás region of Brazil (Figure 67) contains the largest single high-grade iron deposit in the world and the region around it contains a number of other mineral deposits, notably gold at Serra Pelada and the Azul manganese deposit. Although the iron deposits were discovered in the mid-1960s, it took 20 years for export sales to be agreed and development to be completed.

Carajás is situated in undisturbed rain forest and the project necessitated the building of a 890 km railway from the Atlantic coast, and the investment of $2.8 billion by the Brazilian Companhia Vale do Rio Doce (CVRD). Carajás was to be the focal point of a development region covering an area larger than France. The development plan included a major hydroelectric power station and an aluminium smelter. It had government approval as the aim of the project was to meet the urgent need for Brazil to generate hard currency to pay its foreign debts.

Before the construction of the railway and mine, the population of the area was very sparse. The new town associated with the mine site has a population of 11 000 and was planned, as were six other towns on the railway line, but many unplanned towns have also sprung up along the railway as a result of immigration from other areas in Brazil. One side-effect was the establishment of metal works along the route of the railway, particularly pig iron plants that rely on cheap charcoal produced from timber cut from the rain forest. In 1987, it was estimated that 12 of these plants required the annual felling of 5000 hectares of forest. Although Brazilian laws require that 50% of timber used should be from plantations, and that *environmental impact statements* be conducted (as explained in the box 'Environmental impact statements', Section 4.5), the laws have not been enforced. The development of the pig iron plants was encouraged by tax concessions on profits and a duty on imports.

In an attempt to reduce the environmental impact of the project, CVRD has spent $300 million and one of its aims is to reforest 1 million hectares. However, although CVRD has control within its own concessions, it has difficulty in controlling development beyond these areas. The Brazilian government exacerbated the problem as they encouraged agricultural development by large enterprises at the expense of individuals, thus causing significant rural unrest and violence. By 1990, Brazil was the world's third largest producer of iron ore, ahead of Australia.

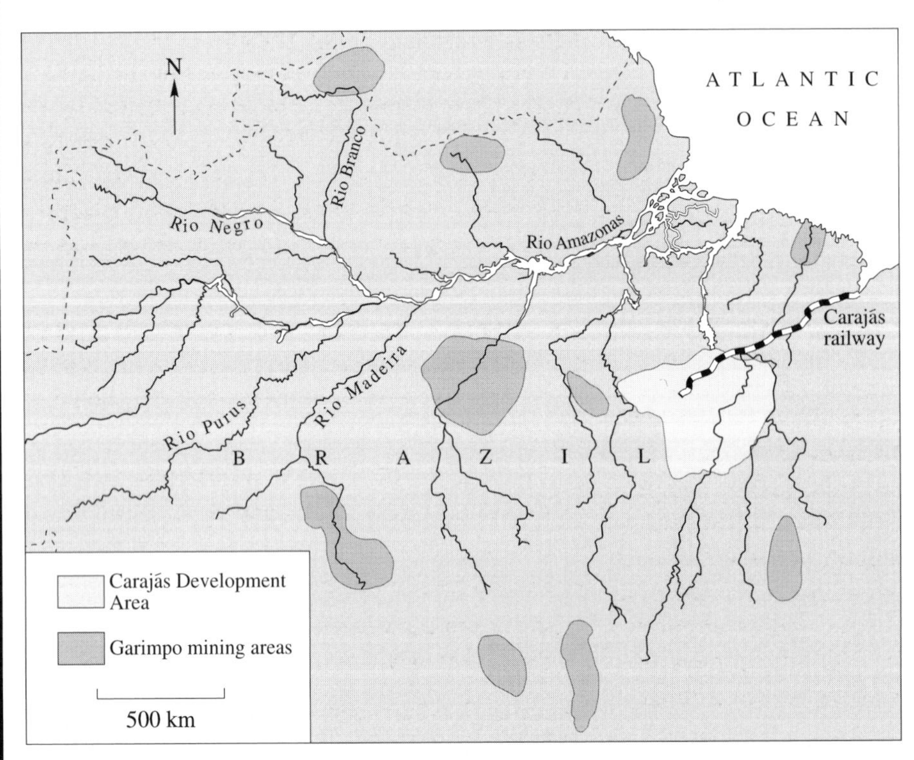

Figure 67 The Amazon basin of Brazil, showing the Carajás region, and sites where garimpo mining is common (Section 4.3.2).

National parks and wilderness areas

Compare Figure 68 and Figure 6 (Section 1.3) with the Postcard Geological Map. What is the relationship between the underlying geology of areas recognized for their special scenic value and those known for their mineralization?

With the exception of the North Yorkshire Moors, the major areas of scenic value shown in Figure 68 are in upland or highland areas of northern England, Wales and south-west England, where the rocks are Palaeozoic age or older. Many of these areas contain mineralization and have been centres of past mining activities as discussed in Section 1.3.

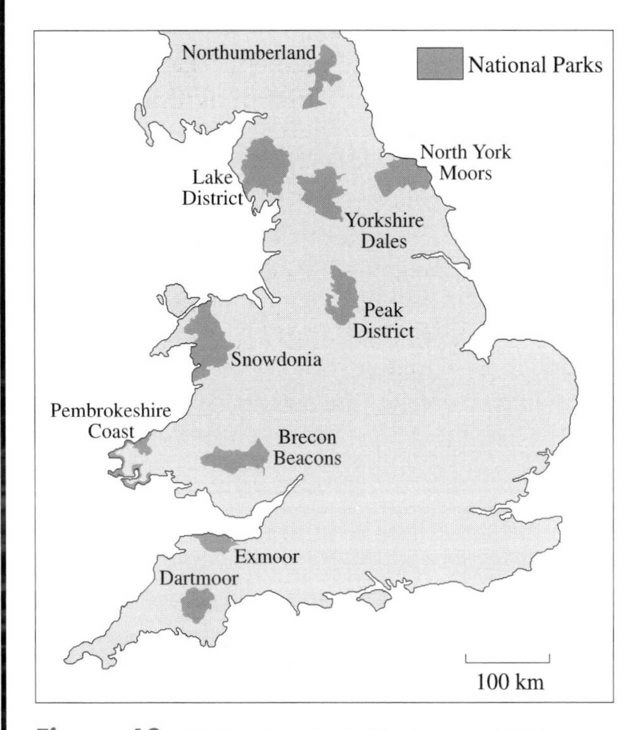

Figure 68 National parks in England and Wales.

The rocks of the Lake District and Snowdonia are Ordovician and Silurian mudstones, sandstones and volcanic rocks with which copper and zinc mineralization is sometimes associated (for example, Parys Mountain, Anglesey). The Carboniferous limestone of the north Pennines, north Wales and the Peak District of Derbyshire hosts hydrothermal lead–zinc (plus barite–fluorite) mineralization (*Metals 1*, Section 4.3.1). Tin and copper are associated with the granites of south-west England.

Although most of the economic mineralization of the UK has been worked out, there remain significant areas of potentially economic, extractable mineralization, but largely in those areas which society regards as aesthetically and environmentally valuable, designated as national parks.

A landmark case was the exploration programme for copper at Coed-y-Brenin within the Snowdonia National Park (north Wales) in the late 1960s and early 1970s. Copper had been mined in the area in the first half of the nineteenth century and the occurrence of copper minerals within a peat bog in an area of Ordovician intrusive rocks was known from the geological literature. The area was investigated by a subsidiary company of RTZ with interests in large-scale copper mining. Their target was a large disseminated porphyry copper deposit (*Metals 1*, Section 2.4) that could be mined as an open pit. An area of potential ore was identified from soil geochemistry, and exploration drilling indicated a resource that was said to be sub-economic, although a major factor in the final decision not to proceed was probably the perceived difficulty of obtaining *planning permission* to mine — especially as much media and public concern had been awakened. Had a large copper deposit been proved, it is questionable whether economic arguments for exploitation would have prevailed over those made by the amenity and conservation lobbies.

In contrast, a major development at Hemerdon on the edge of the Dartmoor National Park was given permission to proceed in 1986 after a public inquiry. The target here was tungsten, and again the method of mining was to be by open pit. Unlike Coed-y-Brenin, there was already a large open pit nearby, the Lee Moor China Clay Mine, and the Hemerdon deposit had already been worked on a substantial scale during World War II. Due to a fall in the price of tungsten, however, the Hemerdon Mine was not developed.

The present policy in the national parks of England and Wales, based on regulation at county and national level, is to test any application against a number of criteria:

- the need for the development on a national basis;
- the impact on the local economy of permission or refusal;
- the availability and cost of an alternative supply;
- the detrimental effect on the local landscape and the extent to which it could be moderated.

The overall effect seems to be that new mining in national parks is not allowed, but decisions not to proceed have so far been based on economic arguments, and the protection of national parks and scenic areas has yet to be tested by a proposal that is truly economically attractive. Although very few mines in the UK today actively extract metals, the current policy is to allow existing mines to continue and underground mines to develop new resources when existing reserves are depleted, although only under strict guidelines.

The conflict between development and conservation is inevitably greatest in countries with dense populations and well-developed planning policies. In the past, mining has been permitted in some countries in a number of national parks, in many cases because mining preceded the establishment of the parks. However, there was a sharp change in many national government policies in the 1980s, and applications to mine in national parks or wilderness areas are now unlikely to succeed in developed countries. Of particular note are:

- the decision by the Australian cabinet in 1991 not to permit mining at Coronation Hill near the Kakadu National Park in the Northern Territory;
- the 1993 decision to stop development of the large Windy Craggy copper–cobalt deposit in northern British Columbia;
- the decision by the Irish Government to stop exploration at Croagh Patrick in County Mayo.

Croagh Patrick is a mountain in western Ireland where significant gold was discovered in the 1980s (Figure 69). However, it is also the site of religious pilgrimages, and when mining was considered, there were immediate protests. Eventually, the exploration permit was cancelled by Eire's Minister of Mines and the Environment. In all the cases listed above, development was stopped by government decisions because the mineral rights were state-owned. The situation is different in the UK where mineral rights are held privately and any decision is determined through the planning process, by county and regional authorities, although controversial applications can be considered at national level by government.

Exploration for mineralization is not allowed in US national parks or wilderness areas. On other public lands, activity is under the control of the relevant federal agency, and the presumption has moved away from allowing mining, to reviewing its suitability. In Australia, the laws are not as restrictive but exploration licences can be reviewed by state governments on environmental grounds.

Governments in many former Eastern Block countries have also shown a swing from the over-riding importance of production to the protection of sensitive areas. A case that has generated much discussion is that of Lake Baikal in central Siberia. This lake is the largest single reserve of freshwater in the world and its protection from mining, agriculture and more especially lumbering became a major issue under Perestroika. In contrast, although many developing countries have regulations on areas that may be mined, currently they are not strictly enforced.

Figure 69 A scenically sensitive area where mining was proposed: Croagh Patrick, County Mayo, is also a site of religious pilgrimage.

Question 36

If an economically exploitable ore mineral deposit was discovered within 10 km of your home, what would you see as possible advantages and disadvantages of a major mining operation?

4.5 The way forward—clean up or control?

Today, the environmental impacts of mining and smelting can be sharply reduced. The main requirements are planning and finance. The question of who is responsible for the cost of clean-up operations varies from country to country and with the timing of pollution. With increased governmental concern, this is an area where changes in regulations and practices are likely to occur in the near future. It has been customary in North America for the 'polluter pays' principle to be applied, but in the UK, in cases where mining activities predate modern planning regulations, abandoned mines are the responsibility of government.

Clean-up operations can also be funded by industry's profits: for example, the US Superfund programme, which deals with various forms of pollution, is funded by a 0.12% levy on the income of large companies. As many mines are entities that are legally separate from their multi-national company parents, which are not responsible for the debts of subsidiaries, a number of countries have instituted 'bond' schemes for mining projects. Before production begins, a company is required to deposit a sum of money called a bond, to pay to restore the site to its original state. A controversial situation occurred at a heap leach gold mine at Summitville, Colorado, when the operating company filed for bankruptcy because it had not made sufficient profit to pay for the first phase of mine closure and clean-up. The US Environmental Protection Agency was forced to meet the $22 million cost of this clean-up.

Provision for environmental protection and restoration is *obligatory* for new mines in most developed countries and must be included in an assessment of the financial viability of each project. There is also a requirement that the project be approved by government. This is known as the *permitting process* and normally involves the preparation of an **environmental impact statement** and the obtaining of approval for remediation and restoration schemes that will be instituted after mine closure. Any deviation from the approved measures is likely to result in legal action. Operating procedures may also require approval.

Environmental impact statements

The first step in evaluating the potential impact of mining is to describe the state of the environment before any development has occurred. In particular, the compositions of soils and waters in the area, which may be naturally enriched in metals around ore deposits. There is no point in demanding a reduction to concentration levels below background.

The potential impact (both environmental and social) of the mining operation at its various stages of development must then be considered through the following questions.

- What can happen?
- How likely is it to happen?
- What are the consequences likely to be?

In order to answer these questions, potential hazards must be identified and their effects under specific circumstances evaluated. For example, water quality can be modelled from a knowledge of hydrology and the properties of the rock being mined. The implications for the environment when an incident occurs can then be predicted. In the event of untreated AMD being released into a major river, models can predict consequences to local ecosystems, such as the impact on fish stocks.

In order to promote good social relations, local communities should be consulted in detail about the consequences of mining. These discussions should address the economic benefits, jobs and wealth creation as well as environmental drawbacks.

The length and complexity of the permitting process is turning many mining companies away from Europe and North America where permitting may take two years, and where consent may not be forthcoming at all if environmentally sensitive areas are involved. Instead, companies are looking to developing countries such as Chile where the permitting process takes about six months, or to other non-industrialized but resource-rich countries that are desperate for revenues, where the process might take even less time.

Whereas, in the past, environmental problems might not have been appreciated by mine operators and were often ignored, today they must be costed at the outset and the whole operation monitored. In fact, the role of the geoscientist in the mining industry has changed greatly since mining operations have been subject to stringent environmental regulation. Formerly the main role of the geologist and mine engineer was simply to determine the most profitable rock to mine and how to mine it, taking account of ore grades and geological problems in extraction. Geoscientists in today's mining organizations are also involved in:

- defining background levels of potential pollutants;
- monitoring the effectiveness of the containment and treatment of wastes;
- monitoring the impact of pollutants on the environment.

The increasing ability of the mining industry to control its environmental effects is exemplified by a gold mine that was opened at Mineral Hill, Montana, in 1989. About $1 million was spent on environmental impact assessment, and vast sums were allocated to ensure the well-being of the natural environment where grizzly bears and bald eagles were among the local wildlife. The operation was based on a reserve of 1 Mt of ore grading 10.3 $g\,t^{-1}$ Au, a total expectation of over 10 t of gold, worth over $100 million at 1992 prices. The mine is essentially an underground operation but ore is treated by conventional heap leaching using cyanide (Section 4.3.2). The whole mining and processing operation was designed for zero discharge of water and total destruction of the cyanide.

Where controls to avoid environmental damage go hand-in-hand with mine production, clean-up at the end of mining is not likely to be as difficult as it might be at sites where operations were not subject to controls. However, most forms of mining require some form of land restoration or rehabilitation.

Rehabilitation

The impact of mining on the land surface can be reduced significantly by rehabilitation *during* mining, if this is possible. This approach has been particularly well applied by the coal mining industry in opencast or strip mining (Section 3.1.3). The area from which the coal has been removed is backfilled with waste (mainly overburden) from the area currently being mined, then stockpiled topsoil is replaced on top of the waste. The rehabilitated area can be re-used for agriculture.

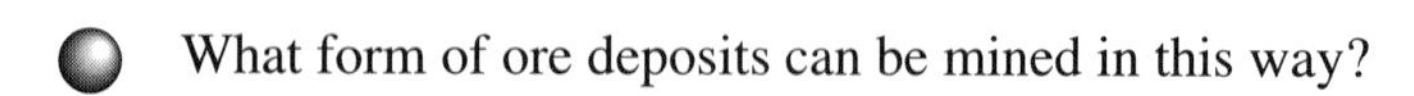

What form of ore deposits can be mined in this way?

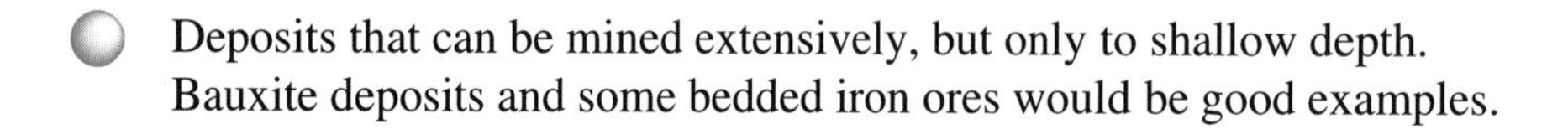

Deposits that can be mined extensively, but only to shallow depth. Bauxite deposits and some bedded iron ores would be good examples.

The dredging of black sands for heavy minerals can also employ simultaneous rehabilitation (*Metals 1*, Figure 50, Section 3.4). In the past, however, metal mines have concentrated on remediation *after closure* (clean-up) rather than *during operations* (control).

Even today, most open pit metal mines are left as holes and allowed to fill with water. In remote areas, it may seem to matter little: in more populated areas holes may be useful as landfill sites. Entrances to underground mines are best sealed and shafts filled with inert material. If there is AMD, a long-term neutralization and control programme must be put in place (cf. Wheal Jane, Section 4.2.2). At present, the backfilling of pits and underground workings is very expensive, although some mineral rights owners have insisted on it, and it must be built into the cost of the whole mining operation. Waste rock and tailings piles can be vegetated to reduce visibility, improve stability, and minimize erosion. Soils may be contaminated with metals (from finely ground minerals) which may be released into acidic solutions. Around smelters, metals may be in a more bioavailable form. Clean-up operations are generally expensive and burial with 'clean' top soil is often the cheapest option. Recently, a promising technique has been proposed for cleaning up contaminated sites. It also has the potential to reclaim and even to *mine* metals.

Concluding remarks

Metal production and mining are often thought of as dirty and polluting. In the past, the drive has been to provide materials for industrial development with little thought of the environmental consequences. With the increased scale of operations in the twentieth century, and thus the potential for environmental impacts to be more serious, there has been a growing realization that unaided

Green mining and land decontamination

Figure 70 *Thlaspi caerulescens*, a hyperaccumulator plant.

It has long been known that some specialized plant species occur as *geobotanical anomalies* in mineralized areas, growing in conditions that would be hostile to most plants (Section 2.6.4). Recently, it has been confirmed that many of these plants do, in fact, take up metals in quantities that would be toxic for normal plants, and some species actually require high quantities of particular metals for healthy growth. These are known as **hyperaccumulator plants.** The dried foliage of some plant species contains up to 40 000 ppm Zn and several thousand ppm of lead and cadmium. A member of the cabbage family, *Thlaspi caerulescens* (Figure 70), is an example that grows on sites of zinc mineralization in central Europe.

Many plant species are now known to be hyperaccumulators and can concentrate high levels of metals such as zinc, cadmium, lead, nickel, copper, cobalt, manganese and chromium. Nickel and cobalt hyperaccumulators grow on soils overlying peridotite rocks. There are two important properties of hyperaccumulators:

- they are capable of extracting appreciable quantities of metals from soils;
- they concentrate metals in organic material so that when the dried foliage is burnt, it produces ash in which the metal is further concentrated 10–15-fold.

On the basis of these properties, what uses could be made of these specialized hyperaccumulator plants?

They could *decontaminate* soils of toxic metals and their foliage could even be *harvested* to provide a source of metals.

Hyperaccumulators could provide a truly 'green' means of cleaning up contaminated land, and in suitable areas could even be a basis for 'green mining'. However, to operate efficiently, large quantities of foliage must be produced, and most hyperaccumulator species have low yields, even when fertilizers are applied. At present, hyperaccumulators have a great potential for decontamination; the question is whether or not they are a practical proposition.

recovery of the natural environment takes longer as the scale of activities increases. The growth of environmental concern amongst the public and by governments, especially in the 1980s and 90s, has resulted in pressure to clean up past activities and to prevent new mining developments. However, the NIMBY (not in my back yard) attitude of completely banning mining from parts of North America and western Europe cannot be the answer; it only exports problems to places where public opinion is not mobilized or where governments and companies put economic gain before the environment.

In the mining industry today, avoiding practices that may spread contamination and building-in environmental safeguards are principles that are becoming as important as maximizing the recovery of metal during extraction. The monitoring, treatment, and management of mine waters is particularly important in controlling pollution.

Increasingly, the principles of sustainable development (Block 1, Section 4) are gaining credibility and being implemented in the mining industry. It is seen as important to maintain a balance in metals extraction that satisfies the need to provide raw materials for the present, without compromising the future. In the 1970s, the 'future' in this context would have meant mainly the 'future *supply* of metals' — the major concern of the times, when it was suggested that the *known* reserves of many metals had relatively short lifetimes until their exhaustion. Today, the 'future' is seen in a broader framework — it includes the 'future of civilization, humanity and the environment'.

Taking action to minimize the environmental impact of the metals extraction industry is only possible through a comprehensive understanding of the environmental consequences of the industry's activities. Efforts are increasingly focused on human health, community well-being and the maintenance of ecosystems. A well-managed, technologically aware and profitable mining industry is most likely to be capable of taking the necessary measures to minimize environmental impact.

Figure 71 The main environmental effects of mining, ore processing and smelting; and of manufacturing, using and disposing of metal goods.

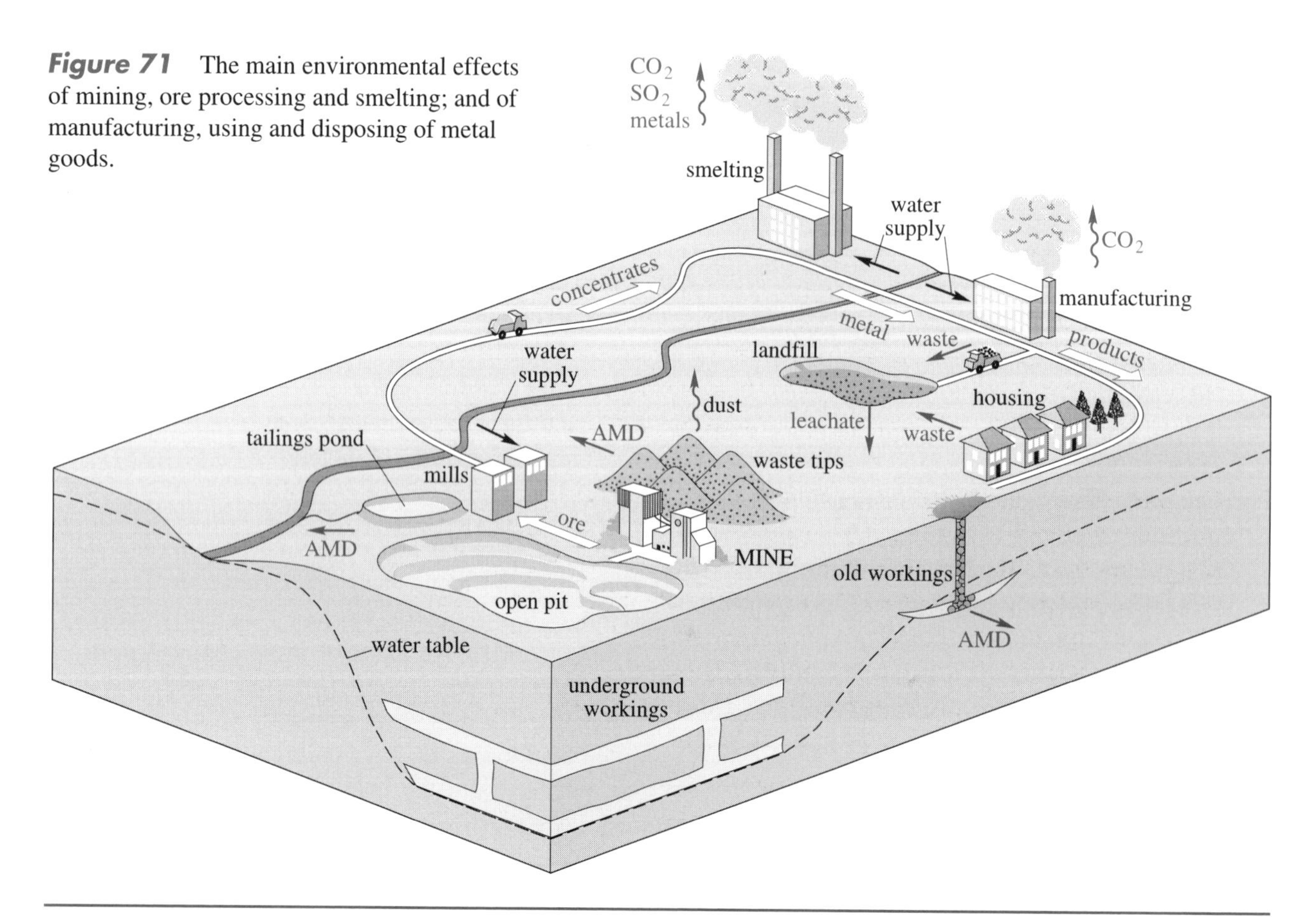

The main environmental effects associated with the extraction and use of metals are summarized in Figure 71 and are the subject of Question 38.

One obvious way to minimize the impact of mining would be to reduce the need for mining by the re-use and recycling of metals, as discussed in *Metals 1*, Section 1.4.2. This is already being done most effectively for lead and aluminium. Such activities are important for longer-term conservation of resources and to help ensure the sustainability of supplies until, perhaps, technology comes to our aid with alternative materials derived from renewable sources.

Finally, try to envisage this scenario painted by Agricola in the 1550s, and consider to what extent it remains applicable today:

> If we remove metals from the service of man, all methods of protecting and sustaining health and more carefully preserving the course of life are done away with. If there were no metals, men would pass a horrible and wretched existence in the midst of wild beasts; they would return to the acorns and fruits and berries of the forest. They would feed upon the herbs and roots which they plucked up with their nails. They would dig out caves in which to lie down at night, and by day they would rove in the woods and plains at random like beasts, and inasmuch as this condition is utterly unworthy of humanity, with its splendid and glorious natural endowment, will anyone be so foolish or obstinate as not to allow that metals are necessary for food and clothing and that they tend to preserve life?

4.6 Summary of Section 4

1. The physical effects of mining include the visual impact of the mines themselves, and their waste tips, associated noise and potentially hazardous dust. Ground subsidence can result from collapse of the workings, especially after abandonment, and from the lowering of the water table.
2. Water is needed in almost all mining operations, for ore processing, for laying dust and even for cooling deep mines, but excess water prevents access to working areas and must be pumped away.
3. Sulphide ores exposed to air and to oxygenated groundwaters by mining undergo oxidation to produce acid mine drainage (AMD). AMD lowers the pH of local streams, rivers and groundwater, often leading to the precipitation of hydrated iron(III) oxides, discolouring stream beds and smothering organisms living there. Toxic metals leached from ores and mineralized rocks by AMD can also contaminate surface and groundwaters.
4. Ore processing can also contribute to AMD, through oxidation of liberated sulphides in finely ground ore and waste. The large volume of fine wastes from ore processing must be safely contained, in tailings ponds, for example. The water in tailings ponds can be treated to raise its pH and precipitate metals before it is released into surface drainage. The use of chemicals in ore processing also requires careful control.
5. Smelters release toxic metals and sulphur dioxide to the atmosphere, thus contributing to local contamination of soils and to acid rain on a regional, perhaps global, scale. The disposal of slag from smelters can create storage problems, particularly if it is susceptible to the leaching of toxic metals.

6 The toxic effects of metals depend to a large extent on their bioavailability, which in turn depends on the chemical form in which they occur — some forms are more easily taken up by living organisms than others.

7 Social impacts of mining can be considerable, especially in developing regions or countries where the sudden influx of modern mining operations and workers into small, previously isolated, rural communities can cause great disruption. In remote regions, whole towns may be founded on the mining of a rich ore deposit.

8 In western industrialized countries, metal mining companies are increasingly compelled to assess the environmental and other impacts of their operations, to minimize damage during operations, and to make financial provision for rehabilitation following mine closure. Mining in national parks and designated wilderness areas is rarely allowed, and only under the most stringent conditions.

Question 37

In what ways might mining in an undeveloped area of a developing country affect local communities?

Question 38

How do you think the recycling of metals could minimize the environmental impacts shown in Figure 71?

Question 39

Imagine you are employed by the mining company that is involved in mining lead–zinc deposits in a setting such as that at Pine Point (the subject of Video Bands 15–17). You are asked to prepare an environmental impact statement when the company wants to open a new mine in an adjacent area. What sort of information would you need to include?

Question 40

Table 7 The extent of the environmental impacts of mining

Environmental impact	Extent of impact			
	local ($10\ km^2$)	regional ($10^5\ km^2$)	global ($10^8\ km^2$)	approximate duration of impact#
visibility	X			short to long term
land take*				
subsidence				
noise				
dust				
atmospheric pollutants from smelting	X	X	X	short to long term
water abstraction				
water pollution				

*Area of land taken for the mine + waste dumps + tailings pond + processing plant, etc.

Indicate duration of impact as *short term* <2 years; *medium term* 2–20 years; *long term* >20 years.

(a) To put the environmental impacts of metal mining and associated activities into a geographical context, consider whether their effects extend locally, regionally or globally. Insert crosses in the appropriate places in Table 7; some examples are done for you.

(b) The duration of environmental effects depends on whether they are accidental (a single event, for example, a breakdown of containment) or a continuous part of mining (on-going for the duration of the operation). Suggest the approximate timescale for duration of impacts *once mining has ceased* (using short, medium and long term as defined) and write your conclusions in Table 7. You may feel that different answers apply in different circumstances, in which case, give alternatives and qualify your answer.

(c) The environmental impacts of mining affect land, water and air. Explain what it is about these environments that controls the extent and duration of these effects.

OPTIONAL FURTHER READING

Barnes J. W. (1988) *Ores and Minerals: Introducing Economic Geology*, Open University Press. This summarizes the formation of many ore deposits, and has a chapter on 'Prospecting for ores'.

Blunden J. and Reddish A. eds (1991) *Energy, Resources and Environment*, Open University U206 text. Chapters 2 and 3 are particularly relevant to the environmental aspects of this Block.

Craig J. R. , Vaughan D. J. and Skinner B. J. (1996) *Resources of the Earth: Origin, Use and Environmental Impact*, Prentice Hall. A comprehensive textbook of mineral resources, now in its second edition.

Evans A. M. ed. (1995) *Introduction to Mineral Exploration*. Blackwell Science. A comprehensive survey of exploration methods and a series of case studies in mineral exploration written by experts in the field.

Woodcock N. (1994) *Geology and Environment in Britain and Ireland*, UCL Press. A wide-ranging account of physical resource occurrence and use in the British Isles; it considers many environmental impacts of mining and resource extraction.

OBJECTIVES

Now that you have completed Block 5 Part 2, you should be able to do the following:

1 Explain in your own words, and use correctly, the terms in the Glossary that relate to *Metals 2*.

2 Outline the sequence of activities involved in the exploitation of ore deposits, and account for escalating costs, investment risks and lead times before mine production commences.

3 Discuss global trends in the levels of production and the distribution of producers of major metals during the twentieth century.

4 Describe the progression of activities typically involved in an exploration programme carried out by a mining company.

5 Discuss reasons for initiating exploration for ore deposits, and the selection of a suitable area for exploration, based on rock associations and regional geological setting.

6 Account for the benefits of remote sensing in mineral exploration.

7 Outline the basic principles behind the interpretation of gravity, magnetic, electrical and electromagnetic surveys.

8 Select the type of geophysical survey most suitable for detecting different kinds of mineral deposits.

9 Account for primary and secondary geochemical dispersion in terms of the processes involved.

10 Interpret data from geochemical surveys of (a) soil; (b) drainage water; (c) drainage sediment; and (d) vegetation.

11 Outline the main aspects of evaluating a mineral deposit.

12 Describe the main forms of surface and underground mining, and recognize the various economic, geological and technical factors that control their viability.

13 Explain the principles of ore processing methods that liberate and concentrate ore minerals, especially their suitability for different ore minerals and grain sizes.

14 Explain the economic and practical significance of ore mineral recovery and energy efficiency in ore processing.

15 Outline the basic principles of metal extraction from solutions and by smelting of ore concentrates.

16 Describe typical mining activities in a major mining region and appreciate how economic and social well-being is closely linked to the prosperity of mining.

17 Describe the potential environmental impacts on land, water, and air of metal-mining activities.

18 Compare the potential environmental impacts of different forms of surface and underground mining.

19 Outline how mining methods and activities of the twentieth century have been affected by environmental controls and concerns.

20 Describe how mining today differs from mining before the twentieth century in terms of methods used, types of deposit mined and environmental considerations.

ANSWERS TO QUESTIONS

Question 1

(a) For an investment at 7% compound interest, the doubling time is approximately 70/7 years (Block 1, Section 2.1). So, after 10 years, the investment of $\$1 \times 10^6$ in the bank would have doubled, that is, it would have grown by $\$1 \times 10^6$.

(b) After 10 years, the mine would be expected to provide a profit of $\$2 \times 10^5 \times 10 = \$2 \times 10^6$.

On the face of it, your profit from the mine would be more favourable by $\$1 \times 10^6$ but you have had to bear the risk of the mine prematurely closing down at any time. In the bank, your initial investment would be safe, so you would have a fund totalling $\$2 \times 10^6$, equal to your profit from the mine. Assuming the mine is not worked out, and could either be sold or kept (to produce a continuing profit), it would be the better investment. However, if reserves were worked out or mining became unprofitable at the end of 10 years, it might not be the better investment.

Question 2

(a) At 1994 rates of output, the lifetime of reserves at Olympic Dam Mine would be $572/3 \approx 190$ years. This lifetime would be *reduced* by an increase in world demand for copper, or restricted access to alternative supplies, leading to increased mine output. It would be *lengthened* if production was reduced due to a fall in world demand for copper, or if alternative supplies became available. The lifetime could also be reduced if a fall in copper price led to a re-evaluation and downgrading of the reserves.

(b) In world terms, in 1993–94, Olympic Dam is most important for copper.

Copper output as a percentage of world copper output is

$$\frac{70 \times 10^3 \times 100}{9 \times 10^6} = 0.78\%$$

Gold output as a percentage of world gold output is

$$\frac{0.62 \times 100}{2290} = 0.03\%$$

Silver output as a percentage of world silver output is

$$\frac{15.5 \times 100}{14\,900} = 0.10\%$$

Question 3

Gold does not feature in Figure 4a because production from gold mining is in very small quantities, yet in Figure 4b it represents 11.5% of the *value* of all metals produced by mining. This is because of its high price, $\$11 \times 10^6\,t^{-1}$, much greater than most other metals produced in small quantities and very much greater than all metals produced in large quantities.

Question 4

(a) In 1930, the USA was the leading producer of iron, copper, zinc and lead, and the second greatest producer of gold. In 1990, the USA's place in the producer league tables had dropped to fifth for iron, second for copper, sixth for zinc, and third for gold. It remained the leading producer of lead.

(b) The main iron producers in 1930 were the USA and European countries that were also important centres of industry; this reflects the high place value of iron ore at the time. In 1990, the main producers were USSR, China, Brazil and Australia, where extensive deposits of high-grade iron ores occur (*Metals 1*, Section 3.3.1). Today, long-distance transportation of bulk materials is not so much of a problem as formerly and, consequently, the place value of iron ore is lower.

(c) Countries listed in Table 3 that have elevated their position among world producers of major metals since 1930 are: for copper, Chile, the USSR, Zambia and Zaire; for zinc, Canada, Australia, China, the USSR and Peru; for lead, China, the USSR and Peru; for tin, China, and Brazil.

Question 5

(a) By 1880, Spain provided 71% of Britain's lead imports (that amounted to $0.71 \times 109\,000 = 77\,390$ tons), which was greater than the home-produced lead (56 900 tons)

(b) Imported lead started to exceed home-produced lead in the early 1870s.

(c) Figure 7 shows levels of UK lead production increasing to 1870, then declining. From 1855 to 1890 imports rose steadily. High levels of imports from the mid-1870s, correlate with an appreciable decline in lead price, which fell to well below £20 a ton. It appears that home-produced lead was squeezed out by cheaper imports, leading to a decline in UK lead mining.

Question 6

From initial discovery, it takes time to fully evaluate a deposit, produce a development plan, carry out environmental impact studies, build the infrastructure for processing ore, organize a labour force and gain access to the ore before production can start. Obtaining approvals from government and making financial evaluations at each stage also take time.

Question 7

(a) In Nevada the main form of exploration for gold in the nineteenth century was panning sediment in streams and tracking upstream to look for the veins that supplied the gold grains.

(b) Modern day exploration includes satellite imagery, which identifies rocks and soils with a spectral 'signature', and geochemical assay, which measures trace abundances of gold and diagnostic elements, such as antimony, arsenic and mercury.

Question 8

The main twentieth-century developments to allow economic mining of low-grade gold deposits are the use of large-scale earth-moving equipment and heap leaching to extract gold from crushed rock. In addition, the gold grains in the low-grade deposits of Nevada cannot be seen. Without modern methods of geochemical assay to reveal ppm levels of gold, the presence of these low-grade deposits would not have been detected.

Question 9

Deposits (a)–(c) are likely to be found in crustal settings (1)–(3) as follows:

a – 3 *(see Metals 1*, Section 4.3);

b – 2 *(see Metals 1*, Section 2.2);

c – 1 *(see Metals 1*, Section 3.3).

Question 10

(a) Tin and uranium deposits are more likely to be associated with granitic rocks (*Metals 1*, Section 2.3, and Section 4.3.2 — tin only); nickel and titanium deposits are more likely to be associated with gabbroic rocks (*Metals 1*, Section 2.2).

(b) Nickel forms sulphide minerals, and many sulphide minerals, like pyrite, decompose on weathering. Uraninite may have been a detrital mineral in the Archaean, but uranium is soluble under today's oxidizing weathering conditions (*Metals 1*, Section 5.3). Only cassiterite (tin) and rutile/ilmenite (titanium) are stable under today's weathering conditions and likely to occur in placer deposits (*Metals 1*, Section 3.4).

Question 11

Gabbroic intrusions are relatively dense and will give rise to gravity highs. They are also likely to contain magnetic iron minerals and to be highly magnetic. The sulphides themselves are unlikely to be detectable by either form of survey — only the associated gabbros will be, because of their high density and magnetic minerals.

Question 12

(a) Pegmatites might be associated with a large granite body that could cause gravity lows. Pegmatites themselves, as thin sheets, do not have a strong gravity signature.

(b) A gravity survey would be useful to find layered magmatic sulphides because they are associated with large basaltic intrusions which would cause gravity highs.

(c) A gravity survey would probably not be useful because porphyry deposits are dispersed and do not have a gravity signature, and associated intrusions intermediate in composition between granite and basalt might not have a strong gravity signature either.

Question 13

The major anomaly of Figure 16b — a feature characterized by closely spaced concentric contours — occurs near the intersection of grid lines 6 and B. Here, the contours record the most negative values of electrical potential and are closely spaced — the kind of SP response that might be expected for a sharply bounded sulphide ore body straddling the water table.

Question 14

Geophysical methods can 'see' beneath the glacial debris (many metres thick) that blankets the bedrock in the Pine Point region. Direct geological observation is little use without exposure of bedrock. Geochemical surveys are only of use if the material sampled reflects underlying rocks. Since the glacial debris may have been transported long distances, geophysical methods are most appropriate.

Question 15

(a) The areas you should have outlined on Figure 20 are shown in Figure 72.

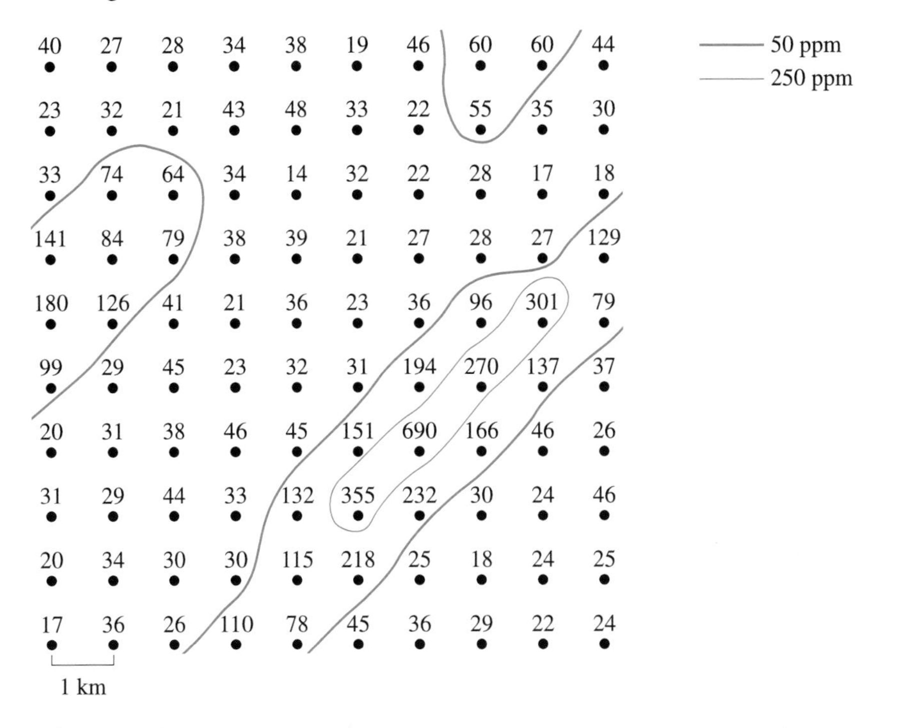

Figure 72 Copper concentrations (ppm) in soil in a gridded reconnaissance survey with regions exceeding thresholds of (i) 50 ppm and (ii) 250 ppm outlined.

(b) Choosing the higher threshold would reduce the area selected for follow-up studies.

(c) Choosing the higher threshold and, therefore, the smaller area would lessen the cost of follow-up work but might result in sites of mineralization being missed.

Question 16

(a) Magmatic segregation deposits containing nickel sulphides accumulate at the base of basaltic intrusions as thin layers. The body of rock is sharply divided into nickel-rich and nickel-poor horizons and therefore primary dispersion is minimal (*Metals 1*, Section 2.2).

(b) Porphyry copper deposits are produced by metal-bearing fluids moving along tiny cracks and into hydrothermally altered rock. There is no sharp division between copper-poor and copper-rich zones, so primary dispersion is broad (*Metals 1*, Section 2.4).

(c) Lead–zinc ore deposits are found in cavities in limestone and are localized. There is usually a sharp division between mineralized and barren zones, so there is little primary dispersion (*Metals 1*, Section 4.3).

(d) Placer deposits are formed by the sorting of dense, hard, insoluble minerals from which lighter minerals are winnowed. Placer minerals are deposited with river and beach sands; although concentrations may be localized, individual grains of these minerals may be more generally distributed. Dispersion is likely to be fairly extensive, but only within the sedimentary deposit itself and the spread of fluvial deposits in particular may not be great (*Metals 1*, Section 3.4).

Overall, porphyry copper deposits show the broadest primary dispersion.

Question 17

The catchment areas associated with sampling points B and C on Figure 23 are shown in Figure 73.

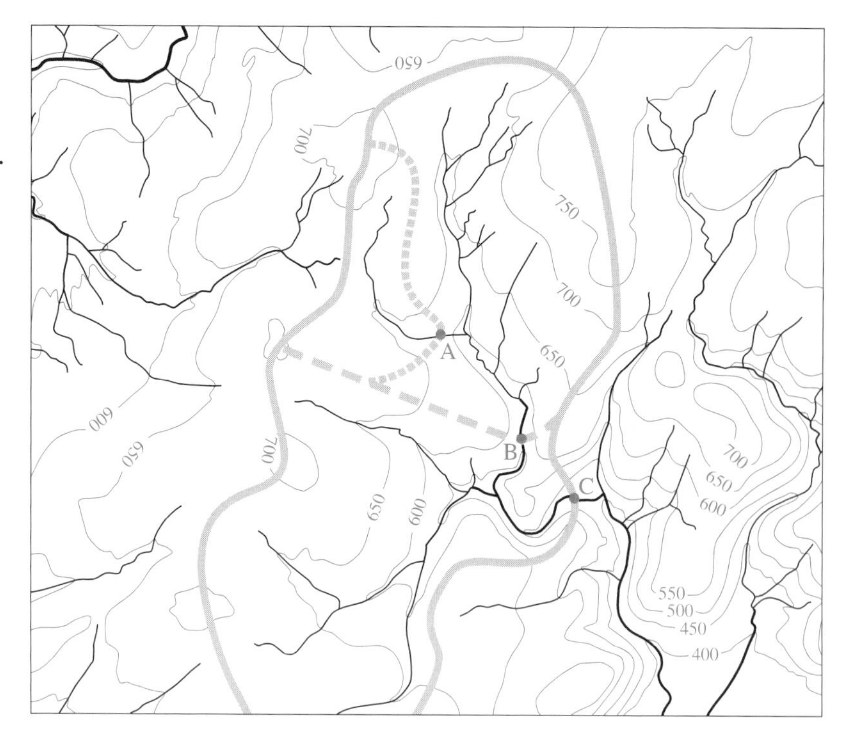

Figure 73 Drainage pattern map showing the catchment areas for points A, B and C.

Question 18

(a) A low-density, easily-broken mineral will be dispersed along with grains of rock-forming minerals. The persistence of the anomaly will be high, but so will its dilution.

(b) A high-density, hard mineral will resist breaking but will be trapped easily. Therefore, the anomaly will have low persistence; the mineral will accumulate to form locally high concentrations.

(c) A chemically unstable mineral will decompose, forming new minerals or ions in solution, to form a water anomaly. Even with a low density, it would have very low persistence.

Question 19

The cut-off points you should have identified in Figure 24 and the likely location of the copper ore body are shown in Figure 74. The form of the ore body is likely to be linear; a sheet.

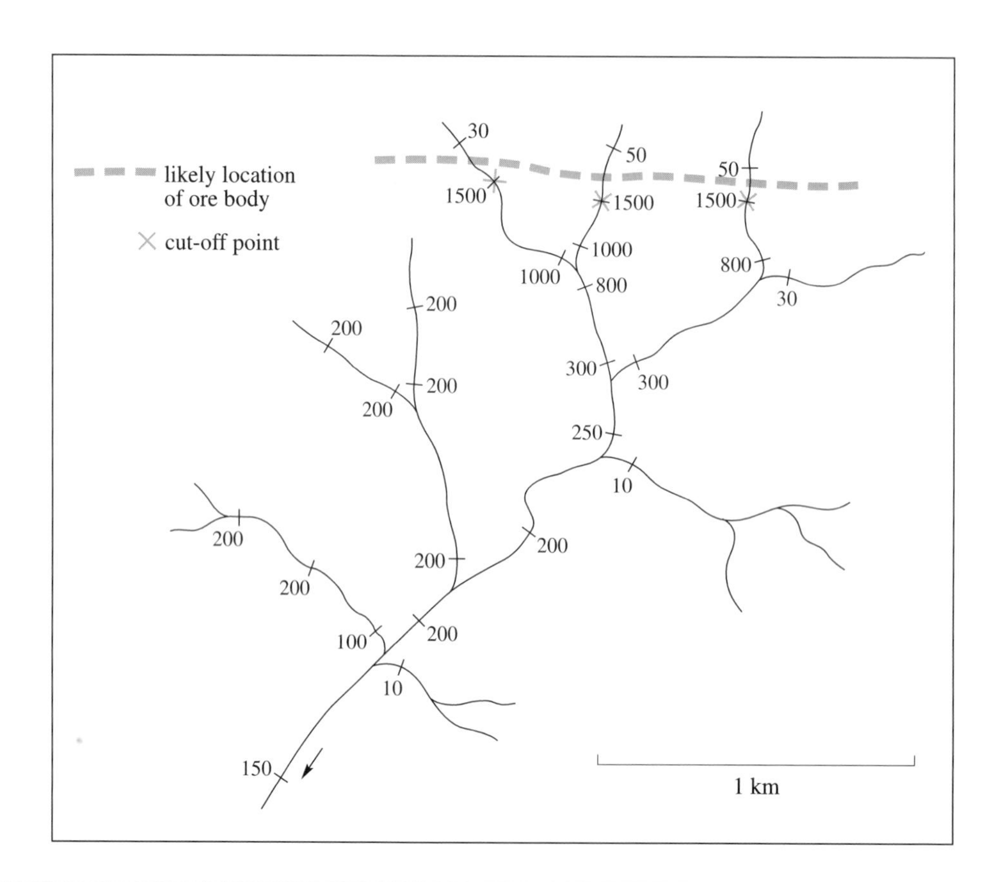

Figure 74 A drainage system showing copper concentrations (in ppm) in the stream sediments, exploration cut-off points, and the likely location of the ore body.

Question 20

(a) Evaluations of (i) the distribution and mineralogical composition of the ore and (ii) the size and grade of the ore body are necessary to define the potential reserve.

(b) An evaluation of the cost of exploiting the reserve set against the potential value of the ore is necessary to assess whether or not mining investment is justified.

Question 21

(a) Generally the reserves (Z) in a confined deposit (Figure 31b) are at a higher *average grade* than those in a large dispersed deposit. The sharp drop in the grade curve on the graph to less than the cut-off grade represents the margins of the deposit. Beyond that point there is no increase in reserves because grades outside the ore body are well below cut-off. For dispersed deposits, there is a more gradual drop-off in grade, so there is a flatter relationship between reserves and grade (Figure 31a).

(b) Cut-off grade can vary with economic conditions (for example, from A to B in Figure 31a) and reserves in a dispersed deposit vary greatly in response (from X to Y). In contrast, in a confined deposit over a similar range of cut-off grades, the reserves would change little. Therefore, the reserves in a confined deposit are less sensitive to economic fluctuations than those in a dispersed deposit *provided that* the cut-off grade is well below the average grade of the deposit.

Question 22

(a) The 'massive' deposit (a) is a good candidate for surface mining; much of the excavation can be in ore; there would be little waste. Simple veins (b) could be worked partly at the surface but must be followed underground to avoid mining excessive waste. The simple geometry makes it easy to mine within the ore body. Most of the reserves in an irregular vein deposit (c) are as pockets that must be mined below ground, and it would be necessary to remove a lot of waste to gain access to the pockets.

(b) As the order of increasing unit costs is from (a) to (b) to (c), for economic exploitation cut-off grades will also increase from (a) to (b) to (c).

Question 23

(a) The lifetime of an individual pit in the Pine Point area varied between 6 months and 2 years. Yet it could take up to 5 years from discovery of a deposit to evaluate it and prepare the site for mining.

(b) Before ore could be mined in the Pine Point area, land had to be cleared of forest; access roads had to be built; drainage channels had to be dug to drain swamps and transport the water extracted by pumping; overburden had to be removed.

(c) It is unlikely that mining a single deposit at Pine Point would be profitable. The ability to maintain continuity of operations by moving equipment from one site to another and utilizing permanent supply routes keeps costs down.

Question 24

(a) Evaluation of a deposit at Pine Point considered:

- the cost of mining;
- the grade of the ore;
- the depth of the ore;
- the metal price.

(b) Lead and zinc grades were determined by assay of borehole core samples to obtain a 3-D picture of the deposit, so that ore tonnages and waste tonnages could be estimated.

(c) Use of 200-tonne capacity trucks was intended to bring about economies of scale and maximize output per day and per mine worker. Continuity was important in maximizing output for minimum investment in equipment, and ensured that the associated processes of ore processing and smelting were not hampered by breaks in supply.

Question 25

(a) The ore body appears to be a near-vertical pipe or sheet resembling the form of a branching tongue.

(b) Ore is mined (i) by stripping from an open pit at the surface and (ii) by tunnelling underground and cutting stopes.

(c) Crushing of ore takes place both underground and in the surface mill depending on the location of the ore.

(d) After blasting, ore is transported by front-loader, tipped into a shaft (gravity); crushed ore is hoisted in a skip, loaded onto a conveyor at the surface and finally the ore concentrate is shipped by rail.

(e) Waste is returned to the mine to backfill mined stopes and help support the overlying rock mass.

Question 26

The ore from the hydrothermal vein deposit would require less energy in order to liberate the ore minerals because of its coarse grain size. Separation could be more easily achieved from coarsely ground fragments than for the magmatic segregation deposit in which grains are usually quite small (Plate 55) and intergrown with silicate minerals (*Metals 1*, Section 2.2).

Question 27

Whether or not to employ a shaking table depends on the *density contrast ratio* of the ore minerals and the gangue in water as the separating medium.

(a) $$\frac{6.9-1.0}{2.65-1.0}=3.58$$

As this ratio is much greater than 2.5, separation of cassiterite from quartz should be very good.

(b) $$\frac{5.2-1.0}{4.6-1.0}=1.16$$

As this ratio is less than 1.25, separation of chromite and magnetite is unlikely to be possible by this method.

(c) $$\frac{7.5-1.0}{4.1-1.0}=2.10$$

As this ratio is greater than 1.25, separation by this method could be used for galena and sphalerite, but may not be very efficient.

Question 28

At Pine Point, primary crushing of ore is done by a cone crusher. Secondary crushing is followed by wet grinding in rod mills and ball mills. The resultant slurry, containing ore minerals and gangue, passes to froth flotation cells for separation of sphalerite and galena from the gangue of calcite, dolomite and limestone, as well as pyrite.

Neither sphalerite nor galena are magnetic, nor are they very conductive, so magnetic and electrical methods would be unsuitable to separate them from each other or from the gangue. In the past, gravity methods (especially the buddle in the nineteenth century) have been used to separate lead and zinc minerals from limestone hosts. However, the presence of pyrite (which has a similar density to sphalerite) at Pine Point would make gravity separation inefficient. During the twentieth century, froth flotation has been the most efficient method for separating sulphide minerals and is well-suited for automation. Because this is a wet method of separation, grinding is also carried out wet, as water is a useful lubricant and subsequent drying is not required.

Question 29

Before iron pyrites could be smelted it would have to be roasted to drive off sulphur. The sulphur dioxide would be environmentally damaging and the whole process would be unnecessarily costly when abundant sources of haematite ore exist which are richer in iron than pyrite and can be smelted without pollution (*Metals 1*, Section 3.3.1). Pyrite has been mined in the past but rarely (for example, in Cyprus) for iron and sulphur for use in sulphuric acid production (*Metals 1*, Section 4.4.3).

Question 30

(a) Mining in the Sudbury area began around 1890 and mining in the deposits of New Caledonia had started some years earlier. These deposits provided a plentiful, accessible and stable supply that ensured lower prices for nickel after 1890, whereas restricted supplies before that time had given rise to higher nominal prices.

(b) Nickel is an important component of steels, especially stainless steel (*Metals 1*, Table 3), and the need for engineering strength and durability of steel encouraged the demand for nickel to rise, especially during World War I. The price of nickel was relatively low, whereas aluminium price remained high and demand for it in engineering applications was low until electricity became available cheaply and in quantity after World War II.

(c) During the two World Wars, the output of nickel was particularly high due to the demand for steel in armaments.

Question 31

(a) The most fundamental considerations for future prosperity of a mining area are the presence of reserves and demand for the product. At Sudbury there are abundant reserves (as defined by current market conditions) and the demand for metals — nickel, copper and PGM — is unlikely to diminish. The big questions relate to the economics of mining. If supplies could be obtained more cheaply elsewhere, Sudbury might become uncompetitive.

(b) A significant increase in the cost of mining in recent years has been due to efforts to reduce environmental impact. A balance must be struck between maintaining the prosperity of a mining area and protecting the environment. Destruction of either could have severe social impact.

Question 32

Underground mining of lead–zinc ores in limestone should not pose severe health problems from dust and gas, although exposure to dust should be minimized, and as lead is a cumulative poison, exposure to any form of it should be monitored. On the other hand, mining a tin deposit in granite that is rich in quartz would generate considerable silica dust, which carries a significant risk of miners developing respiratory disease. In addition, uranium-rich granites produce high levels of radon gas which is also a problem when inhaled. Provision of strict dust-control measures, such as spraying and maintaining good ventilation, are particularly important in this case.

Question 33

The Wheal Jane discharges of toxic metals were almost inevitable without adequate measures in place to control the flow of waters issuing from the mine. The control operation at Wheal Jane was set up *after* the problem arose. Forward planning could have put preventative measures in place *before* problems occurred.

When measures have to continue in the long term, there are obviously financial implications, especially if a company goes out of business — provision of adequate funding to support management of mine waters is essential. It would be more satisfactory for a mine to be made safe during operations, for example, by backfilling to limit the access of groundwater to mineralized rocks.

Question 34

(a) The cadmium concentration in the soil around the Avonmouth smelter is in $mg\,l^{-1}$, whereas in the Carnon River (Figure 63) they are in $\mu g\,l^{-1}$, a concentration three orders of magnitude smaller. There could be several reasons for this, including the following:

- different concentration levels in the 'starting materials' — cadmium in the Carnon River has been leached mainly from low concentrations of metals in ore and waste, whereas cadmium around the smelter has been liberated by smelting ore concentrates, a process aimed at producing pure metals;
- the concentration in the river is being *transported* by the water at the instant of sampling, whereas in the soil metals have *accumulated* over a long period of time — if we took into account how much water had flowed, the amount of cadmium transported *per year* in the Carnon River would be quite high.

(b) Lead concentrations in the soil are some ten times greater than those of cadmium, but that doesn't necessarily mean that the lead is ten times more harmful than the cadmium. The toxicity of any element depends on its effect on the metabolism of organisms and this varies from element to element as shown in *Metals 1*, Table 8. Toxicity may depend less on the concentration of a metal than on the chemical form in which it occurs, because the form determines its solubility and hence the extent to which it can be absorbed by organisms — its bioavailability. It should be borne in mind (as noted at the end of Section 4.2.2) that the simple oxides of lead are the most likely form of lead to occur around smelters and they are also the most soluble form.

(c) Concentrations of both lead and cadmium are lower at a depth of 30 cm than at the surface where fall-out of metals accumulates. This suggests that migration downward through the soil is slower than accumulation at the surface.

Question 35

First, smelting involves heating ore mineral concentrates which releases toxic elements such as sulphur and some volatile trace metals that tend to be held 'safely' in minerals during mining and ore processing operations. The spread of atmospheric pollutants, like sulphur dioxide, from smelters is generally greater than that of dust and contaminated waters from mining. Secondly, smelters are frequently close to populated areas, whereas mines are more often in remote areas.

Question 36

The advantages to any area of opening a mine are mainly economic. Mines need labour, local services and equipment. A new mine could reduce unemployment, increase prosperity of other businesses in the area and attract new forms of industry.

On the other hand, there might be the disadvantages of visual impact, noise and dust in the immediate vicinity, and heavy road use if ore concentrates were shipped out of the area by lorry. Draining a mine would cause the water table to drop, and consequently, local supplies of water from boreholes may be liable to fail. Surface and groundwaters might become polluted with toxic metals if containment and treatment of mine waters failed.

Question 37

Mining in an undeveloped area where modern civilization has not spread, often has severe effects by upsetting the social balance and culture of the indigenous population. This is caused not only by the influx of mine personnel in great numbers but also by the employment of local labour, creating a cash economy. The building of the infrastructure (roads, railways, electricity, and power lines) to support mining and the processing and smelting of ores is likely to stimulate the economy and the development of other resources in the area. Such development may be seen as a benefit to local communities, but almost inevitably leads to destruction of the way of life that existed previously.

Question 38

Recycling of metals back through the smelter or through manufacturing would mean:

- less mining and, therefore, less land taken for mining and less disruption of communities;
- less ore processing and reduced need to dispose of rock waste;
- reduced demand for water and reduced production of AMD;
- less transportation of ore and concentrates;
- reduced energy consumption.

However, there will be energy implications and the potential for pollution associated with the separation of metals from used products.

Question 39

An environmental impact statement anywhere should contain the following information.

1 A definition of the initial state of the environment. This involves ecological and geochemical surveys to assess wildlife, vegetation and background levels of potential contaminants in soils, surface drainage and groundwater.

2 An evaluation of the impact of proposed workings, roads, disposal of waste rock, and pumping to drain workings etc. on the local environment.

3 Proposals to monitor and minimize impacts during operations, and contingency plans for possible breakdown in control procedures.

4 Proposals to restore the site after mining ceases and provision of guaranteed finance.

Environmental impact depends on the specific form of the mining operation, and at Pine Point could be assessed by examining the impact of existing mine sites in the area. Mining at the surface is visible during operation but is unlikely to cause annoyance in such a sparsely populated area. Although destruction of the environment would occur at the mine sites, it would be relatively localized. Roads and drainage channels could be more permanent. After use, pits would be allowed to flood. AMD is unlikely to be a problem in Pine Point mines as any acid produced by oxidation of pyrite would be neutralized by the limestone. A greater problem, in the short term at least, is posed by tailings because storage and settling ponds can cover large areas. Eventually tailings can be landscaped and revegetated.

Question 40

(a) Table 8 is the completed version of Table 7. Visibility, land take, and subsidence have only local impact, as does noise. Effects of water abstraction and pollution, and of dust are usually local, but may have regional consequences. Only gaseous pollutants are likely to have implications that extend to a global scale (acid rain, poor air quality, global warming).

Table 8 The extent of the environmental impacts of mining

Environmental impact	Extent of impact			
	local ($10\,km^2$)	regional ($10^5\,km^2$)	global ($10^8\,km^2$)	approximate duration of impact#
visibility	X			short to long term
land take*	X			short to long term
subsidence	X			long term
noise	X			short term
dust	X	(X)		short term
atmospheric pollutants from smelting	X	X	X	short to long term
water abstraction	X	(X)		medium term
water pollution (AMD)	X	(X)		short to medium term

*Area of land taken for the mine + waste dumps + tailings pond + processing plant, etc.

Indicate duration of impact as *short term* <2 years; *medium term* 2–20 years; *long term* >20 years.

(b) Noise and dust are short-term effects but air pollution by gases (e.g. carbon dioxide) may continue to have an impact well after the cessation of the operation that caused it. Water abstraction and pollution effects are likely to be severe in the short term but may continue to have medium-term effects when pumping has ceased. It often takes many years for water table levels to be re-established, and for damaged ecosystems in rivers and lakes to recover. The impacts of visibility and land take are likely to be long term, even permanent, unless massive effort is put into restoration work.

(c) The extent and duration of environmental impacts depend on the rate and scale of movement of the medium involved because that is what controls rates of spread and the extent to which pollutants become neutralized or diluted.

Land is relatively stable, affected by natural erosion and deposition processes at the surface, and by large-scale very long-term tectonic processes at depth. Although it may take a long time for land to recover naturally from the effects of mining, the physical effects are generally of local extent. However, land reclamation may bring about recovery on a relatively short timescale.

Water includes surface run-off, seawater, ice, and groundwaters. Surface water run-off is usually the most rapid way in which pollutants on land are dispersed by water, especially in solution. However, it is localized compared with air movement. Drainage contaminants are usually diluted to insignificance on entering the sea where currents disperse them through great volumes. Groundwaters, by contrast, are generally slow-moving, may reside for a long time in rocks and thus retain chemical pollutants for long periods.

Air can transport gases and small particles in suspension; it forms a vast global circulation system, which dilutes local anomalies but is capable of spreading material over very large areas in quite a short time (the extent of radioactive fall-out from the Chernobyl incident in Block 4–2 is a good example).

Natural processes eventually clean up pollutants on land, in water and in the air. Some work more rapidly than others; for example, rain dissolves sulphur dioxide thereby cleaning the atmosphere, but making acid rain.

ANSWERS TO ACTIVITIES

Activity 1

Although your knowledge of exploration methods is rather limited at this stage, you might be surprised at how much you could already deduce and what recommendations you could make.

(a) There is a gravity high in the north-east corner, and a gravity low near the southern margin of Figure 12b.

(b) The gravity high is likely to be associated with basalts or gabbros and the gravity low with a granitic intrusion.

(c) (i) Detailed geophysics may refine the position of the gravity or magnetic highs or lows, but cannot prove that mineralization is present.

(ii) Geochemical sampling of drainage channels could reveal the presence of ore minerals in sediments or a metal anomaly that might be indicative of mineralization.

(iii) Field mapping would be little use as there is no rock exposure.

(iv) Drilling the bedrock would be too costly as a reconnaissance tool unless soil or drainage geochemistry combined with geophysics have located a likely target.

(d) Water analyses are useful in evaluating whether or not any sulphide mineralization exists near the surface within quite a large area because sulphides are liable to decompose on weathering and, if the metals released were soluble, they could be detected. In this case, water analyses would be hampered by the fact that the streams do not flow all year. Stream sediment samples would be more appropriate. These would indicate whether or not anomalous metal concentrations were present in the areas drained. The streams in the north-east would be best for a drainage survey, where sulphide mineralization could be associated with the dense, basaltic rocks indicated by the gravity survey.

(e) If the drainage survey indicated anomalous metal occurrences confined to a particular catchment, carrying out a soil geochemistry survey over the area might pinpoint the source. If the ultimate source were not exposed, drilling (although expensive) might be justified.

Activity 2

(a) The areas coloured blue on Plate 71 (50% of the data; regions with less than 25 ppm copper) are mainly in the Northern and Grampian Highlands of Scotland. The area is shown on the geological map in *The Geological Map* booklet as mainly metamorphic schists and gneisses, but includes areas of intrusive igneous rocks and Devonian rocks as well. However, not all areas of similar metamorphic rocks have such low copper values. There is also an area of blue in northern England, corresponding to Carboniferous rocks.

(b) Areas of red in Plate 71 (10% of the data; containing more than 72 ppm copper) are restricted in their distribution. The most extensive areas are in Skye and Mull and are related to volcanic igneous rocks. There are also red areas in the Midland Valley of Scotland over Carboniferous rocks. In fact, all these highs are related to basaltic volcanics.

(c) Background levels of copper in (i) the red areas are in the range 72–183 ppm, and (ii) in the blue regions are in the range 6–18 ppm.

(d) In the red regions, 183 ppm could be the most suitable threshold. In the blue regions the threshold could be 25 ppm.

(e) Copper anomalies (concentration levels well above background) might indicate potential sites of copper mineralization. The sharpest anomalies, but not necessarily the highest, are in the areas of low and intermediate copper backgrounds, i.e. red spots on a blue background. These anomalies might be worth a look for mineralization, as they indicate a high level of copper enrichment in the sediment, and might be more fruitful than anomalies in areas where background levels of copper are higher (and relative enrichments lower).

(f) Some of the colour boundaries on Plate 71 closely match the white lines — the geological boundaries — on the geological map. Colour (concentration) boundaries may be of use for large-scale mapping, particularly in combination with similar data for other elements. However, in an area where exposure is good, field mapping is the more direct means of proving the geology. Mapping by stream sediment geochemistry may be useful where exposure is very poor.

Activity 3

(a) Pit 1 (Figure 34b)

Mass of ore $= 19 \times 10$ (squares) $\times 3.8$

$= 722$ (mass units)

Mass of waste $= 0.5 \times 19 \times 53$ (squares) $\times 2.6$

$= 1309$ (mass units)

Stripping ratio of pit 1 $= 1309/722$

$= 1.8$

Pit 2 (Figure 34b)

Mass of ore $= 32 \times 10 \times 3.8$

$= 1216$ (mass units)

Mass of waste $= 0.5 \times 32 \times 90 \times 2.6$

$= 3744$ (mass units)

Stripping ratio of pit 2 $= 3744/1216$

$= 3.1$

For an inclined ore body, the stripping ratio *increases* with depth (and hence size) of the pit.

(b) In Figure 34c, pit 1 excavated to level 1 would excavate 50×3.8 mass units of ore and 100×2.6 units of waste giving a stripping ratio of $260/190 = 1.4$.

Pit 2 excavated to level 2 would excavate 100×3.8 mass units of ore and 400×2.6 units of waste giving a stripping ratio of $1040/380 = 2.7$.

Pit 3 excavated to level 3 would excavate 150×3.8 mass units of ore and 900×2.6 units of waste giving a stripping ratio of $2340/570 = 4.1$.

Again, the stripping ratio *increases* with depth and the size of the pit. In practice, if the intention at the outset was to excavate the mine down to level 3, the margins of the excavation at each level could be taken out to the boundary outline of pit 3. In this case the stripping ratio would actually *decrease* with depth from 6.8 for level 1 to 5.5 for level 2 and to 4.1 for level 3.

Activity 4

(a) Sites A, B and C, upstream of the mine and tributary discharges into the Carnon River represent background concentrations. Background levels of arsenic and copper in dissolved and particulate forms are less than 0.1 mg l^{-1}, with dissolved arsenic having the highest concentration and particulate copper the lowest at sites A and B. Background pH is around 7.

(b) (i) The peaks of particulate arsenic (1 mg l^{-1}) and dissolved copper (0.8 mg l^{-1}) are reached downstream of the County and Nangiles Adit discharges, at sampling point E, suggesting that they arise from either or both the County and Nangiles Adits. Peak concentrations of particulate copper and dissolved arsenic (both about 0.4 mg l^{-1}) are reached downstream of the tailings pond discharge.

(ii) The pH falls below 5 downstream of both the County and Nangiles Adits, so the discharges from the adits provide most of the acidity (AMD). Note the sharp *rise* in pH just upstream of the discharge from the tailings pond; this is a consequence of lime neutralization and could be due to some leakage of the tailings water upstream of the main discharge, or to an unmarked discharge between E and F.

(c) Below the County Adit, dissolved copper is more abundant than dissolved arsenic, but below the tailings pond the two tend to converge. In the case of particulates, the arsenic component is much greater. This observation concurs with the information given earlier in the Section that arsenic tends to form ionic complexes which can be adsorbed onto sedimentary particles.

(d) The concentrations in Table 6 are measured from the mine water discharges, whereas those in Figure 64 are from the Carnon River and are diluted by less-polluted river water.

(e) See Table 9.

Table 9 Copper and arsenic contamination from discharges into the Carnon River

Location of discharges	Concn of Cu/ mg l^{-1}	Flow rate/ $l\,s^{-1}$	Flux of Cu/ $g\,s^{-1}$	% of total flux	Concn of As/ mg l^{-1}	Flow rate/ $l\,s^{-1}$	Flux of As/ $g\,s^{-1}$	% of total flux
County Adit	1.08	330	0.356	88	0.21	330	0.069	33
Nangiles Adit	2.71	4	0.011	3	14.70	4	0.059	29
tailings pond	1.24	30	0.037	9	2.61	30	0.078	38
total flux			0.404				0.206	

(f) The County Adit contributes by far the largest proportion (86%) of the total copper flux to the river, while contributions of total arsenic are at roughly similar levels for all three sources.

ACKNOWLEDGEMENTS

The author would like to thank the Block Assessor, Dr Richard Edwards, for his helpful comments; Dr William Jones for his extensive comments and suggestions; also Dr Keith Atkinson, consultant on exploration and ore processing; Mr Mike Gill, consultant on mining history; Dr Peter Lightfoot, consultant on mining at Sudbury; Dr Charles Moon, consultant on environmental aspects of mining.

Grateful acknowledgement is made to the following sources for permission to reproduce material in this block:

Text

Neale, G. (1994) 'Tin mine's lethal cocktail blamed for swan deaths', *Sunday Telegraph*, 11th December 1994, © The Telegraph plc, London, 1994;

Figures

Cover: Satellite composite view of Earth, copyright © 1990 Tom Van Sant/ The Geosphere® Project, Santa Monica, California, with assistance from NOAA, NASA, EYES ON EARTH, technical direction Lloyd Van Warren, source data derived from NOAA/TIROS-N Series Satellites. All rights reserved; *Figure 8: Metallstatistik 1979–1989*, 77th edn, 1990, Metallgesellschaft AG; *Figure 10:* Edwards, R. P. and Atkinson, K. (1986) *Ore Deposit Geology*, Chapman and Hall; *Figure 11a:* Spartan Air Services Limited, Ottowa, Canada; *Figure 16:* Heiland, Tripp and Wantland (1945) *AIME Transactions*, 164, pp. 142–154, American Institute of Mining, Metallurgical and Petrological Engineers; *Figure 18:* Siegel, H. O. (1968) 'Discovery case history of the pyramid ore bodies, Pine Point, N.W.T., Canada', *Geophysics,* **33**, Society of Exploration Geophysicists; *Figure 22:* Rose, A. W. et al (1979) *Geochemistry in Mineral Exploration*, Academic Press Inc (London) Ltd, © Arthur W. Rose et al; *Figure 30:* Barton, R. M. (1964) *An Introduction to the Geology of Cornwall*, Truro Bookshop; *Figure 37:* Dr P Lightfoot, Ontario, Canada; *Figure 38:* C. J. Hawkesworth; *Figure 39(a)*: Inco Limited, Copper Cliff, Ontario; *Figure 39(b)*: Dr P Lightfoot, Ontario, Canada; *Figure 40:* Ontario Geological Survey (1989) *Ontario's Mineral Wealth,* Ontario Geological Survey, Information Brochure; *Figure 53:* Alcock, R. (1988) in Taylor, G. P. and Landolt, C. A. (eds) *Extractive Metallurgy of Nickel and Cobalt*, The Minerals, Metals and Materials Society; *Figure 55a:* adapted from Souch, B. E. et al (1974) 'Magnetic ore deposits – a symposium', in Brocum, S. J. and Dalziel, I. W. D. (eds) *Bull Geol Soc Am*, **85**, Geological Society of America: *Figure 58:* Inco Limited, Copper Cliff, Ontario; *Figure 59:* Hamersley Iron Pty Ltd, Perth, Western Australia; *Figure 60:* Rossing Uranium Ltd, Windhoek, Namibia; *Figure 61:* Apex Photo Agency Ltd, Plymouth, Exeter; *Figure 62b:* South West Water, Exeter; *Figure 65:* Still Pictures; *Figure 66*: H. Mathews (1992) Unpublished PhD thesis; *Figure 69:* P. C. Webb; *Figure 70:* A. J. Baker, Hong Kong Baptist University.

Physical Resources and Environment